Colonel Jonathan
An American Story

John Francis Wilson

RIVERSONG
BOOKS

An Imprint of Sulis International
Los Angeles | London

Riversong Books
An Imprint of Sulis International
Los Angeles | London

www.sulisinternational.com

Library of Congress Control Number: 2018941140
Paperback ISBN: 978-1-946849-24-3
eBook ISBN: 978-1-946849-25-0

The document on the cover, "Military Warrant," is the property of the New London Historical Society. Used by permission. Fig. 4 ("Lucretia Latimer, Power of Attorney") and Fig. 7 ("Foster's Commission") is located in the New London Historical Society archives. Used by permission. Fig. 8 ("The Colonel's Resignation Letter") is located in the Connecticut State Archives in Hartford. Used by permission.

All other photographs ©2018 by John Francis Wilson.

CONTENTS

PREFACE

Every person named in the story I am about to tell is a real, historically documented person. The names are all real as well; not a single one is a mere artistic creation. The story itself, in its broadest construction, is also real and is mostly based on solid historical evidence. I say "mostly" because we are dealing with a time before photography and audio-recording changed the way we reconstruct the past. We are, after all, looking back more than a quarter of a millennium. The people of those times, even the ones who left voluminous correspondence or detailed autobiographies, have furnished us only crumbs, hints, indistinct footprints, shadowy clues, indistinct whispers and fleeting glimpses. And the people in this particular story wrote almost nothing and certainly almost nothing about themselves. Instead, they left us shards and slivers, the sort of stuff that survives when grandma's favorite pitcher falls off the shelf, and its debris is swept outside and under the back porch. To tell the story, we must crawl down into the sticky darkness, painstakingly gather it up again, glue it all back together, and even then be satisfied with a pitcher bearing many cracks and missing pieces.

So, along with what can be *proven* to have happened, there are elements of the story that *probably* happened. This probability rests on the surviving bits and pieces and generally rises to what lawyers and judges might call the "preponderance of the evidence." But that still leaves us with some cracks and missing pieces, and so, with great restraint and a mighty squelching of authorial license, there are some things of which we can only say that they were *possible*; the best we can say of them is that they do not contradict what can be known for sure. Into this category we must place all dialogue and all attributing of motives. What else could we have done?

There you have it—full disclosure. So now with a clear conscience, I can tell you the story of a remarkable man and his remarkable family, who lived in remarkable times and who have left an impact that intertwines with the history of America and extends from the eastern ocean to the western one. It is a story worth rescuing from beneath grandma's back porch and gluing back together, despite all the difficulties in doing so.

ONE: THE SWORD

There Were No Drones

Sumner County, Tennessee
Saturday, August 30, 1806

The old Colonel sat on a fallen log, looking out across the broad green meadow. The pasture land was punctuated here and there with brown-gold stacks of hay and bordered with massive old oaks and ancient trees of a dozen other species. A large flock of dark-feathered turkeys scampered about in the near pastureland, and a family of white-tailed deer moved silently among the more distant trees, calm but attentive. The leaves were showing the beginnings of color, the first suggestion of fall. It would be the Colonel's last. Behind him, the fine two-story house he and his sons had literally cut from the forest seemed firmly rooted in the Cumberland soil. Massive logs, hewn into massive planks two feet wide and one foot thick, secured by skillfully mixed mortar, gave the house an impression of strength and permanence. At the side of the house stood a tall chimney, fashioned from expertly cut white sandstone, reaching up into the sky. Behind the house, in a separate building, there was a well-equipped kitchen. A section of a weathered old fence built of stalwart pickets still attends the house at its flanks, a reminder of the time when this place had been as much a fortress as a residence.

This was not the Colonel's first house, nor his most impressive one. Of course there had been the modest log structures he and his sturdy sons had built when they had first arrived in the Cumberland a decade and a half ago. But the house on his mind today was more than a thousand miles away in the verdant forest a few miles west of the old colonial port town of New London, Connecticut. He had built that house so very long ago for his new sixteen year old bride Lucretia. It was to be the house where the two of them would put down their roots, raise their family, and spend their lives. That first house had also been built to last, firmly planted in the old colony of Connecticut, among the descendants of the Puritan settlers who were the fathers and grandfathers of the Colonel and his teen-aged companion. Completed in 1745—more than 60 years ago—it was the prototype for the house behind him, right down to the arrangement of the doors and windows, and the interior floor plan—though of course that earlier house had been built of finely milled lumber instead

1

of roughhewn logs—lumber from his own family's impressive mill driven by the aqueous power which it had harnessed on "Latimer Brook."

He would never know the full story of that first house, of course, now so far away in space and time—how some of his children and grandchildren would continue to live there and how a century after this day of reminiscence the house would be consumed by fire and its very location all-but-forgotten. But even now that old beloved home may as well have no longer existed, as far as the Colonel was concerned. It belonged to another time and place. Once he and his family had turned their faces toward the wild and unknown lands far to the south and west, beyond the dark green mountains, they knew full well they would never see their home place again, nor the family and friends they had left behind. Perhaps that is why the house they had built here in the wilderness copied as closely as possible those in Old New England: continuity in the midst of radical change.

Fig 1: The Latimer home in Chesterfield (built 1745)

The Colonel was a big man, tall and strong even at the age of eighty-two. It was a family trait—the height and bulk. Even back in New London, where the Latimer brood had walked eight miles to church on Sundays, people remembered them, boys and girls alike, as a "tall and robust race." Such a hike was for them no more than an agreeable recreation, it was said. This natural vigor, succored and sharpened in colonial New England, had been tested more than once here in the wilderness.

He had the look of a leader. His hair was abundant and snowy white, parted in the middle, extended an inch or two down his neck. There were ample sideburns and in general the posture of a man who was determined not to let the years or the abundant aches and pains stoop him. When he sat, he sat up straight, and when he stood, he stood tall. Even now he exuded confidence and an aura of wisdom and of inner and outer strength.

Mano e Mano

The Colonel came by these attributes honestly. His great-grandfather Robert, the first of his line to arrive in the New World from England, was a bit of a mystery to him. He knew he was a sea captain, and that the ship which came to be his, built in New London, was called the *Hopewell*. And he had heard about Robert's partner, Mr. Channell, poor fellow. Mr. Channell, it seems, had once imbibed a bit overmuch while in the town of Boston and took it in his head to jump into the Charles River for a sobering, but unfortunately final, dip.

The results, the Colonel knew, were disastrous for Mr. Channell, but serendipitous for the Colonel's great-grandfather Robert. He bought out his over-washed partner's share in the business and continued to run the *Hopewell* back and forth from Boston to the distant Barbados Islands, selling goods along the way from New York to Virginia and bringing back copious amounts of rum from the islands of the Caribbean. Robert had the rough edges characteristic of the crusty New England mariners of his time. He was hardly a Puritan. But he provided well for his family, settling them in a nice house in New London when it was still a new and tiny village. It was a town full of sailors, with a harbor full of boats. Sadly, one day around 1670 Captain Robert set out for yet another voyage to the far-away islands and never returned.

The Colonel's grandfather, also named Robert, sometimes existed as a momentary flash of vague and distant memory for him, but usually only a name. He was, like his own father, a man who worked with his hands, handled money well, and gradually created a family fortune. He doted on his grandson and even left him, at the age of four, a nice two-year-old calf and "one good ew" in his will. This Robert was a surveyor, a builder, a selectman of the town, and an accumulator of real estate. It was he who first acquired the swampy land west of town that became the Colonel's home base for much of his life—a place called Chesterfield.

But this Robert Latimer was best known as a soldier. Not a professional soldier, but a militia-man—a soldier of the people. He was a man's man and a leader of men, and was again and again selected by his peers as an officer in the local militia. Most people knew him as "Captain Latimer," and in fact, that is the way he is remembered on his gravestone which can still be seen in Ye Antientist Burial Ground in New London. For those who believe in such things, one might suspect that in the Colonel's veins had always coursed the martial blood of this grandfather.

Like his father the sailor, this Robert could not be called a man of great piety. He was one of those "seculars" in Puritan New England who were so crucial for the economic well-being of the society, but created such a dilemma for its spiritual self-understanding. He didn't bother to have his children baptized until he had accumulated three of them, and did not himself become a member of the church until he was sick, had already written his will, and sensed the hand of the Grim Reaper upon him.

The story the Colonel liked best about his grandfather was a famous one in New England, even though there were those who thought it nothing but folklore. Still, the famed president of Yale, Timothy Dwight, chose to tell it as a fact in his bestselling book of the day, *Travels in New England.*

What happened was a common occurrence in medieval England, but no one had ever heard of such a thing in America. As the story was told, the inhabitants of New London and those of nearby Lyme got into a tussle about a boundary line between them. There was a two-mile strip between the Niantic River, on one side, and Bride Brook on the other, a marshy plot at a spot called Black Point that both towns wanted to claim as their own.

After years of tense confrontation, the citizens decided to settle the question in an ancient manner. There would be a personal combat between two champions representing their respective towns, *mano e mano.* The winner would take all. Lyme chose Matthew Griswold, and New London chose Robert Latimer. On the appointed day the people from both towns gathered on the disputed plot and Matthew and Robert fought it out with their fists.

As it happened, the Colonel could claim a family victory regardless of who won, since his wife Lucretia was a Griswold. The fact is, at least according to the tale, Matthew Griswold gave Robert Latimer a thrashing and the land went to Lyme. The Colonel smiled when he considered the irony of all this. Much of the land in dispute ended up belonging to the Latimers anyway. And one of his first duties as an officer in the Revolution had been to protect the Griswold home in Lyme from the Redcoats! Ah well, we must let bygones to bygones, he thought, his lips forming a nascent smile.

The Flower of Young Society

The Colonel was named for his father Jonathan, who, like his grandfather Robert before him, was known to his neighbors as "Captain Latimer." In fact, the life of this first Jonathan Latimer seemed very similar to that of his father, Robert. There was the hard physical work, the acquisition of land and fortune, the same practical, hard-nosed and mildly impious approach toward life he had learned from the Latimer men before him. But despite the rough edges, it was this Jonathan who lifted the family into the society of New England blue-bloods. This he did in the time-tested way; he "married up." Spectacularly so.

Jonathan managed to win one of the six beautiful daughters of a prominent citizen by the name of George Denison—maidens who were, by common consent, the flower of young New England society. A few months after the death of Mr. Denison, a Harvard-educated lawyer and man of great power and influence, Jonathan and the lovely twenty-year-old Borodell Denison had become man and wife. In this way, the Latimers were joined not only to the highest levels of their contemporary society, but to the very foundations of the American Colonies as well. Borodell Denison, you see, was the great-great-granddaughter of William Brewster, the spiritual leader of the Pilgrims who had arrived in America on the ship Mayflower in 1620, almost exactly a century before her marriage to Jonathan.

Jonathan's bride had other illustrious forebears as well. Her grandfather Daniel Wetherell was perhaps the most prominent public servant in New London in his day. And her great-grandfather, also named George Denison, was famous in his own time, fighting in Cromwell's army in the old country, and returning with a bride, Ann Borodell, who was so beautiful and elegant that people called her "Lady Ann." Such people as these, mostly born in England, formed the backbone of the American Colonies and produced the stalwart leaders who themselves would eventually create the United States of America.

The marriage of the Colonel's parents Jonathan and Borodell would last fifty years and would place the Colonel and his ten brothers and sisters in the privileged and ruling class of the Colony of Connecticut.

The harsh call of a flock of crows suddenly brought the Colonel back to his own time and place. When his family had arrived in the Cumberland the contest between the white settlers and the Native Americans was not yet finished, and life itself was an uncertain, day-to-day proposition. The gentle life of civilized New England, where one's children learned some Greek and Latin, and then might well attend Harvard or Yale; where the evenings were spent in reading or stimulating political or theological discussions, was a dim memory here. This was instead a wilderness of huge trees and almost impenetrable cane breaks; of untamed waters and uncharted hinterlands. Wild creatures prowled the forests—bears, panthers, deer, and buffalo—in numbers that staggered the imagination. Furthermore, the native inhabitants were not finished with this place; they meant to exact vengeance on those who were wresting it from them. Yes, there were Indians still in Connecticut, but beaten, broken ones. Here the fires still burned. Looking back on those early days, a friend who had spent his youth among families like the Latimers remembered people like them as "bold adventurers" who were "compelled to use freely first the rifle and the ax before the plow and the sickle." Life consisted of "unremitting vigilance and hard manual labor." "There were no drones in the early settler's hive," this fellow said.

Not long after their arrival in the Cumberland the Latimers had tasted the bitter consequences of the desperate struggle for this land in the most tragic of ways, as we shall see.

The Warrior

Colonel Jonathan and Lucretia may have had their origins among the blue-bloods of New England—firmly planted in the ruling class—but weak or spoiled by wealth they were not.

The Colonel's title was not honorary. It was earned in the heat of battle. He had been a soldier since his youth—fighting first for his King and then for his newly independent country. In a way, all this seemed like a dream to him, this lovely fall day in the wilderness. Like something which had happened to someone else, or something someone had read in one of the few leather-bound books that had found their way into the forest.

The Colonel was one of those men who seem again and again to be nearby when truly significant events occur. And not just nearby, really. Rather, people like the Colonel are often important participants in those events. They are a crucial part of them. Part of the reason such events happen at all. But somehow it seems that when the group portrait is made, by which the event will be understood long afterward, these people are missing from the center of the picture. They are not even on the front row. They are rather somewhere at the back, hard to see, easy to miss, and thus easily forgotten. The narratives that survive and thereby solidify the past as others will remember it tend quite arbitrarily to overlook such people—and history proceeds without them.

In our own time the Colonel, of course, is mostly forgotten. That is the undeniable truth of the matter. But if you were to mention his name to George Washington, there would be a smile of recognition: "Ah, old Colonel Jonathan. A good man!" Or the famous martyr Nathan Hale: "A man I truly admire, and a mentor to me." Or even the traitor Benedict Arnold: "My old New England friend—whatever happened to him?" Such men as these somehow were situated in the center of the group portrait, and have remained there, but not the Colonel, though for each of them he was a person of consequence.

This is why, though he was certainly present at Saratoga when General Burgoyne surrendered to the Americans, and though he was certainly commended for his contribution by General Horatio Gates, and though the famous scene of the event hanging in the Capitol rotunda in Washington, D. C. was painted by a man whose family the Colonel had known well, and had literally watched grow to manhood, despite all this, you won't find Jonathan Latimer in the picture anywhere.

Then, again, maybe he *is* there after all, somewhere at the back. Perhaps he is behind that tree.

As he sat on the old log there in the Cumberland, and contemplated the still forest, and his long life, he wondered whether he should have drawn a bit more attention to himself. Perhaps he should have written a book or two—put his remarkable life down on paper. Or maybe it was better this way—to feel satisfied with one's place and portion, whether others had noticed or not.

His reverie was suddenly interrupted by the sound of his wife Lucretia's voice, strong enough to reach his rustic resting place, but, as always, gentle, dignified, and warm. "Come in, Jonathan. Dinner is waiting. We need to make this a short evening and get our rest. Tomorrow the whole tribe will be here for Sunday dinner."

Dinner on Station Camp Creek

Station Camp Creek, Tennessee
Sunday, August 31, 1806

Sometimes, after church, the whole Latimer clan gathered at the Colonel's home near Station Camp Creek to feast and catch up on recent events. On particularly special occasions family members who now lived several miles away came to the home place as well. Almost 15 years had passed since the Latimers had arrived in the Cumberland. During these years they had taken seriously and literally the charge given them in the Good Book to "be fruitful, and multiply, and fill the earth, and subdue it." There would eventually be almost a hundred grandchildren, many of whom the Colonel lived to see. Some of them had childhood memories of New England, but most were pure-born children of the forest. And every member of the family cherished those Sunday gatherings where all, or at least most, of the tribe could feast and talk and remember. The women-folk and the girls laid claim to the house at such events, sitting on every available chair, bed, box, or even fire-log, eagerly sharing their lives and gossiping about their neighbors. The men sat on logs outside, or leaned on fences, and did the same.

But for the younger male grandchildren, of whom there were always a dozen or two, the most wonderful part of such events came when Colonel Jonathan agreed to sit with them under a huge tree not far from the house and tell them stories of war. No one on the frontier knew more about the battles that had created this new land in which they lived —the United States of America. But the Colonel could also talk about the French and Indian War, years before the Revolution, when he had been a soldier of the King of England. And who but their grandfather could remember dining with General Washington, or the ferocious actions of the Hessian soldiers at New York or Saratoga, or the unbelievable scenes of carnage after confrontations with the French and their Indian allies so far up in the North as might as well be the moon? Grandpa had been there, and he had seen those things, things that others could only read in books. If one could read, of course. And if one could find a book.

And on very special occasions he would agree to go into the house, unlock a mysterious old trunk and bring out his sword.

Nothing...absolutely nothing...stirred the hearts of the Latimer boys like looking at that magnificent weapon and imagining where it had been and what part it had played in momentous events. The sword was very old. Grandpa had had it for over half a century. The boys thought it was surprisingly small—only a little over three feet long—and very slender, almost delicate. It fact it was called a "small sword" by the experts—the kind of sword that officers carried during the French and Indian and Revolutionary Wars.

The handle was made of pierced silver with all sorts of wonderful figures and decorations. The egg-shaped pummel at the top had something that looked like a glove from a medieval suit of armor on one side and on the other, a strange wide-eyed creature peering out from among the swirling decorations. Was it a bear? A lion? Whatever it was it was wearing a military uniform and had its right arm folded across its chest as though it was defending itself from a blow.

And the disk-shaped cross guard was even more interesting. There was a drum, and all sorts of swirling vines and leaves and other mysterious things. And what appeared to be a wolf leaping out to bite something that looked like a scaly fish, his front paws curling downward, his sharp teeth at the ready and his huge eye glaring menacingly. Or was it a bizarre creature, half wolf and half fish, biting its own tail? The boys speculated on these things endlessly.

"Grandpapa," someone was sure to ask, "did you ever kill a man with this sword?"

"We won't talk about that sort of thing," he would reply, gravely shaking his head from side to side. "And anyway, it's an officer's sword. Its' use is more to point and to command than to injure or kill."

The Colonel would suddenly jump to his feet, point the sword to his left and then to his right, and shout with full voice, "Forward to the line boys! Give those rascals what for!" Then he would thrust the sword straight up toward the sky. "Ready, aim, FIRE!" The last word was so loud that the boys always flinched and threw their heads back in alarm, though the Colonel had done this before dozens of times. This charade always made the Colonel throw back his head, too, and laugh.

Fig. 2: The Colonel's sword

"Tell us about the war up on the borders of Canada, Grandpapa, when you fought against the French and the Indians."

This was an assignment which the Colonel always approached with a mixture of enthusiasm and dread. The soldier in him wanted to relive those days, but the old man, weary of the pain and suffering he had seen for so long, only wanted to forget. Still, it was a way to stay in the lives of his grandsons, and in some sense, a way to extend what he knew was otherwise a shortening shadow.

"Well, boys, strange as it seems, I have fought against the French, and I have fought with them. And I have fought against the Indians and I have fought with them. For that matter, I've fought for the King of England and I've fought against him. Soldiers follow their orders, you know, and one day they tell you the fellow who used to be your friend is now your enemy. And the next day it's the other way round. I'll tell you for sure boys, that war is a very strange thing, and it doesn't pay, if you're called to fight one, to think much about anything except what's right in front of you."

"My first trip up toward Canada was in June of 1756, half a century ago. We thought of ourselves as British then—loyal subjects of His Majesty, you know. When we heard there was trouble up on the northern border we wanted to do our part to stop it. We couldn't have the French coming down and threatening our quiet New England way of life. One thing His Majesty needed, we were told, was to drive out those Frenchmen living up in Nova Scotia who were called Arcadians. They couldn't be trusted, we were told. The King sent soldiers up North to move them out to someplace where they wouldn't be such a threat. They were packed up like salted-fish and shipped south. We began to see them at our home in New London in January. The ships sailed into our port and unloaded them by the hundreds. Some were re-packed into carts and sent away—we didn't know where. And a lot of them eventually ended up way down in Louisiana, where they still live today. And you may know that as we speak your Great Uncle Eusebius is probably right down there with them. Speaking French like a native. At least that's what we hear."

The saga of Uncle Eusebius is another story—which we will tell in due time.

War in the North

"Anyway, I gathered up some of the farmer boys around our place in New London County and shaped them up the best I could. It was early June when we left. We met down at Gardiner's Wharf and crammed ourselves on a boat there. Off we went, along Long Island Sound, past the town of New York, and a hundred miles up to Hudson River to Albany. Our job up there was to attack Ticonderoga and Crown Point. My men were young and excited, but I wasn't. After all, I was thirty-two years old and father of four young children and had a farm to keep up. And anyway I had been up there before and knew what to expect. And you can bet that your Grand Mammy was none too happy about the situation."

"We got there and found that the British General Shirley had some hare-brained scheme to use our 'country boys' to scatter the French and the Indians without so much as one professional officer to plan and lead the fight. Then the politicians jerked him out of the picture and sent in another couple of scoundrels named Loudon and Abercrombie. We marched miles and miles up to Lake George, and when we got there we found that the British were going to put a bunch of fuzzy-faced Redcoat junior officers over our good Connecticut officers, even our Colonels and Majors. Even our own Connecticut General Lyman, who was a far better commander than those British society fancies, didn't get their respect. Our boys didn't like this situation a bit and threatened to go back home."

As he spoke, the Colonel's face began to get more and more red and his voice louder and louder. Then he caught himself, thought a moment about how useless is was to be angry about things that happened so long ago, took a deep breath, and calmly resumed his story.

"As it turned out, the British generals themselves decided their schemes wouldn't work. All we saw of battle were the burned out farms and the dead bodies from earlier fights. All the poor fellows we found scattered on the ground had been scalped. A bloody mess where their hair used to be. You boys should thank the Good Lord if you've never seen a human being scalped. We made the long trip back home wondering why we had gone up there in the first place. Not a very good story this time boys. But you have to know the truth: War sometimes is glory, but mostly it is blood and disappointment and misery."

With that, Colonel Jonathan put the sword back in its leather scabbard and sent the boys, who were a little disappointed themselves, off to inquire about dinner.

The French and the Indians

Jonathan was very reluctant to tell his grandchildren the realities of that war against the French and the Indians. In fact, he had continued to serve as a captain in the Connecticut Militia in 1757 when the cold cruelties of war became all too real to him. And he had seen things that were better forgotten. He had come back home to Connecticut after several frustrating months of inaction in the frigid camps of Lord Loudon. While there, his feelings about the British military, and particular its officers, had ripened into disdain.

Nevertheless, duty called, and duty was a cherished value in Puritan New England. And so, in May, 1757, at the call of the Assembly, he accepted the task of serving as Captain of the Fifth Company of the Third Regiment of the Militia of the Colony of Connecticut. Even before this reappointment, he had been busy keeping his men sharp, and in preparing for the next campaign in the North. Old Jonathan Hempstead, his father's good friend, who wrote down almost everything that happened around New London in his diary, and thereby provided a vivid record of the times, noted on March 17, 1757: "I delivered unto Samil Richards

Capt Jonathan Lattimer Junr & John Bradford Selectmen 1 Cheast & pail of Bullitts & in it 750 flints."

Now Jonathan and his men waited for word summoning them north. Many of their fellow New Englanders were already there. Once again their commander was General Phineas Lyman. More than once, when the Colonel wanted to show his grandsons what day to day life was really like in the military, he pulled from his pocket an old crumbled paper that had somehow survived, retrieved from the old chest in his bedroom. Across the top were the words "General Orders of 1757." The boys would gather around and listen with rapt attention as he read:

GENERAL ORDERS OF 1757
By Phinehas Lyman Esqr., Majr. Genll. and Colonel of the
Troops Raised by ye Colony of Connecticut To act in Conjunc-
tion with His Majesty's Regular Troops, Under the command of
His Excelency ye Earl of Loudoun, ye Next Campaign.

Orderd
That ye Drums all Beat ye Reveille at Half After Four oclock in
ye Morning & Every Company Turn out immediately & Parade
on ye Places of Rendezvous where ye officers are to Meet and
Call them over & See that ye Men are all clean & well Dress'd &
to Note Every Defect, & that Every man Dress Neat & Clean
when on Duty.

That ye Commanding officers of Each company See that their
Men are Exercised from ten to twelve oClock A.M. and from
Four to Six P:M:, that the Places of Parad are Kept clean and
Neat.

That the Drums Beat ye Tattoo at Seven oClock at Night &
Every Company to turn out on ye Paraid. The officers to Meet
em and call em over & as soon as Dismised Every man to Return to His Quarters & Not to Be Absent without Leave & to
Keep still & Behave Orderly.

That No officer or Souldier Goes out of Town without leave
from ye Commanding officer.

That ye officers Take care to Be Punctual to the Exact time of
Performing Every order, & to see That ye Souldiers Do ye Same,

& By No Means To Get into a Loose way of Doing Duty.

That for Every Breach of order ye Offender Be Confined & a Report thereof to Be Made By ye officer of ye Guard as Soon as Relieved.

Given Under My Hand at Fondiës in Claverack ye 2nd Day of May 1757

P. Lyman

The Horrors

The Colonel thanked God regularly that his call to the Canadian border did not come until August. When it did come, the call was urgent. It was what people in those days called an "alarm." The story that came with this alarm was gruesome and terrible to contemplate. On the third day of August, three thousand Canadian militiamen and their Indian allies had arrived at Fort William Henry and surrounded the place. The Fort was situated at the southern end of Lake George on the frontier between the French and English colonies. Realizing their situation was hopeless, the defenders of the Fort surrendered on August 9. The French promised them, and the women and children who were with them, safe passage back to Fort Edward on the Hudson, a few miles to the south.

But something horrible happened. The Indians understood the essence of warfare differently from their European allies. For them, it was about plunder, the taking of slaves, and the display of courage and even of cruelty to the defeated. The French had promised that all these things would be theirs, but instead had negotiated surrender and were sending the enemy away unharmed. This could not be permitted, the Indians muttered among themselves. It was no way to wage a war.

At five in the morning the troops and their families began to leave the fort in a column and head for Fort Edward, protected by a few French soldiers. The Indians waited until the last of those in the fort were outside the gates and then rushed forward. The attack was rapid, vicious, and from the attackers' point of view nothing more than taking what they had been promised. They would wage war in the proper way, as it should be waged. The road was soon covered with dozens of dead bodies, scalped and covered in blood, clothing stripped off as booty. Some of the dead were soldiers, some were women and children. Hundreds of the survivors were taken away by the Indians—human plunder.

The French officers were mortified at this breach of the European ethics of warfare but the damage was done and their reputation as civilized soldiers was permanently soiled. And back in places like New London, when the word arrived of what had happened, there was outrage.

This was the atmosphere on August 11, when Jonathan Hempstead wrote in his diary: "One quarter of the whole militia of the town marched for Albany, to defend the country; Jonathan Latimer, captain." This time the trip north was made on horseback—a quicker if more exhausting method of travel. When they arrived, they found that the French, as horrified as the British with the turn of events, were not able to move on to attack Fort Edward as they had planned. Their Indian allies, now that they had what they had come for, headed for home. So once again, the Colonel and his men experienced not the thrill of battle but rather the sad exercise of gathering up the mutilated bodies and settling into the routines of daily life, parades, and drills. And as winter was beginning to set in, they were soon once again on their way back home to Connecticut.

Ironically, it was left to Mother Nature to avenge the massacre. Smallpox had been spreading inside the Fort before the siege, and the clothing taken away by the Indians as plunder carried the microscopic seeds of death. A terrible epidemic was soon raging among the villages of those who had waged war on the white men in their own way—and now paid the heavy price for it.

Griswold Hears the Unpleasant Details

When the boys found out that dinner was still an hour in the future, they were distracted by the chance to shoot at squirrels with their Uncle Charles' rifle, out among the trees behind the house. The Colonel returned to his thoughts, turning the old sword this way and that, and remembering how it felt in his hand in the heat of battle.

Despite his many years as an officer, and the many battles he had experienced, he had always been a rather reluctant soldier. In those days soldiering was an avocation for most men, not a vocation—even for the leaders. The American way was to have every able-bodied man serve in a local militia unit. Aware of the oppressive professional armies in Europe, who preyed upon the common people and answered only to the Kings, Americans chose to carry their own guns, elect their own officers, and to fight only when they were directly threatened. Their new Constitution would lay all this out as a "right." The guns they carried were their personal property. Only rarely did they wear a uniform. Their training consisted of Saturday morning drills in front of the local courthouse. Every man must do his duty. Missing a session might mean a 50 cent fine—or even a full dollar.

Jonathan's father before him had the look and bearing of a leader, big and good-looking, confident without being arrogant, and having the respect of his Connecticut neighbors. These were the qualities which led to election as captain of the local militia. And when the older Jonathan's body began to give out, it seemed natural that his son, who looked and acted very much like him, though not his oldest son and heir, would become captain in his place.

The younger Jonathan did not shirk from his duty, but he did not think of himself primarily as a soldier. What he valued was life on the land—a nice farm with fat cows and a big vegetable garden—a fine mill beside the beautiful stream that ran through his property, which even today is called Latimer's Brook—surrounded by his honored wife Lucretia and his well-behaved children. It was the sort of lifestyle also favored by his younger contemporary, the Virginian Thomas Jefferson. It is true he was a "public man" in a way. At various times he served as Justice of the Peace, or Selectman of the town, or Captain of the militia, because the institutions these positions represented were necessary in order to preserve the life of a prosperous colonial farmer. The ambition which drove some men to seek for more did not plague him as it did some, however. But a man cannot pick the time or the place of his birth, and Jonathan had, for good or ill, come to adulthood in a time and place of momentous events, and therefore was drawn into those events with little chance of doing otherwise. But he was not, like General Washington, or Mr. Jefferson, a man with burning ambition to be either rich or famous. He did what he had to do, and was satisfied with that.

The Colonel's reveries were again interrupted, this time by his widowed son Griswold, who was now living with Jonathan and Lucretia.

"Been telling the boys tales about the old days?" Griswold asked.

"The French and Indian War," Jonathan replied. "But I don't tell them everything, as you must know."

The Colonel had spent much time and energy in recent years securing the future for his large family as best he could—parceling out land to each of them with meticulous care to be fair and equitable. Griswold's inheritance would be the Colonel's own house and farm.

Griswold had come to the Cumberland with his older brother Witherel, years before the rest of the family. The brothers both carried the names of their distinguished forebears in Colonial Connecticut. In fact, Matthew Griswold, their mother's cousin, had only finished his term as governor of Connecticut five or six years ago. Together the two brothers had blazed the trail in the new land for the Colonel and the rest, who would come later. Griswold had taken over the care of his brother-in-law Eusebius Bushnell's children when Eusebius got himself into hot water and had to take off for parts south (a story we will save for later). He became a sort of surrogate father for the children and even signed the bond for Clarissa Bushnell's marriage in 1795. He and his wife Polly had served as witnesses on the deeds for the Colonel when he began to buy land in Tennessee back in the 1790s.

Sadly, though not yet forty years old, Griswold was already a widower. Since he was alone, his father had suggested that he come live with him and Lucretia, care for them in their declining years and then have the farm and house as his own. This kind of arrangement was the social security safety net of the frontier, and it worked rather well. The Latimer clan all thought the arrangement was only right, given Griswold's services to the family.

"Why don't you tell the whole story, Dad," Griswold asked, "Don't you think they need to know what war is really like?"

"I'm afraid they'll learn that soon enough," replied the Colonel. And then, despite the painful memories, he began to tell Griswold what he had not wanted to tell the boys. It was an account that Griswold had heard before.

In March, 1758, the Connecticut State Assembly had once again confirmed Jonathan a captain under Colonel Fitch and Major Israel Putnam. Putnam was already in the process of becoming famous and was destined to become a legendary hero of the American Revolution. He and Jonathan would fight alongside each other many times during the succeeding decades. The next few weeks had been spent trying to recruit a full complement of men to return to the North for a third campaign against the enemy, responding to an appeal by the new British Prime Minister, William Pitt.

The Colonel was not enthusiastic. Pitt promised to treat the provincials better, and that helped, but there was still that incompetent Abercrombie to deal with and Jonathan was apprehensive. So far the British had mostly come out poorly in this war, and he didn't look forward to more of the same. If it were not for the fact that his own people in New London might suffer from a British defeat, he would have been tempted to step aside from the whole affair. But duty pushed aside reluctance.

A huge army, the largest ever amassed in North America, gathered at the ruins of Fort William Henry, destroyed since Jonathan had last been there. There the men from Connecticut found a huge camp with row upon row of tents. There were thousands of Scotch Highlanders, regular British soldiers, and thousands more men from the colonies.

"We were relieved at first to find that young Lord Howe was there and in charge, instead of Abercrombie," the Colonial said to Griswold.

This relief was short-lived, however; Abercrombie was soon back in command.

"He ordered the huge assemblage to be loaded on boats on July 5. About 7:00 am on that day we set out for the north end of Lake George in hundreds upon hundreds of boats. It was a glorious sight, I must admit. Flags were flying and bands were playing. The scenery was beautiful, and you could almost convince yourself that you were a part of a wonderful holiday parade."

"But the Angel of Death confronted us soon enough. Abercrombie put the Connecticut men under Putnam in the very front, along with Rogers and his rangers, and then followed behind us with the main army. The gallant Lord Howe insisted on going with Putnam to the very front as well. We soon found ourselves lost in the dense woods and our well-organized columns fell into chaos. And then shots began to ring out at us from a French unit, also lost, scattered among the trees. We were horrified to see young Howe fall dead. And then, to add to the horror, some our own men mistook us for the enemy and began killing their own fellow-soldiers. The thicket was full of dead men, but somehow we finally got the best of the French in this 'little skirmish'—as the books call it. More than 200 French soldiers died."

"My men also learned the cost quickly. For the generals, death is a statistic; for us, at the front, death had a name. A good man, from Massachusetts, my First Lieutenant, young Jabez Howland, was struck down. The very next day it was Chris Stubbins, a young man only married two or three years before. I remember their names, and can see their faces, to this day."

"Little did we know it then, but there were to be many, many more. We spent the night in the forest and then moved on toward the Fort. And then, the next horrible day, that madman Abercrombie ordered us to rush up a rise into a hail of bullets. The road was too narrow for such a large army, and our men were scattered about in confusion. We outnumbered the French four to one, but we had no artillery to protect us. The French had piled dozens of big old trees in our path, making it impossible to move ahead with any confidence. Bullets flew everywhere. *Two thousand* of our men went down. The ground was covered with bodies and drenched in blood."

Another eyewitness to these events would later describe the battle this way: "The scene was frightful; masses of infuriated men who could not go forward, and would not go back; straining for an enemy they could not reach, and firing on an enemy they could not see; caught in the entanglement of fallen trees; tripped by briers, stumbling over logs, tearing through boughs; shouting, yelling, cursing, and pelted all the while with bullets that killed them by scores, stretched them on the ground, or hung them on jagged branches in strange attitudes of death."

After the carnage, Abercrombie ordered the British army to pull back. Many hundreds lay dead, and nothing whatsoever had been accomplished. The Colonel shuttered as he tried to push the memory back into deepest part of his mind.

He turned abruptly and made for the house, carrying the sword back to the private place where he kept it. As he walked he talked in a voice much more quiet than usual, almost a whisper.

"Never speak to me about the glories of war," he said, not so much to Griswold as to himself.

TWO: NEW YORK

The Quiet Years

Colonel Latimer returned from the wars in the North determined to settle down as a colonial gentleman farmer and raise his growing family in the quiet beauty of the fields and woods of Chesterfield in the county of New London. There were already seven children, and others were appearing on the scene with some regularity: Nicholas, Griswold, Joseph, Nathaniel…

The older children began to marry and create families of their own. Family patriarchs like Jonathan felt two significant obligations to their children in those days. The sons should be provided with the means to make their own way, usually with gifts of land. And the daughters should marry as advantageously as possible. Jonathan and Lucretia had only two daughters who reached marriageable age, but this was quite enough to trigger an entirely new phenomenon for the family, namely, the appearance of suitors.

The courtship of Hannah, the oldest daughter, went well. The young man was Daniel Rogers, of a well-known and particularly pious local family. It is true that they were known for their somewhat problematic history of holding to such heretical ideas as the equality of all races and genders, the separation of church and state, and the evils of slavery. But Daniel seemed a moderate young man of mature and respectable habits, and there were times when the Colonel himself was inclined toward those same radical ideas about equality. And as for Lucretia, daughter of a pious Christian clergyman, she agreed with them wholeheartedly. Besides this, Daniel was Hannah's second cousin, once removed (his mother was a Denison). All in all it was a good, safe choice and young Daniel quickly found his place within the Latimer clan, and in fact felt more a part of it than he did with his own tribe.

That left only one more eligible daughter, the frail but beautiful Borodell, named for her equally beautiful grandmother. But there was no hurry in finding a match for her. When the Colonel returned from the wars in the North, she was still only ten years old.

In the meantime, the family settled into country life. Jonathan's father had given his brother Robert a large house on Main Street in New London and he became the family's urban representative, along with other town-dwelling brothers, among them Daniel, Amos, Henry, and George.

The Colonel, however, preferred some peace and quiet, and some distance from the evils of the town.

New London was flourishing, its port full of ships, its warehouses brimming with goods for transport and resale, its streets full of sailors of various colors and tongues—from old England to the Caribbean. Despite the economic possibilities in town, Jonathan still preferred the more traditional life in the country, plowing fields, raising livestock, and teaching the children the value of hard work and upright living. His one concession to public life was serving as a Justice of the Peace, a significant position in the colonies, and a sign of the respect afforded him in his community.

Connecticut was still steeped in its Puritan culture and remained a dominion of the Saints. Chesterfield was eight miles from the nearest meeting house, but this was no deterrent to the family's religious activities. Every Sunday they set out like an assemblage of pilgrims, well-washed and wearing their best, tall and hardy, full stride ahead. It was a beautiful walk, full of the lovely scents of the fields and the gentle nudging of the sea-breezes. Other worshippers joined them here and there along the way and by the time they reached the meeting house their weekly procession formed the majority of all those who had gathered for prayers that morning.

The young people enjoyed this weekly ritual, but the Colonel, whose religion tended to emphasize the practical, thought the whole thing was a bit too time-consuming. So he recruited a number of neighbors, and together they petitioned the Assembly (remember that in those days there was no separation of Church and State in Connecticut) to create a new parish a little closer to home. This is necessary, the Colonel and his friends explained, because "we live remote from any meeting-house for divine service and are in a great measure destitute of the privileges of the gospel." Jonathan even offered land for the new meeting house, to be built on a hill just south of his own house, and to include an adjoining burial ground. Latimer Hill, as the site was called, was at the time a veritable jungle, full of rocks and ridges and vines and briars, but a lovely place for a church. Here, in its burial ground, would be the final resting place for many of Jonathan's loved ones.

By this time Borodell Latimer was prettier than ever and at seventeen, fair game for a suitor. Just at the most opportune moment, one appeared. His name was Eusebius Bushnell. His family was an old and respected one. Eusebius was, in fact, Borodell's second cousin. His father had attended Yale and his younger brother was to be a renowned surgeon. The

Latimers knew him well, even though he had grown up in Norwich, twelve miles away. In those days twelve miles was a long way.

However, Jonathan and Lucretia were not of one mind when it came to this handsome, polished, even eloquent young man. Jonathan had always wished that he himself were more articulate in discourse. He admired people who spoke and wrote with ease and clever turn of phrase. Eusebius was certainly one of those. Furthermore, Jonathan fancied himself a good judge of character, a quality of great importance for a military officer for whom the accurate evaluation of a man's inner strengths was often a matter of life and death. Almost eight years older than Borodell and, in his mid-twenties, already something of a man of this world, Eusebius possessed a notable presence and an air of confident maturity. He exuded self-confidence and brimmed with ambition.

Borodell, it must be said, was entirely taken with him.

Jonathan thought he would be just right. Lucretia was not so sure. His relationship to the Latimers came through her side of the family, and families talk among themselves with a candor not displayed to outsiders. She had heard things. It is true that he was half a Griswold, and the Griswold's distinguished themselves with high achievements. But there was something in Eusebius that made Lucretia uneasy. The words flowed smoothly from his lips—this was an indisputable fact—almost *too* smoothly for Lucretia. But his ambition, though admirable, seemed a little too undisciplined for her taste. Her Puritan clergyman father had taught her the value of moderation and the virtue of clear, honest, straightforward conversation. Eusebius seemed in these areas to be somewhat less than one would hope for. And though she was loath to say so to anyone else, at times he even seemed to her to stretch the truth in his attempts to persuade others with his ideas. And when is one's risk-taking a virtue, and when it is foolhardiness? She expressed these feelings to Jonathan, but in that gentle, circuitous, feminine way expected of women like her in those days.

And Jonathan, who thought and listened with much less subtlety, missed her hesitations entirely. It was not that he lacked respect for her point of view. Quite the contrary; he honored and often depended upon it. But even people who have lived together for a quarter of a century sometimes fail to communicate.

On September 13, 1772, Borodell Latimer and Eusebius Bushnell were married.

The Clouds

There was, however, little time to celebrate. Within a year the increasingly dark clouds were beginning to gather.

First, there was the ominous poster that appeared on almost every wall in the county of New London. It spoke of a meeting held in nearby Norwich on September 8, 1774, in which delegates from the area around New London discussed the "present state of this county" and how they were being threatened with "the loss of our liberties and constitution rights."

The local militias were encouraged to begin having drills, gathering ammunition and weapons, and to pay due attention "to the cultivation of military skill and the art of war."

This notice made Lucretia shudder, anticipating the worst, and knowing that her husband's life was sure to change, as would their families' and their neighbors'. But she was also confronted with another trial, a far more personal one. Not long after the wedding of her daughter, she had discovered that she was once again pregnant. This would be her thirteenth child, who would come into the world in Lucretia's forty-second year. The pregnancy ran its course, and there was a baby girl. Given her mother's age, no one was surprised that the little girl was very weak and sick from the beginning of her struggling existence. The family insisted that she be named Lucretia, honoring the mother who was for them all a tower of strength. But little Lucretia could not overcome the physical challenges that ravished her tiny body. She did not grow as she should. She often would not eat. She cried incessantly. In eight months she was gone, the last to arrive in the family and the first to leave it.

Lucretia's grief was deep and dark. Despite her inner strength this trial might have bested her, had she not become at just this crucial moment a sort of surrogate parent to a new eighteen-year-old teacher in town— freshly graduated from Yale. After all, ten of his thirty-two students were Latimers, and he would often be in Jonathan and Lucretia's home.

His name was Nathan Hale.

To the People of America:
Stop Him! Stop Him! Stop Him!

Station Camp Creek
Sunday, August 31, 1806

Griswold wandered away to find shade under the trees and the Colonel, having carefully put the sword in its place and returned outside to enjoy the pleasant breezes, was left to his own reflections. The past flowed freely into his mind, swirling like those gentle Tennessee breezes around him. He remembered how he had returned to Connecticut after the horrors of the war with the French and the Indians confident that he could now live a peaceful, pastoral life with his lovely wife Lucretia and their growing family. There would be hay to harvest, cattle to feed, town meetings and church services to attend. And, in fact, almost two decades slipped quietly by, doing those very things.

There were a dozen sons and daughters now, and would have been thirteen, had baby Lucretia not suddenly left this earth just before the War of Revolution began—her sojourn in human society no longer than the time she had spent in her mother's womb. She was the first of their children to go before them into the next world—but would not be the last. The older children were grown now, and had homes of their own. They all looked back with fondness on the simple rural life in the Chesterfield District, miles out in the country, a world away from the relative hustle and bustle of New London City.

But then the earth began to shake, and the heavens to tremble. Only two weeks after little Lucretia had left them, the Latimers and those around them were startled by the sudden arrival of an express rider from neighboring Massachusetts, shouting about horrible atrocities committed by the British in the towns of Lexington and Concord and calling for volunteers to meet the challenges to the liberty of the colonies.

The clouds of war were once again gathering in the skies of New England, and Jonathan's heart grew heavy. He had no illusions about what lay ahead. He had seen all this before. But things were different now. He was no longer a young man. Unlike the young hotheads stirred to passionate patriotism by the rider from the East, his own feelings were tempered by the unspeakable things he had seen on the Northern Borders in that time when he himself was young. Then, war seemed to be an exciting adventure—a sort of competitive sport where a man could prove his mettle before his colleagues and test his limits. But now the phrase "Lexington Alarm" carried no romantic nuances for him, no excitement in the face of adventure—only cold, hard reality, and the anticipation of blood.

The very night the rider had appeared in New London, the citizens had gathered in young Nathan Hale's schoolhouse, where so many of the students bore the name Latimer, and began working themselves into the kind of frenzy from which Wars have always gained their initial sustenance. Teacher Nathan himself, young and idealistic and passionately eager to right the wrongs of this world, gave an articulate and fiery address. The crowd roared its approval. The people were ready for arms.

And, of course, Jonathan understood and shared their concerns. He knew what would have to be done and, more to the point, he knew who was going to have to do it. Sure enough, there came first the call for volunteers to ride to the aid of the citizens of Boston. Seventy men stepped forward.

And then the question: "Who will lead our men?"

And then the inevitable answer, "Why, Jonathan Latimer, of course!"

He would have the rank of Captain. His younger brother Daniel would be his sergeant. Horses were secured. Minimal supplies gathered. Amid the shouting and general stirring the men rode off immediately in a great cloud of dust, Jonathan at the lead.

Looking back at those momentous times, now passed for thirty years, the old Colonel could remember the faces of the men who rode with him—many of them the men of Montville, the town nearest his farm. Amos Avery, Samuel Hillhouse, Ebenezer Weeks…he could have named them almost every one.

But by the time the patriotic horsemen had arrived near Boston, along with hundreds of other New England farmers, merchants, laborers and such like, the action of over. There was little to do beyond demonstrating to the British that there were going to be consequences for their attempts at oppression. Ten days later, Jonathan and his men were home again— one hundred miles to Massachusetts and one hundred miles back.

That is not to say that things returned to the *status quo ante*, however. Those ten days laid down a bright red marker; they were a preface to almost a decade of war. And not a war far up on some northern border like the one with the French and Indians. This was a war which would encroach upon a man's hayfields, invade a man's Indian corn patch, and inhabit his family's kitchen.

Life in New London did not change immediately. In May, Jonathan was once again appointed a Justice of the Peace. Then men began choosing sides. They were given no choice. Friends became enemies. Those who represented law and order, like Jonathan, were confronted with violence which grew not from criminality, but from passionate conviction. He was not surprised when one day he found this broadside nailed to every available wall, pole and wagon side in the county of New London:

To The
PEOPLE OF AMERICA
Stop him! Stop him! Stop him!

One Hundred Pounds of Lawful Money Reward!
A Wolf in Sheep's Clothing!
A TRAITOR!

Whereas Isaac Wilkins, of the Province of New-York, has made his escape from the place of his former residence, after having betrayed the confidence of his constituents, and villainously consented, that they, and their posterity, should become abject Slaves to the mercenary, and tyrannical Parliament of Great-Britain; and hath, in divers other instances, endeavoured to destroy the Liberties of America, in which Freedom will reign amidst the most sanguinary machinations of her inveterate enemies—Therefore, whoever apprehends the said Isaac Wilkins and secures him, that he may be sent to the Provincial Camp, in Massachusetts-Bay, shall receive the above reward. By order of the committee. New London, May 4, 1775

"This will be our world for a while," Jonathan thought, wondering at the same time who this Isaac Wilkins of New York might be, and what he had actually done.

Dinner in the Great Forest

The Latimer grandsons had been sitting under the great oaks in such wonder at their patriarch's stories, his almost magical sword, and then the excitement of the squirrel hunt, that they hardly noticed the time. But inside the house, the women had finally finished their monumental task and were ready to call the family together for a great feast. There was no table in the house sufficient for such a host of hungry frontiersmen, so the plan would be for everyone to take a pewter plate and fork and line up to receive the bounty before them. Portions were determined by the mothers and grandmothers, careful that everyone was treated equally, and that nothing would be wasted. Then everyone would return to the shade of the trees, find a log to sit on, or maybe simply a fence to lean on, and eat the delicacies set before them.

The women were cutting huge chunks of beef from a freshly butchered yearling calf, tender and swimming in melted fat, and laying them on the big plates. And there was also fried chicken, of course. And next to that were pots of vegetables grown in the garden beside the house: green beans that had been cooking all morning surrounded by big slices of bear bacon, okra, carrots, sweet potatoes, squash, and ears of roasted Indian corn. There was a mess of wild greens, picked in the forest by the children and thrown into a big pot with smoked ham hocks for flavor. There was the usual hot cornbread, but today there was also a mountain of hot biscuits made from the precious family store of wheat flour.

Uncle Witherel, who was the sort of unofficial spiritual leader of the clan, being as he was a ruling elder in the nearby Ridge Presbyterian Church, led the family in a solemn prayer of thanksgiving for the feast before them, and for the blessings of this new and verdant land, and for the strength to survive their times of grief and loss. Rather too much praying, from the grandchildren's' point of view, and given the plethora of wonderful smells wafting upward around them. But substantial Puritan upbringing, transported thousands of miles into the wilderness, overcame the temptations of the flesh, and they remained quietly respectful to the final "Amen."

For a while, there was almost no conversation—only the sounds of enthusiastic consumption. But soon the plates were empty, and then even the second plateful was gone. And, of course, everyone had left some room for a huge slice of wild blackberry pie, hot from the stone oven, and a piece or two of tangy honey-sweetened gingerbread.

But then the women folk gathered up the plates and pots of leftovers and disappeared into the house, and the boys once again gathered around their venerable grandfather, eager for more stories.

"Grandpapa! Tell us about Mr. Hale, the schoolmaster, and how the British hanged him, and how he died a hero," said young Charles Latimer, son of Witherel. Only ten years old, Charles was entirely a child of the great forest, and unlike many of his cousins, had never lived in New England. For him, stories from that time and place were like the sagas of the Bible. And Nathan Hale, hardly known yet by the larger public, was often remembered and discussed by the Latimers. They were, after all, a part of his story.

"For that, you need your uncle Robert," the old man said. "Of us all, he was the closest to Nat Hale. After all, Robert was a scholar in Nathan's school before the War even started." Lucretia, who would hardly have been expected to be a part of the usually all-male after-dinner storytelling, when she heard Robert's name, moved over to where her fifth son, now in his forties, sat in the shade, enjoying the afternoon breezes.

"The grandbabies want to hear about Nathan Hale," she said. "And you're the one to tell them."

Robert Latimer Tells His Story

Robert had always seemed rather frail, even in childhood. But maybe what was interpreted as frailty was no more than a sort of scholarly inclination, rare in this active family. Certainly, Lucretia had seen the most promise in him among all her sons for a life of the mind. And for that reason, he had been allowed an education beyond the basics.

He was an eager young soldier nevertheless, and was the only Latimer to show visible wounds from the Revolution. He had been wounded while still a teenager; severely enough to prevent him from active service any longer. And then, toward the end of the conflict, there had been a terrible fight with a Tory who had confronted him when he was alone in the woods. He would never talk about the fight, but would only admit that the grotesque scar on his right hand, which, in healing, had drawn his fingers almost into a ball, came from a blow by the Tory's broadsword.

Reticent when it came to his own story, Robert had never been shy in telling the story of his teacher, who 'til his dying day he never called anything but "Mister Hale." He moved over to the little gathering of youngsters and began his tale.

"It was in the early summertime," he said, looking out into the nearby pastureland as though he could see all the way to New London. "It was 1774. The air was full of talk of wars and rumors of wars. Some said the British ships were firing on Boston, and that troops were gathering. But life went on in our community. The men in the county, including lots of Latimers, had built a new school-house and painted it red. And now there was talk of a new teacher—a young fellow from Yale who came with high recommendations."

"Your grandmammy had told me I could go to school when the new teacher came and I was very excited, even though it meant I would have to stay at our Uncle Robert's house in town many nights instead of being in my own bed in Chesterfield. I'll never forget the first time I saw Mr. Hale. He was tall and strong and spoke quietly but like a poet. And, so the girls tell me, he was the best-looking fellow ever to set foot in our neighborhood. Like some kind of Greek god, they use to say."

He laughed at this, though the grandsons found this detail a matter of little or no interest.

"It was still summertime," Uncle Robert continued, "but Mister Hale got right to it. Thirty boys were gathered together and began their studies. And something else, something we had never heard of. Mister Hale said he would also teach the girls if they wanted to read some books—

27

and several of them did. They had to come to his school early in the morning—five o'clock! And he studied with them for two hours before the rest of us even got there. Of course, they didn't stay once the boys arrived. And lots of folks wondered what good it would do to have girls reading books."

Fig. 3: Nathan Hale's School in New London

"What a teacher he was! Tough on us if we didn't work hard and answer correctly. That you would expect. But he was also the liveliest teacher you ever saw, throwing himself around the room like a madman sometimes. And reading with such passion that sometimes we all laughed and sometimes we all cried. And as stern as he was in class, when the school day was done he would come out in the yard and play all the schoolboy games with us. He was big and strong and could always best the lot of us when it came to running or lifting or throwing something."

"He wasn't shy about showing off his prowess. He could stand in a barrel and just jump up in the air and land in the barrel next to it, and then do the same again—barrel to barrel to barrel. Or he could put his hand on a fence as high as his shoulder and just jump right over it like he had springs for legs. We all wanted to be just like him, and that included knowing about books and writing pretty sentences as well as being athletes."

"Those were the days when things were getting tense with the British. There were ships in Long Island Sound full of British sailors who looked like they were up to no good. And we heard rumors that they had fired on Boston from ships just like the ones we were seeing. People were taking sides, some were Tories and some were not. Everyone was on edge."

"Months went by and things got only worse. Then, one day in April of 1775 a man came riding into New London shouting that there had been big trouble in Lexington and Concord, and that the British were killing people there, and that we might well be next. That very night there was a big meeting at Miner's Tavern, and a big crowd of men and boys were there, very excited and agitated. And Mister Hale got up and gave a speech like you never heard. He said we had to act before it was too late. That it was time we acted like free men and not like slaves; that the Parliament of England was way out of line. He had everyone hanging on every word. We all wanted to take off then and there and teach those Redcoats and their Tory friends a good lesson."

"But we had to finish the school term and Mister Hale did, too. So we couldn't go with the first group that took off for Boston. But Papa went. In fact, he was the Captain in charge. And Uncle Daniel was a sergeant. Fifteen men went from around Chesterfield, and more than fifty more from around New London as well. They rode off on horses, and we were excited and amazed. They were back in New London in ten days or so and to our great disappointment they reported that things had calmed down, at least for a while, and they hadn't had a fight with the Redcoats after all."

"But things were still tense, you can believe. There were still those British ships all up and down Long Island Sound so close we could see them, and more than once the sailors came ashore and stole our livestock, and everything else they wanted, and shot at our people if anyone objected."

A few weeks later George Washington was appointed as commander of something very new—the Army of the United States of America. Then the Connecticut Legislature published the list of those they expected to form and lead the militia of that State. Jonathan did not have even to look to know that his name would be on the list.

Robert continued:

"Papa was made a Captain in the Third Company of the Seventh Connecticut Militia, and one of the first things he did was to bring Mister Hale along with him, as his First Lieutenant. Of course, he had to recruit all the men for his unit—that's the way it was done. And I'm happy to say he let me join up as a fifer, even though I was only fifteen years old. Uncle Robert, your grand pappy's brother, was the other fifer and I guess Papa felt that he would keep an eye on me."

"We didn't go off to battle right away, and of course I was disappointed at that. In fact, we found ourselves digging trenches and building fortifications for the town of New London, pretty unglamorous work, I must say. But also guarding the shoreline, which was a little more exciting. The British commander, named Wallace, was blockading our harbor and keeping us all very jumpy. He even damaged our lighthouse."

Lucretia, who had been listening to all of this from a distance, could not resist adding, "And that is when troops for our side began arriving in the area. I remember that some of them were sent over to Black Hall, my family's place at Lyme, to protect my kinsman Matt Griswold, who was deputy governor at the time. I was very worried about all this, though I had great confidence in your grandfather, who was in charge of defending New London and the towns around there. And in the middle of it all your uncle Jonathan Junior decided to get married!" Jonathan, who was the Colonel and Lucretia's second son, standing nearby, turned aside and looked off into the woods, struck with a painful memory of his bride Elizabeth, who had not lived to see the Cumberland.

"It was difficult for Papa to keep his troops in line," Robert continued. "They were not far from home, and guard duty was boring, so they tended to wander off, or just generally loll around instead of acting as proper soldiers. It was difficult for them to understand the seriousness of the situation. He had to be pretty hard sometimes; to be sure we were ready for action."

"And it's a good thing he was. One day at the end of August we saw the British Captain Wallace bringing his ship into Stonington Harbor, just across the river from us in New London. He meant to steal some ships there, and as many cattle as his men could round up. When the militia at Stonington, included several of Mama's Denison relatives, tried to stop them, the British sailors began firing all sorts of cannons at them. Papa ordered half of his men to march toward Stonington, right into a storm of cannonballs. There was terrible damage to the town, but the Lord did not allow the British to take even a single life. The firing slowed when the enemy saw Papa's men coming and stopped altogether when the Sun went down. So that was that."

"By now we had been soldiers for fifty days, but we were all itching for more of a fight than we had seen so far. After the stir-up at Stonington it was back to digging trenches. Once in a while, we were able to capture an enemy vessel in the Sound. That was always exciting. Once, I remember, we took one with its owner and three black slaves on board. But mostly, we just kept digging. And Mr. Hale was fit to be tied. We all wanted action, but he, most of all."

"A few weeks later there was the big battle at Bunker Hill in Boston, where our men gave the Redcoats something to think about. Your Uncle George, who still lives back in Connecticut, was there and fought and saw it all. The Americans had the British surrounded in Boston, and General Washington himself sent a letter to the officials in Connecticut and asked for us to come and help him out. But people in our neighborhood were very worried about this. Sending so many of our young men there will leave us 'naked and defenseless,' they said. But as September was ending, we marched away, regardless. We were finally going to war."

"Word came that your Uncle George had gotten very sick, so your Uncle Witherel joined up with Granddad's company to go to replace him. He was eighteen years old at the time." Robert glanced toward Witherel, offering to let him take over the narrative, but he only nodded and gestured for Robert to continue.

"We got a taste of military marching right away, he and I. New London, Norwich, Providence, and finally Cambridge. Mr. Hale was Papa's aide and paid the bills for our living along the way. Our feet were soon blistered and burning, and every muscle ached from fatigue, but we were excited and ready to do our duty. And we were very proud when we heard that General Washington had said 'the new levies from Connecticut have lately marched into camp, and are a body of as good troops as any we have.'"

"But what we landed in was a siege. And I will tell you now that nothing is more boring than a siege. Just setting there, week after week, trying to starve your enemy out. Mr. Hale filled his time writing in his diary about everything that was happening. I'm proud to say the name 'Latimer' appeared more than once in his little book."

"We arrived the first day of October, 1775. Your granddad was an important man there and, of course, that made us Latimers very proud. He was 53 years old and at the height of his career. We often saw him talking to General Washington and the other commanders, though at the time he was still only a major."

"We were camped at a place called Winter Hill in Cambridge, and it wasn't bad. A sort of fort had been built on top of the hill. But as time passed the men got more and more restless and some started doing bad things. There was lots of thievery, for instance. A couple of days after we arrived we got a good lesson in military discipline. We were all called out to watch the punishment of a fellow named Bunker. They tied the poor man to a horse's tail and dragged him to Winter Hill. Then they gave him a terrible beating—thirty-nine lashes. Then they carried him back to the main guard, still screaming in pain, and made him stay there until he could get together eighteen pounds of lawful money to pay for the horse he had stolen."

"Sad to say, lots of horses disappeared during this time, mostly officers' mounts, taken by men tired of the siege and needed a good ride home. It even happened to Papa. We were all crestfallen when his wonderful bay stallion turned up missing. He was a wonderful mount—six years old, fourteen hands high, a great natural trotter with a white face and white feet—worthy of an officer. I can still see that horse now, like it was only yesterday. Papa was so upset that he had an ad put in the New London newspaper offering the exorbitant sum of three dollars reward for his return. I think he thought one of his own men had decided to go back to his farm in New London in this grand style. Still in all…we never saw the horse again."

"The months went by, and the weather turned bad. Winter Hill was high ground and there was a terrible cold wind most of the time. We were in tents and were usually covered with snow and hardly ever warm. As for the war, the British were about two miles away, and once in a while there was some shooting back and forth, but all in all not much action. Our main job was to keep the roads blocked. Occasionally one side or the other got hold of a prisoner. General Washington came up from time to time to see how we were doing. Those days were marked as something special. But most of the time we just tried to amuse ourselves by playing checkers, socializing, or putting on wrestling matches. Mr. Hale was quite interested in the wrestling and especially when we had a big match between our men and those stationed on Prospect Hill. Though he was a man of strong religious discipline, he accepted that in this case evening prayers might be omitted in favor of the wrestling match—provided, of course, that no wagering was allowed. He was also a very good checker player and sometimes came to Papa's tent to have a game with him, especially on rainy days. I enjoyed watching them try to outmaneuver each other."

"Papa decided there was no good reason for me to stay half-frozen on Winter Hill and determined to send me back home. Of course, I didn't like that, but I didn't have much say in the matter. I especially hated to leave Mr. Hale, who was by far my favorite person. It was not pleasant on Winter Hill; I'll admit that. Men were even beginning to die, and there were many, many desertions. The desertions made General Washington very angry. He got together a list of all the names and sent it back to Connecticut to Governor Trumbull and asked him to punish the deserters when they got home."

"Mr. Hale not only stayed out his enlistment, but he also signed up to stay on even longer. It was a fateful decision, as we know now. He spent the last few days helping Papa with his payroll and such matters. The tents were folded, and the Connecticut men marched off for home—those who had not already done so. On December 11 Papa set out himself. His last contact with General Washington was not a particularly happy one. The General appreciated that Papa had done his duty and kept his promises, and the sendoff was polite enough. But I think Papa wonders to this day what the General was really thinking and whether he was offended that Papa was leaving. Of course, we know that Papa's greatest contribution to the Revolution still lay ahead, but who could have known that on that cold, cold day in December?"

A few days later Nathan Hale received a letter from Robert Latimer. Robert's mother had taken a look at it before it was sealed—to see that it was appropriate and worthy of the family's reputation. She remembered it well, and, as it happens, the letter has survived to our own day and rests in the archives of Yale University.

Capt. Hale:

I think myself under the greatest obligations to you for your care and kindness to me...Though I have been so happy as to be favored with your instructions, you can't, Sir, expect a finished letter from one who has as yet practiced but very little this way, especially with persons of your nice discernment...I am sure, was my Mammy willing, I think I should prefer being with you to all the pleasures which the company of my relations can afford me.

[Signed] Robert Latimer
P.S. My Mammy and Aunt Present Compts

Other letters went back and forth between Robert and Nathan Hale in the early months of 1776. In one Robert says, "You write me that you have got another fifer and a very good one too, as I hear. Which I am very glad to hear. Tho' I sincerely wish I was in his place..."

"Uncle Robert," young Charles interrupted, "Tell us again—what did a fifer do?"

"Every infantry company had its fifer—two, in fact—along with a couple of drummers," Robert replied. "Our job was to give the men a signal so they would know what was expected of them during the battle. We had to learn different tunes to mean different orders—one for advance, one for retreat, one for the order to fire—things like that. Now a fife plays a tune high and shrill, and you can hear it even when the bullets are whistling around you."

"When the whole regiment was ready to march, the fifers and the drummers from all the companies got together to play the marching tunes. They called that the 'band.' And what a sound it made—it stirs my heart just to think of it!"

"Could you still play a fife, if you had one, Uncle Robert?" another of the boys asked.

"You can bet I could!" Robert said. "Every tune is branded in my mind, you can believe that. And especially that one they called 'Yankee Doodle'!"

The Call of Duty

The Colonel's consciousness had drifted far away from the Cumberland as Robert talked, and he found himself reliving those tumultuous times so vividly that the old emotions were resurrected. This very private reverie was broken when Robert turned to the Colonel and said, "Before I finish the story of Mr. Hale, maybe you should tell them about what happened in New York. That will help them understand."

With a touch of reluctance, the Colonel agreed. "I've had some low moments in the course of war," he said, mostly to himself, "but nothing can equal the fight for New York City in 1776 and the dreadful events that accompanied that fight. That was truly awful, and I shudder to this day when I remember it."

"Then maybe you shouldn't," Lucretia called out from inside the house, where the increasingly animated and loud talk among the men outside could be distinctly heard. She had heard this story more than once, and she did not like to hear it. The Colonel's response was not to stop his narrative, but to speak much more softly, as though sharing a secret.

"I got home from the business in Boston near the beginning of 1776. It was still cold, and the fields lay in waiting for the coming of spring. Everything in me was eager to exchange the practice of war for the practice of farming. I wanted to watch the crops grow through the summer and to harvest them in the fall. That was what I really wanted." He paused, pensively.

"But it didn't happen that way."

The Colonel's eye began to glisten, something no one would have seen in his warrior days. It was clear to the more perceptive of his grandsons who surrounded him that a particularly painful memory was assailing him somewhere deep inside.

"I had hardly gotten settled before my father died. It was hard to accept—that he was gone. He had already seemed old and feeble when I left for Boston; that's true. He was, after all, almost eighty years old. But he had always been our tower and strength, and he seemed as steady and enduring in our eyes as ever he had been. But, looking back, we realized that there had been a slow decline. The shoulders stooped. There was the hint of a shuffle in his walk. You could see him grimace now and then as some hidden pain cut through his body. His eyes and ears were beginning to fail him as well. He was never the same after my mother Borodell died. He had lived five years more after that, but the joy of life was gone."

Lucretia, who could still hear the Colonel clearly, despite his attempt at *sotto voce*, and at the same time see his silhouette against the glow of the evening fires, felt a pain cross her body like a miniature bolt of lightning. "He could as well be describing himself now," she found herself thinking.

A few days after their father's death, the Colonel and his brother Daniel placed a notice in the *Connecticut Gazette*, offering to cover any outstanding debts of their father Jonathan. It took almost a year to settle his rather complex estate. He was, as they say, "land poor." He owned seven hundred and seventy-five acres of land, some of it very valuable, like the hundred acres within the town of New London, and hundreds more west of town in Chesterfield. But there were debts of almost 528 pounds (about $135,000 in today's money) and not enough cash to pay them. Colonel Jonathan and Daniel had to sell some of the Latimer land to pay these debts. Nevertheless, all eleven of his heirs were remembered in his will. This was an example of family loyalty that the Colonel remembered and tried himself to follow. "The father of the family needs to be sure all his children get off to a good start," he used to say.

In the midst of these family matters, the war once against interrupted the Colonel's plans for a year of quiet farming.

"In March," he continued, still as much to himself as to the grandsons, "word came that the Redcoats were headed for New York. General Washington and the Congress were truly alarmed about this news. They gathered up the troops who were still in Boston and Cambridge, where we had spent the cold winter before, to try to chase the British away. We couldn't let them take over New York. We couldn't even let them get close. If they did, New England would be cut off from all the other colonies, and they could take us down like trapped animals."

"So I wasn't surprised with what happened next. The recruiters went out in full force and gathered up all the boys they could find on the farms of New England. These boys and their officers began to march into New London by the hundreds. You could hear the fife and drum and the thump, thump, thump of marching feet from daylight to dark almost every day. The boys who were too young to fight, and all the girls, stood in awe by the roadsides watching the massive parade, and shouting encouragement."

"Go get 'em, boys. Go get 'em!"

"And then, to add to the excitement, General Washington himself showed up in New London. He was worried about the way things were going and anxious to get our men recruited and on their way to help his regulars in New York."

"He arrived on a Tuesday. It was a day no one there would ever forget. Now, of course, I had seen the General often by this time and served by his side. I'm proud to say that even if we weren't exactly what you would call 'acquaintances,' he did know my name, and called it out when he saw me. The General was one of the most impressive men I ever knew—maybe the most impressive. He was tall and dignified and made you feel a bit taller yourself, just to be in his presence. I know the other side of the man, too—maybe better than most. But I tell you that to this very day, I admire him as much as any man I've ever known."

"Nathaniel Shaw had a big dinner for General Washington in his fine stone house in the city. Nathaniel was the naval agent for Connecticut and an important man in the war. The house was packed with army and navy officers. General Spencer and General Wadsworth, my commanding officers, and the famous General Greene were there. The dining room in Nathaniel's house couldn't begin to hold the crowd. Outside in the streets, and down at the dock, only a few yards from Shaw's house, the locals and the soldiers were everywhere. It was one huge crowd—shouting slogans about victory and just generally building up the spirits of everyone."

"When the festivities were over, late in the night, the General went on over to Lyme and stayed the night at John McCurdy's place. The excitement caused by his visit lasted for weeks after he was gone."

"Over the next several weeks the recruits kept arriving. Finally, toward the end of June, the boats begin to load up with the soldiers and their officers and move off down Long Island Sound toward the City of New York. There was always a crowd there to shout them on their way. My good neighbor and friend Colonel Sam Selden asked me to be his Lieutenant Colonel and how could I refuse? He needed help. The poor man was getting up in years, and I knew he wasn't in good health. He had a large estate and twelve children—and the prospect of a few more years to enjoy the fruits of his long labors. Looking back, he shouldn't have gone. He had done his part. But that is the man he was. So, as I say, how could I refuse him? And the next thing I knew the General Assembly had appointed me a Lieutenant Colonel, so what else could I do?"

Once again, there was a pensive pause.

"And how could we know that in less than half a year Sam would be dead?"

"The time came to gather up our men, get them organized into companies, and load them on the boats. I stood with Sam Selden on the dock and looked them over. 'Sam,' I said, 'they don't inspire a lot of confidence, do they? A lot of them don't even have guns…or shoes that will last. Rag-tag farm boys, that's mostly what they are. A little light on the scales."

"'Sorta like me,' Sam replied."

Jonathan's last bit of business at home was to call together the Chesterfield Society to discuss the selection of a minister for the new congregation that would meet on land donated by the Colonel and his family. That done, he was ready to leave the next day. The family gathered to see him off. The children were full of excitement, but Lucretia was once again quietly grieving as women had grieved for ages, sending their men off to war.

As he finished his preparations, Jonathan stepped into the room where Lucretia was sitting, reading a little leather-bound book of poems in French, something her father had taught her to do when she was very young. He touched her gently on the shoulder to get her attention.

"Lucy, I want to ask a favor of you," he said.

"Anything, John. You know that," she replied.

"I want to send word to the county judges that you have been given power of attorney for me while I am gone."

"But John, is that sort of thing done? I am a woman after all." She punched the word *woman* a little, and spoke in such an ambiguous cadence that one could not be sure whether she was serious, or whether she

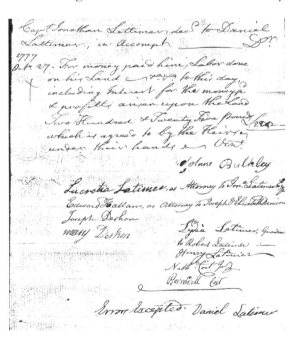

Fig. 4: Lucretia Latimer, Power of Attorney

was playfully skirting a rhetorical line between irony and sarcasm.

"Who cares whether it is done!" Jonathan replied, picking up the same cadence and skirting the same line. "No one represents me better than you, and no one is more qualified or more respected than you down at the courthouse. Whenever there is any document to sign, whether it has to do with my father's estate or with anything else, sign for me if you think it wise, don't sign if you don't."

"That is exactly what I will do," she said. She patted his shoulder, and he reached up and put his hand on top of hers and held it there for just a moment.

In a few hours, he was on the dock, seeing to the logistics of departure for the Fourth Battalion, Colonial Selden's regiment, General Wadsworth's Brigade, General Spenser's Division, Connecticut Militia. At the beginning, as the boats pulled away from New London, there were four hundred and sixty-four men in the Regiment, ready for what may come.

War in the City

The journey west to New York City took ten days. The boats stayed close to the north shore of the Sound all the way; wandering too far to the middle would make them easy prey for British ships lurking in the area.

Everyone was in place as ordered by General Washington by July 4. Selden's men were sent to occupy a series of buildings clustered around the South end of Broadway at the corner of Queens Street, less than a mile from Number 1, Broadway where the General himself was en-sconced in the mansion called Richmond Hill House. This proximity to power did not mean that Selden's men were in the center of the General's plans, however. Jonathan was aware, if the rank and file were not, that they were there to play an auxiliary role, albeit a fairly important one. They were to have more use of shovels and picks than of muskets—which may have been as well, since many of them had no muskets, any-way. They were not the General's first team, but they were to wait in re-serve, and do what they could when they could.

In the meantime, these conservative, religious, fresh-faced country boys were suffering the sudden shock of the City—something entirely new to them.

It was not new to Jonathan. He had been in the City many times, espe-cially during the 50's when he was a soldier in the war against the French and Indians. But the City was now larger, more brazen in its fleshly temp-tations, and an even bigger obstacle to military discipline than it had been in the old days. Some said that of the 30,000 residents of New York City, 500 were prostitutes. Jonathan did not doubt it. And the men, used to having their wives or mothers clean up and cook for them back home, soon turned their make-shift barracks into pig-sties, crowded, filthy, congenial haunts for vermin and microbes.

In fact, the first invasion of Manhattan was not the work of the British, but of the microbes. The men slept on the floor, cooked their own food, left the debris scattered in halls and cupboards, and drank water of doubtful origins when they were thirsty. It was not long before the Bloody Flux made its debilitating appearance and a third of the young Connecticut soldiers were writhing in agony on the hard floors. It was a malady that usually did not kill—but made you wish you were dead.

With all these distractions, the men had no way of knowing about the momentous events that had occurred over in Philadelphia that same day that they arrived. Only hours after the deed was done, a courier rushed away to New York with a sheaf of copies of one of history's most famous documents in his saddle-bag. He arrived on the 9th of July. General Washington first read the document for himself, in private. Then he ordered all the troops to gather in strict formation at their respective parades to hear it for themselves. Within sight of some of these men, and within a few minutes march for most, were tens of thousands of British and Hessian soldiers, bent on their destruction. And the waters around this scrubby and poorly prepared army were filled with hundreds of British ships, their guns trained on the island. This was the setting when with great solemnity each colonel had the document read to his men, who listened in awe:

> When in the Course of human events, it becomes necessary for one people to dissolve the political bands which have connected them with another, and to assume among the powers of the earth, the separate and equal station to which the Laws of Nature and of Nature's God entitle them, a decent respect to the opinions of mankind requires that they should declare the causes which impel them to the separation.

> We hold these truths to be self-evident, that all men are created equal, that they are endowed by their Creator with certain unalienable Rights, that among these are Life, Liberty and the pursuit of Happiness.—That to secure these rights, Governments are instituted among Men, deriving their just powers from the consent of the governed,—That whenever any Form of Gov-

ernment becomes destructive of these ends, it is the Right of
the People to alter or to abolish it, and to institute new Government...

Jonathan stood next to Sam Selden and listened. Not a man of demon-
strative emotion, his lips nevertheless tightened, and his eyes narrowed,
and he fought back the tears. He was happy for his new country, but as a
man of the real world, he read between these majestic lines a tale of
many more battles, much more blood, and unseen, but certain, horrors to
come.

As the reading continued the troops became more and more restive as
Tom Jefferson's complex sentences fell one upon the other. They had
heard already what they needed to hear. Never mind the technicalities.
Feet shuffled and whispers collected themselves into murmurs and, the
moment the last words were read, were transformed into triumphant
shouts.

"I do not excuse what happened next," the Colonel said. "But these
men, untrained and undisciplined, yet asked to risk their very lives for
what this sheet of paper represented, could hardly be blamed. They took
to the streets and, along with the civilian patriots, they let fly all their
pent-up emotion—fear, anxiety, excitement, and commitment to their
new country, the 'United States.' It has been called a riot, and perhaps it
was. Some of them rushed over to Bowling Green and pulled down the
statue of King George that was standing there. They showed it great disdain and disrespect, but in many ways, they cannot be blamed."

"Anyway, things sobered up a few days later when some British ships
came sailing around the south end of York Island showering us with
cannon balls and filling the air with smoke. The civilians panicked and
ran away and the young soldiers tasted a touch of what was to come."

"Not a very tasty dish, I'm afraid."

"But spirits were still high and the men were eager for action. Then
something happened that many took as a very bad omen. It had been hot
and steamy and everyone prayed for rain. But on the twenty-first of August—it was a Wednesday, I well remember—when the rain came. It
seemed a visitation of death itself. A huge black cloud covered the city
and lightning began to crash down around us. Soldiers caught outside
began to be hit by the bolts of fire. It was a scene from Hell. More than
one man was seen to catch on fire and fry into ashes in a few seconds."

The grandsons shuttered and looked at one another with a mix of horror and fascination at the mental picture which formed itself in their
minds.

"The next day the Sun was shining and the steam was rising again. But something far worse was about to hit us. The British were moving on to Long Island like a plague of locusts. We could easily see the smoke from their activities from where we were. Word came from General Washington, 'Bring your men back to the east, over the river; we will meet the enemy on Long Island because if he gets across the river, our cause is in horrible danger.' Then he spoke to the men himself—told them to be brave and fight for the cause. What a formidable figure he was! Tall and dignified, seemingly confident and with no hint of fear. They cheered him 'til they were hoarse."

"As it happened, most of our own New London men weren't on the front lines when the fighting started. And a good thing, too, for they were a motley crew for sure. Not that the boys at the front were much better. And there they were, facing the most powerful and well-disciplined army in the world. And then there were the Hessians, German boys not any older than ours, but trained for war and tough as nails. They might just as well have been demons from Hell for the fear they put into our boys. We heard the guns and the shouts of battle ahead of us. We began to see hundreds of our soldiers stumbling back from the front— or running full speed. They were covered with dirt and blood. They had seen their neighbors trying to surrender in the face of overwhelming force, and then seen the Hessians plunging their bayonets into one defenseless farm boy after another, as they pleaded for mercy, hands in the air. At least that was the story they came back telling. One thing was sure —their faces were the very portrait of horror."

"As officers, of course, we had more information than the poor fellows around us. But it was not good news. We were sorely beaten and almost surrounded. The General decided we had to get ourselves away from there. And I will give it to him; he planned a very clever retreat. We disappeared back across the river to New York right under the enemy's nose —and to his great surprise."

Disaster at Kips Bay

The British had by this time descended on the waters around Manhattan like a satanic host. Jonathan's task was to keep his men working hard at building defenses for the invasion which was sure to come soon. They would create a string of barriers to make things as unpleasant as possible for the invaders. But in the midst of this activity, Washington and his generals decided to try to keep the British army off the island entirely.

Colonel Selden, with Jonathan at his side, was to guide his men back across the East River once again, to a place called Coble Hill.

Jonathan stared for a moment into the distance, looking back over the years to that tragic day in Brooklyn. His face twisted in an involuntary grimace, but for some reason, he felt the need to continue.

"Our men weren't on the front line when the Redcoats made their move through the cornfields. But they could see what was happening and knew they were going to share in its bitter fruit. Thousands of well-trained and well-disciplined troops marched at us in perfect formation. From time to time they would stop and rain bullets on us in great torrents. We could hear our men at the front screaming out in pain and see them falling by the dozens.

"General Washington was there with us, but he told us to stay where we were and wait for further orders, then he rushed off into harm's way. Despite his efforts, we could see our men giving way. The hail of bullets continued and men continued to fall. Those who cried out for help got none. It was, as it always is with raw recruits, nothing but every man for himself. When the firing stopped there were hundreds of our men dead, hundreds wounded and hundreds captured. We were outnumbered two to one, not even counting the thousands more Redcoats still on the ships. The General ordered us to lead the men back across the river to Manhattan."

Washington's skill in organizing and getting his army back across the river without alerting the British is considered a brilliant bit of military leadership. But for many of the men, it was a nightmare. It started raining again soon after the action was completed and kept raining for two days. Campfires wouldn't burn. Everything got wet, including gunpowder. Cooking was impossible. Many of the men had neither a tent nor even a coat. Some had no shoes. The battle trenches filled with rain and some soldiers had to stand guard in water waist deep. Food was scarce and consisted mostly of foul-tasting hard biscuits and raw pork. And the surrounding waters were full of ships which were in turn full of enemy soldiers waiting for the right conditions to attack again.

Despite the painful memories, the Colonel had started his story and intended to finish it.

"By the morning of August 30, 1776, we had our men back on Manhattan, digging in all along the east side, looking the monster in the river in front of us full in the face. My, what a bedraggled, sour-faced lot we were! And there was absolutely nothing better ahead. That was something that the greenest one of them could plainly see. Some of our men were put in the ditches at a place called Turtle Bay, but most were further south, just at the edge of the city. Less than half of the fellows we had brought from New London were even able to stand guard. The rest were lying wherever they could—sick unto death with the city's diseases."

"The British took their time. The Hessians would shout across the river at us, insulting our manhood and predicting our sorry end in thick German accents. It was almost two weeks before the ships in the river began to move and we knew the time had come. We didn't know where they would land, and we pitied the poor souls who would have to face them first. We figured the chances would be good that we would be those poor souls."

"But it didn't turn out that way. The small armada of flatboats, full of Hessians, who were loudly singing hymns, and Redcoats, who were filling the air with curses, began to land between our men, at the weakest link in our defense chain, a short distances north of us, in a cove called Kips Bay. The ships in the river turned sideways and began to fire their cannons at the shoreline, ahead of the troops jumping out of the boats. The troops there in Kips Bay were even greener and more ill-prepared than ours. But the finest army in the world wouldn't have stood a chance at this point. Few of the boys even got off a shot. A few, at the very front, tried to surrender. The rest watched in horror as the Hessians simply walked up to the now-unarmed boys and ran them through with their bayonets."

"That was it. That was enough. The second and third lines threw down everything that would make it hard to run…including their guns, in some cases…and off they went as fast as their weary and wobbly legs would carry them. The men in our units soon heard about all this and caught that dreadful disease called 'panic' as well, and even though the enemy wasn't moving directly against them, they too began to run like the very thunder."

"We shouted at them, called them every name we could think of, cursed them at the top of our voices (and on the Sabbath, too—God forgive us!), but nothing would stop them now." The British didn't come after us. They stopped in a big meadow to regroup. But our boys didn't notice. They weren't looking in that direction. They were looking for some way *out*. And a short distance away, the British drummers sounded a steady beat, beat, beat of the drums, signaling that the mighty enemy army was once again on the march."

"About that time General Washington and his staff showed up at full gallop. I have never seen him in such a state. He was yelling orders, and curses—both of which were ignored by the terrorized farm boys. My old friend Putnam was with him, every bit as mad as the General. They rode into the middle of the exploding shells and whirring musket balls, lashing out at their troops with their horsewhips, trying to pull it all back together."

"But it was no use. Some of his aides pulled General Washington out of the fray before he was hit. If they had not rescued him from himself, history might have been very different from what it is—that's for sure!"

"Meanwhile, Colonel Selden ordered me to gather up as many of our men as I could find in boiling confusion and try to get them to safety. I saw him ride off to the Post Road, heading north, with the men who had already gathered together, shaken and frightened as they were, some bleeding, many with no weapons or gear of any kind. As always, he was encouraging them and urging them on, this time not to battle, but to an organized and honorable retreat in the face of hopelessly uneven odds. We had to hurry. If the enemy could stretch across the island from east to west above us, we were no better than trapped rats."

"I gathered up whatever men I could find, and headed north with them. Sam Selden was ahead of me, but I could see him, along with Captain Eliaphat Holmes and some other officers, heading up the Post Road.

"The day's evil was not spent. Suddenly, with no warming, coming towards our men, marching with precision and confidence, we saw a formidable party of Hessians. They were heady with their success and showing the swagger of conquerors. They pointed their bayonets menacingly at our men and shouted 'Halt sofort! Sie sind unsere Gefangenen!' There was no way of escape. A half dozen of them surrounded Colonel Selden and pulled him down from his mount. Two others attacked Captain Holmes, but he was a very big and very strong man, and he tore himself away and cried out to the men to rush through the bayonets and escape. Many did; a good many more could not."

There was intense fighting now, with men being hit on both sides. Several enemy soldiers fell, mortally wounded. More than fifty Americans had been taken captive and faced the terrible prospect of incarceration on the prison ships posted around the island. Few would survive that ordeal. When they realized that they had a high-ranking officer in their power, the Hessians moved away quickly, dragging Colonel Selden with them. Some paused long enough to fire once more into the mass of retreating Americans. By the time Jonathan could catch up to the action, Sam Selden was well down the way to the west, hopelessly restrained by the Hessians. He looked back and caught Jonathan's eye for a brief moment, signaling with a nod to the north that it was up to him to lead the men on the safety.

It was the last time Jonathan ever saw Sam Selden.

Thrust into Command

Only later would he learn what had happened after his friend was taken away. The confrontation had taken place just on the outskirts of the city, near what is today the corner of 23rd Street and 3rd Avenue. From there it is only a short distance to the infamous Debtors' Prison near the City Hall on Wall Street. That is where they took Colonel Selden. Not young and not well, dreadfully fatigued by the action of the last few hours, Selden soon felt the ominous heat of fever gradually taking over his body. The British guards, when they realized he was an officer, tried to give him some treatment, but too late. By October 11 the fever had done its work. Sam Selden was dead. The British buried him in a nearby churchyard. It would be left for Jonathan to console his family back in Connecticut, and to take command of the Fourth Connecticut State Levy in General Wadsworth's Brigade.

Meanwhile, the Colonel's son Witherel found himself in what passed for a uniform once again. This time he was not under the watchful eye of his father. He was almost twenty now, a private in the 2nd Division of the Connecticut Militia, and could expect to be treated like one. His unit had not been summoned, yet, however, and, it seemed to him, spent most of its time marching around from town to town in Connecticut.

Jonathan led the exhausted and dispirited militia men of Connecticut up the postal road northward, toward Harlem Heights. They camped briefly at a spot which the locals called "Two Mile Stone"—where a milestone measured the distance from the town center at the southern tip of the island. Here Jonathan took stock of loses and appointed officers to replace those who had lost their lives a few hours before, writing out the warrants in his own hand.

Washington's scattered troops were reassembling on Harlem Heights. Jonathan Latimer and his men took the place they had been assigned there. The British were not far behind. The days had seemed like centuries. For so many, these were the last days of their lives. There was more desperate fighting to keep the enemy from running over their encampment on the Heights. That was when the gallant Colonel Knowlton, a Connecticut man, was killed in a place called the Hollow Way, and a sergeant named Leffingwell became entangled in a very unfortunate set of circumstances (a story soon to be told).

Jonathan finally had a moment to pick up the "return" that colonels were supposed to fill out periodically—a report on the status of their men. Sam Selden's name was on the document. Jonathan could not bring himself to remove it, or to replace it with his own. He simply listed himself as the unnamed "Lieutenant Colonel." The reports from his captains were distressing. Thirty-nine men were missing, killed or captured, since the last report. Of the 458 men listed, only 251 were "present and fit for duty." There were 114 "sick and absent" and another 43 "sick and present." By New Year's Day of 1777, only a remnant of these would remain.

These memories tired the old man like a day behind a plow. Though pressed by his sons and grandsons to continue, he made excuse. "I've got to check the horses before the darkness comes," he said, and wandered off toward the barn. But the story was still playing in his head. On the 20th of September, he had submitted another report to the General and this time he wrote a word after Colonel Selden's name: "late." Then, at the bottom of the page, he wrote his own name. It was several weeks before the full impact of those terrible days could be assessed. Jonathan had gathered his men together, taken note of the missing, and sent in this report:

> September 15th, A. D. 1776.—Dead and missing on that day: Samuel Selden, Colonel.
>
> First Lieutenants: Benjamin Brewslon, John Comstock Second Lieutenants, Charles Williams, John Wheately. Sergeants killed or taken on that day: John Steadman, Edward Parker, Timothy Teffeny. Corporals missing on that day: Luther Geer, James Stair, Zabish Winship.
>
> Privates killed or taken on that day: Jonathan Wood, killed or taken, Caleb Chester, do. Nathan Beeby, do. Daniel Osgood, do. Reuben Chapman, do. Edward Church, dead, Thomas Copor, prisoner, John Nonsuch, do. Byal Lord, killed or taken, Liger Lord, do. Peter Duke, killed or taken, Ebenezer Packet, do. Fortain Quamono, dead, 16 Sept. Jacob Tuomiwos, killed or taken, Jediah Richards, do. Asher Raide, do. Able Moses, killed or taken, Zeblun Benneat, do. John Foog, do.

More than three decades ago, yet still so clear in the mind. These men, mostly really only boys, rising early, excitedly climbing onto the boats in New London, never to return.

Then, on September 21 word came that a massive fire was burning in New York City. Before it was stopped, one thousand buildings were in ashes. Word was that Washington was not sorry, and in fact thought it better that the city burn than that the British have it. And the day after that, Nathan Hale, who was like a son to Jonathan, who had been arrested in the town of New York amid the smoking rubble, was condemned as a spy and hanged without mercy.

THREE: NO MERCY

The Firing Squad

Harlem Heights
September 23, 1776

The Colonel pulled his watch from its pocket and checked the time. 11:00 am. An hour earlier the American soldiers had been summoned by the hundreds to the grand parade on Harlem Heights near a residence called "Kartright's House." All the regiments stationed below King's Bridge on the island of New York had received the order, including those who were now Jonathan Latimer's men. They stood in straight lines, at formal attention. Two smartly dressed Continental soldiers emerged from a nearby building which served as headquarters. They were leading a young man in his twenties. Behind these three figures came the firing squad. Their rifles rested on their shoulders. Their eyes were focused in a discipline-imposed emotionless glaze, staring straight ahead. The young man's eyes moved right and left, open wide as if they are taking in as much of this beautiful world as they can, while they still can. His lips are drawn into a tight line. His hands are bound and therefore cannot tremble. He is dressed in a non-descript way—tattered shirt and trousers, hopelessly worn-out shoes. Anything that might be distinguished as military has been stripped away.

Jonathan knew this young man well, and his family, too. Like many of the militiamen gathered on the field this crisp morning, he was from Jonathan's neighborhood—nearby Norwich to be exact. The problem with being a militia officer is precisely this—many of the men under your command are friends or the sons of friends, neighbors or the sons of neighbors, relatives or the sons of relatives. No matter what happens you are required to wear the face and demeanor of an officer, and to hide within your uniform the heart of a friend or a father.

The young man's name is Ebenezer Leffingwell. He is the son of John and Hannah Leffingwell.

The incident which had touched off this chain of events had occurred almost exactly a week before. Washington had ordered his army to abandon the town of New York and retreat to the north of the island of Manhattan. He had sent the brave Colonel Knowlton with a few hundred men to hold off the advancing British forces who were accompanied by thousands of Hessian mercenaries. This, he hoped, would allow his troops time to escape. With Knowlton's courageous leadership, the Americans had handled themselves well, desperately trying to erase the bitter memories of the panic at Kips Bay. General Washington's Adjutant, Reed, had come down from headquarters to see how the defenders were doing and to arrange for reinforcements. On his way back he noticed a soldier who was, as Reed put it, "running away from where the firing was, with every mark of trepidation and fear." This is what he reported to the Court Martial which had been called together four days ago.

"Go back and fight!" Reed had shouted to the man.

At this point began a series of misunderstandings and miscommunications which are common in the heat of battle and often end in tragedy. The Americans were running low on ammunition. Sergeant Leffingwell, popular with his fellow soldiers, and a dependable—and heretofore always brave—colleague had been ordered to leave his unit to try to find more bullets. Ironically both Leffingwell and Reed understood their task to be the same—to come to the aid of Colonel Knowlton's vastly outnumbered forces.

"I follow my orders, Sir!" Leffingwell answered. By this, he meant that he intended to do what his commanding officer had told him. He made a theatrical turn back to the lines, but once out of Reed's sight, he started northward, and away from the action, once again.

When Reed realized what Leffingwell had done he was infuriated. It was, for him, Kips Bay all over again. He turned aside from his own mission and rode after Leffingwell. When he caught up with him, as he told the Court Martial, "I struck him with my sword, and wounded him in the head and hand. He bade me keep off or he would shoot me; he presented his piece, and I think snapped his piece at me. It did not fire. And when I raised my own piece and pulled the trigger, it failed as well. Otherwise, I would have shot him on the spot. As it was, I dragged him back here and thus he stands, a coward, before you today."

Leffingwell, not a man for whom thoughts became words with any speed, hurting from his wounds, and awash with a storm of emotion, never explained himself at all. Rather he fell into a tortured silence. Had he been fleeter of tongue he would have said that he understood himself to be under orders to go north, not south. And thus he had found himself in that dilemma which often falls upon those whose only choice is to obey orders—just whose orders shall I obey? And instead of explaining this painful dilemma to the Adjutant, he simply feigned obedience to him, and then went on his way. Yes, he was terrified. There was no denying that. But he was not running away from his duty. And yes, he had pointed his gun at Reed. After all, the man was trying to kill him, driven by what seemed to the Sergeant an irrational rage. He reasoned this way: I owe it to my colleagues to carry out my original orders, and this man stands in my way.

Adjutant Reed, on the other hand, was still stinging from the reaction of his commander, General Washington, who had been almost beside himself with rage when the militia had buckled at Kips Bay. Reed had never seen Washington in such a state before and remained stunned by the whole affair. And here is this blasted scoundrel, running away again!

Given the General's state, the respected standing of his Adjutant, and what appeared to be the plain facts of the case, the Court Martial could hardly rule any other way than the way they did.

Ebenezer Leffingwell was to be shot.

Reed had met with the field commanders to read the Generals orders of the day. They were to assemble their men on the Grand Parade, near Cartright's House, to watch the execution. The significance of the location was not lost on Jonathan. His men were camped the closest of all to the place, between General Washington's headquarters and the fortifications constructed just to the south of the parade ground. Beyond the fortification, further south, were the troops of General's Putnam and Greene. It was clear, Jonathan Latimer thought, that Washington and his advisors had little confidence in the militia men. Had they not run away at Kip's Bay? Were they not an unpredictable, ill-trained, undisciplined rabble? He obviously wanted to be sure they saw one of their own shot down before their eyes, as a warning to others whose courage might falter. Jonathan was inwardly enraged.

The field commanders were solemn and silent. Adjutant Reed asked if there were any questions. Finally, Jonathan spoke:

"I am wondering whether the General will attend the firing squad in person so that he might observe that our men have little to eat, no coats, and in many cases, no shoes…" He stopped short of advising that the situation called for compassion, not fear mongering.

Reed's eyes grew steely and cold. "Sir, you are, I realize, new to field command. I am sure that you will consider your further career in the military before you have anything more to say."

Jonathan was unaffected, though some of his fellow field commanders dropped their heads and wished to be elsewhere. "I have no ambition beyond the care for my country's freedom and the proper respect for my men," he said.

"And I will relay this sentiment to the General," Reed replied. "You are all dismissed."

Standing on the Grand Parade, Jonathan looked at his men, their bodies at attention, eyes full of dread. The late morning mists swirled around them, and the ground was only now losing its thick covering of frost from the night before. There had been little or no sleep. Some stared vacantly ahead, rendered silent by the penetrating cold. Some wore battered shoes; some only cloth wrapped around naked feet. There they stood, still shivering from another night on the frost-covered ground, wet with the persistent rain, unprotected by any shelter from it, wearing tattered and filthy clothes, berated not only by the regulars but even by their fellow militiaman from other colonies as cowards and incompetents.

Never mind that Jonathan's men had not even been present when the panic hit. Never mind that their colonel had been dragged away, along with many of their colleagues, into a captivity leading to almost certain death. They were from Connecticut, and that was enough. It was not fair. But it was not fair that Ebenezer, who was a good man, well-liked, conscientious, but nevertheless slow of tongue, should be kneeling, waiting for a dozen musket balls to carry him into Kingdom Come.

There is an old saying "All is fair in love and war." Maybe in love; but certainly not in war. It is the stronger or more clever side, or perhaps the luckier one, that emerges the victor—not the one that is more virtuous or deserving. And when the hail of bullets crashes into the ranks, it does not bring down those who deserve to die, but only those with the misfortune to be standing in its path. This was a fact Jonathan could verify through a surfeit of experience and one which would, many years hence, reveal itself to him in the form of an unspeakable personal tragedy.

But now, as the sudden and reluctant commanding officer of a battered, even pathetic, regiment of farm-boys and field-hands, he must sternly take the side of the General. This is the duty of leadership. There must be discipline, and sometimes this is the way attention must be drawn to that undeniable fact. But these boys—and most were only boys —had no training, no equipment, no uniforms, and no idea of the larger picture. Abstract issues about the taxing policy of the British Parliament or the procedures involved in importing and exporting colonial goods had no particular bearing on their daily existence. All they knew was that they were in constant danger of being horribly mangled by an artillery shell, or struck down by a musket ball, or, worst of all, thrust through with the point of a ruthless Hessian bayonet point.

And the fact was that their hearts were with Sergeant Leffingwell. They understood him and they trusted his report of what had happened—far more than they trusted Adjutant General Reed. Or even General Washington. Or even Jonathan Latimer. Every day since the sentence, their murmuring had grown louder and louder, their anger more intense. It was not fair, what they are doing to him. It is not right. Have we come here to be treated this way? Maybe we should go home and let the Generals and Colonels and Majors and Captains fight this damned war.

Becoming more and more aware of the undercurrents among the private soldiers, Reed began to become very uneasy about the course of things. He still felt the verdict was correct and the sentence just. This he felt as a soldier. But as a man, there was just that tiny touch of uncertainty. What if, in fact, he had misinterpreted the situation? And, perhaps more important, even if he had not, was it wise to do something which might collapse what little was left of the goodwill and confidence of this rag-tag crew of farm-boys? He had been much more affected by the sentiments Jonathan had expressed than he had seemed to be.

He approached the General with these new doubts and urged him to rethink the matter.

"But we cannot afford to have men running from the enemy. Our cause is lost if these men cannot be counted upon to stand and fight," the General said.

"You are entirely correct, sir," Reed replied. "I bow entirely to your wise judgment. I simply note that what is whispered today among the men may be shouted tomorrow. And words may transform themselves into actions with perilous consequences."

On the parade ground, the firing squad was taking its place and preparing to fire. The drum roll had begun. The prisoner stood as erect as he could, determined to die like a man. The blindfold was tight, painful, and effective: a prelude to eternal darkness.

Suddenly a figure could be seen running from the headquarters to the officer in charge of the execution, putting a small piece of paper in his hand. The officer read it to himself and then gestured for the attention of the troops—as if he did not already have their attention.

He began to read:

GENERAL ORDERS. Head-Quarters, Harlem Heights, September 23, 1776.

Ebenezer Leffingwell, being convicted of offering violence to his superior officer, of cowardice, and misbehavior before the enemy, was ordered to suffer death this day. The General, from his former good character, and upon the intercession of the Adjutant-General, against whom he presented his firelock, is pleased to pardon him; but declares that the next offender shall suffer death, without mercy.

The troops shuffled and emitted carefully stifled grunts in each other's direction, fearing to react in any overt way. But when the order "at ease" was sounded, they could contain themselves no longer, and the murmurs became louder and louder until they were transfigured into a great shout.

"They will fight again now," Jonathan thought, immensely relieved.

Only a short time later did the Americans learn that while this affair had been unfolding, there had been another death sentence. This time there was no sudden act of mercy. There was no last-minute interruption. And in this case, there had not even been a trial. Less than ten miles away from the Colonel's camp, near the still smothering town of New York, the body of another young man, also an American, tall and handsome, and twenty-two years old, was almost at the very moment of Ebenezer Leffingwell's deliverance, swinging grotesquely from the limb of an apple tree.

The Apple Tree

After the siege of Boston, as the months moved by, Robert Latimer had lost contact with his teacher Mr. Hale. Many years had passed before the Latimer's were able to put together the story of what happened to him. The story had its beginning during the days of furious fighting on Long Island, the terrible events of Kips Bay, the retreat of the Americans to the northern parts of the island of Manhattan, and the struggles near Harlem Heights. The British appeared ready and able to overwhelm the southern part of the island and the city of New York in awesome numbers at any moment. General Washington desperately needed to know what they were planning to do next. The outcome of the whole war depended on what they were going to do next.

And so, for perhaps the first time in its very short history, the United States of America needed a spy. Washington asked Colonel Knowlton to find him one. Nathan Hale, at the time, was flat on his back with a bad case of the flu. But when he heard that Knowlton was secretly meeting with his officers to ask for a volunteer, he dragged himself out of his sickbed and stumbled into the meeting, determined to finally meet a challenge that would test his courage to its limits. When Knowlton made his plea, there was silence in the room. Then, from the back, a voice, at the same time weak yet confident.

"I will undertake it, sir."

No one had much respect for spies in those days, and the men in the room were shocked when they heard Nathan, a paragon of Christian integrity, volunteer for a task based on lies and deceit. But for Nathan, duty trumped even respectability. His comrades in arms were cold, sick, discouraged, and about to be trapped. He must do what had to be done.

Nathan Hale created a new identity for himself and set out for Long Island, disguised as a Dutch school teacher looking for work, hoping to mix with the British soldiers there and find out what they were up to. He began his mission on September 15, very near the time when Sergeant Leffingwell and Lieutenant Colonel Reed were having their fateful confrontation a few miles to the north. Only hours later, the gallant Colonel Knowlton would lie dead on the battlefield. Less than a week later, as Nathan moved rapidly toward his own fate, much of New York City would burn to ashes. Fateful events were packed into those few days like too many clothes in a suitcase.

By September 18, Nathan was in Brooklyn, talking, prodding, questioning along his way. Now he made the short trip across the river into New York City. Nathan had once lived there several months, and he was a striking man, tall and handsome, far from ordinary. Would anyone on the island recognize him for whom he really was? There was no time to dwell on mere possibilities. He did his work. On September 21, about midnight, the city caught on fire. Tension filled the air and was sucked into every man's lungs—especially those of young Nathan Hale. In the midst of the chaos, he quickly caught a ride back across the river to Long Island, plans, maps, and notes from his investigation hidden in his shoes. Now all he had to do was quietly cross Long Island into friendly territory again. The end of his dangerous mission was in sight.

But this was not to be. Within only a few hours, the brave young Nathan Hale had been betrayed, arrested, and sent in chains in the brig of the ship *Halifax* to face the British General Howe in Manhattan. He was well aware that spies were given no trial, received no quarter, and that there would be no mercy. He was determined to meet his fate with solid courage, dying for a cause he was sure was worth dying for. His captors dragged him before General Howe and the questioning began. He denied nothing. He expressed only one regret; that he had not been able to do more for his country.

The General was impressed with the good-looking young man before him. He could tell by his vocabulary, his articulate speech, and his calm demeanor, that he was no ordinary foot soldier. But there was never any question as to his fate. The rules of war were clear. He must die.

"May I have a chaplain to attend me?" he asked.

The answer was "no."

"Then perhaps a Bible?"

Again, "No."

Some hours passed, and it was Sunday, the Lord's Day. Nathan waited patiently as his executioners looked for a suitable tree in the park near his prison. They found one in the nearby apple orchard. They also located a length of rope and a step ladder. Everything was ready.

Nathan spent his time writing a letter to his family and silently praying for a gentle journey into the next world. The letter, of course, would never reach his loved ones and its contents are forever lost. Hours passed. Uncharacteristically, the British executioners were behind schedule. When they came for him at 11:00 a.m. he walked beside them with firm resolve, taking some comfort in the bright, beautiful day, absorbing the beauty like a stranded man drinks his last drops of water before the arid desert heat destroys him. He was soon surrounded by lovely apple trees.

"How incongruous it was," he thought, "to die in such a handsome place!"

The executioner ordered Nathan to climb the ladder, his hands still tied behind his back. He let him speak a few words about how he gave his life willingly for his country, regretting he could not do more.

"Swing the rebel off!" shouted the executioner.

The ladder was torn from under his feet. There were several minutes of agonizing struggle. The ladder was violently kicked to the ground. And he was gone.

But his body was not taken down. It was left swinging grotesquely in the apple tree for three whole days, decomposing in the bright New York sunshine. Only then was it thrown in a nearby grave, where it still lies, somewhere among and beneath the skyscrapers of modern Manhattan.

The Latimers did not know all these details, of course; historians gathered them together many years later. And it was just as well, for they would not have wanted to know them. And they certainly would not have wanted to share them with the flock of wide-eyed cousins, sitting together there in the bright Sunday sunshine on the frontier of the new land for which Uncle Robert's beloved teacher had sacrificed everything.

Sunshine Patriots

Two days after the affair of the firing squad, and three days after Nathan Hale was hanged, Jonathan received an order from General Washington, sent to all field commanders. The general had been out among the troops and saw that "this army is in want of almost every necessary—tents, camp-kettles, blankets, and clothes of all kinds." So he ordered the commanders to "use their endeavors to procure such clothing as are absolutely necessary; but at the same time I confess, that I do not know how they are to be got."

Jonathan had an idea, and he acted quickly upon it. He called one of the men under his command, Edward Hallam, whose daughter happened to be married to Jonathan's brother Robert, along with another soldier, and gave the two a note, scribbled on a small piece of paper:

> The Bearers…are in Consequence of the late General orders permitted to pass Kings Bridge on their way to Connecticut to procure Clothing for Col. Selden's Regiment, if the General will permit them.

The document was signed "*Jona Latimer, Col. Harleam Heights. Sept 25, 1776.*"

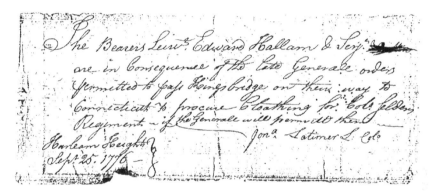

Fig. 5: The Pass from Harlem Heights

The people back home would have an opportunity to provide at least a modicum of warmth and comfort for their cold and exhausted sons and fathers.

On the 30th orders came from Washington that the officers under General Wadsworth, and that included Jonathan, should gather their tools, as a part of the "Engineer's Department" and begin working with all haste on the fortifications. All the men were to have their arms with them from the break of day, every day, since it seemed that the enemy was ready to attack once more. "*As the preservation of our Country may depend very much on a strict obedience to this Order, it is hoped that commanding Offi-*

cers of Brigades and Regiments will pay a special attention to it," wrote Washington.

Jonathan would do the best he could. Of the 490 men under his command, less than half were now fit for duty. Most were passing their days in misery—weak, burning with fever, and sick unto death—and for the most part practically naked.

General Washington and his field commanders were at the point of desperation, having lost one engagement after another and now expecting another attack at any moment. And the troops, particularly those without even shoes, and those who were within days of the end of their enlistment, were becoming more and more unreliable. They were prone to plunder, to rebel against orders, and even to desert their posts. When Jonathan received Washington's orders on the first day of October the desperation bleeding through them was palpable. First, the general ordered that James McCormick, a deserter, be hanged at 11:00 am the following day before the assembled troops. He ordered punishment for any officer whose men left the camp. He told the field commanders to place guards at the back of the men when they were marching who were to shoot anyone they saw running away.

These were, indeed, as Patrick Henry famously had said a few months before, "the days that try men's souls." It was no time for "summer soldiers" and "sunshine patriots," the golden-tongued Mr. Henry had declared. Jonathan could not repress a cynical smile when he remembered these words. "We needn't worry about summer soldiers and sunshine patriots," he thought. "My men are freezing."

"And as for deserting," he thought, anger rising within him, "most of them are too sick to run away."

As it turned out, the work on the fortifications was of little consequence. A few days later Washington decided that the troops should once again move north, leaving all of New York Island to the British. They were ordered to cross Kings Bridge and move toward White Plains, eighteen miles away. For officers like Jonathan, the hardest part of this task was moving the hundreds of men too sick to walk. That and the fact that, despite the stern warnings from headquarters, those who could were deserting by the hundreds as well, and many of those who stayed were more and more liable to disobey direct orders given to them.

Meanwhile Witherel Latimer and his companions, stalled at New Haven, finally got their order to join the action. They were to head for West Chester to serve under General Sullivan, who had just been released by the British after being captured on Long Island a few weeks before. But they were joining an army in retreat.

It was October now. The trees were glorious in reds and yellows, but the armies took no note of them. In fact, the colorful display was for them only a sign that the bone-chilling cold of winter was about to descend upon them. In a few more days the British army caught up with the Americans near White Plains and once again the air was full of bullets and cannon balls, and the screams of dying soldiers. Jonathan shuddered at the memory. There had been a dreadful confrontation in front of the entrenchments his men had helped to create. Now they stood in front of these entrenchments and faced yet another alarming Hessian vanguard marching toward them. Soon they were forced to retreat, stopping when they could behind trees and stone walls to get off a few shots at the advancing enemy. Finally, backing up the steep incline of a hill called Chatterton's, they were able to fire a deadly volley into the Hessian line that stopped their progress, though the hill was lost. It was an orderly retreat—an honorable one. Jonathan's men did not turn and run. He was proud of these half-naked farm boys.

This time Witherel shared in the horrors. When he and his companions arrived at the battle site, they were met with cannon fire from the west, where the Hessians had captured American guns and turned them on the defenders. Dead men lay everywhere, but no one pulled away from danger until darkness stopped the encounter. Then the guns were silenced. This meant that now one could clearly hear the groans and cries of those being carried to a nearby house to have their arms and legs amputated. The British troops could be seen not far away gathering up the dead. Some they were burning in large bonfires. Others they were throwing carelessly into pits, covering them with a thin layer of soil, leaving many limbs, and even some heads, with no covering at all. This gruesome task gave the British a chance to see the corpses of some American soldiers up close. One of them later noted that "many were without shoes or stockings and several were observed to have only linen drawers on"—no shirt, no waistcoat, only a hunting shirt, and a rifle.

For the rest of his life, Witherel could not think of this day without shuttering.

Under the cover of darkness, Washington withdrew his tattered army toward the hills to the north and made camp near North Castle. Fortunately for his troops, the British general decided not to follow them. Instead, he turned back ruthlessly to clean out whatever opposition still remained on Manhattan Island, a task he easily accomplished. Washington headquartered at Peekskill, and for a few days the Colonel and his son could enjoy brief moments of one another's company.

Most of the army was to eventually cross the Hudson and move on into New Jersey; the exhausted boys from New England, those who were left, stayed behind to guard the stores of supplies and the crucial river crossing-points. They had agreed to stay out their tour of duty, but no more than that. Washington and his generals had offered various incentives to get them to stay: a bounty of twenty dollars, a suit of clothes, one hundred acres of land (some day), and assurance of adequate rations. The men believed none of this, and would not have stayed even if they had believed it. Let others do their part now; we want to go home.

Jonathan was freed from the onerous task of trying to persuade these disillusioned men to stay in New York by a letter which reached him at the camp at White Plains. "The General Assembly of the State of Connecticut takes great pleasure in informing you," the letter said, "of your promotion to the rank of Colonel. You are hereby ordered to return to New London as soon as practicable, where you will assume the command of the Third Regiment of Connecticut Militia, replacing Gurdon Saltonstall, who has been promoted to Brigadier General. Your assignment shall be to defend the entrance to Long Island Sound, the town of New London, and the adjacent coastlines."

It would be only a matter of weeks before this regiment would begin to be called "Latimer's Regiment." Jonathan was approaching the zenith of his career as a soldier.

Cat-o-Nine-Tails

But all that lay ahead; for the moment there was still the British Army to contend with, establishing itself on New York Island and planning further assaults on the Americans. Jonathan's men were ordered to camp at Philipsborough, along the Hudson River, to guard the roads and waterways in the area against enemy movements toward the American army.

And then there were the court marshals. The troops, particularly the boys in the militia, tasting an end to their ordeal, were becoming more and more unruly and difficult to keep under discipline. Ill-clothed and fed, they often could not withstand the temptation to plunder or even steal supplies from their own storehouses. Angry with their lot, they sometimes boiled over in violent or even cruel treatment of prisoners, Tories, or even innocent citizens. And then there was the rum. If a jug should happen to appear out there in the dark among the men serving a cold, lonely and dangerous guard duty, it might disappear—too fast, and too abundantly, into the pit of an empty stomach. The head fogged up.

The sense of judgment wandered and tripped upon itself. Lives were put in jeopardy.

Discipline must be maintained. All these offenses must be punished. Again and again, General Washington reminded his officers of their duty to keep order. The result was a parade of almost daily court martials and afterward, a string of public punishments. Again and again, the troops were made to stand and watch, attentive to the lot of those who failed to control themselves.

The Colonel remembered one case in particular, not because it was the most important, or the punishment the most severe, but because it was the first after he had learned that Sam Selden was dead. As a field commander, he would no longer simply sign off on the punishment of offenders as a proxy for someone else. The responsibility would be his alone.

On November 18 he selected a panel of judges and ordered them to meet the next day to deal with whatever offenders were presented to them. There was only one. It was a young Irish immigrant named Matthew Connor who found himself in the American army fresh off the boat. One of Jonathan's captains, Elijah Bingham, brought the boy before the Court Martial. He was surly and defiant. Whatever his crime, he certainly was showing no signs of contrition.

"What is the charge?" asked the president of the Court, another of the regiment's captains whom Jonathan had selected for the task.

"Drunk while on guard duty," replied Captain Bingham, spitting out his words and obviously still boiling with anger, "followed by a string of oaths, directed toward his comrades and even his captain."

"And what is your defense?" asked the president.

"My defense is that I found a jug half-full of kill-devil and I drunk it up. Wouldn't you?" the boy snarled.

"And why did you do such a thing while on guard duty?"

"I was cold and needed a warm-up. And bored besides. Go ahead and put it to me, the lot of you. I can take it." The young man's face contorted into a cynical smile and he stood as tall as he could, being bound hand and foot.

"And 'put it to you' we shall," said the president. "Your behavior cannot be condoned. You have endangered the lives of your fellow soldiers and dishonored yourself and our cause."

The members of the court conferred briefly, whispering to each other.

The president turned to look directly into the young man's eyes. "We find you guilty as charged," he said. "We will recommend to Lieutenant Colonel Latimer the following punishment: that you be brought before the entire regiment and given fifteen stripes with the cat-o-nine-tails on your naked body."

Matthew Connor did not flinch, but he felt his stomach clinch at these words. He had seen the cat-o-nine-tails at work on the backs of other men. Still, he had gotten off rather easy. While the judges knew that discipline was necessary, they also felt some sympathy for poor wretches like Matthew Connor. They could have suggested as much as one hundred lashes—which would have left life-long scars, or worse. They could have recommended that he also be drummed out of the army and sent off to fend for himself. But they did not, and they knew their commander well enough to believe he would agree with their decision.

A note was written and taken to Jonathan's tent. He read it and without any hesitation simply said: "Tomorrow—at 10 o'clock."

Daylight dawned, and the regiment stood at attention in the cold morning air. A whipping post had already been erected, since simply seeing one of these had a sobering effect on the troops and helped them measure their impulses. Matthew Connor was marched out before the regiment, naked to the waist, his hands bound in front of him. At the post, the soldier in charge lifted Connor's arms above his head, itself a painful process, and hooked them on wooded pegs driven in the post high enough to stretch the prisoner's body to the point of pain.

Now the young boy who served as the regimental drummer stepped forward. He was a big boy, though not yet fifteen years old. His size was bad news for Matthew Connor. For "minor" punishments like his, the executioner was by custom the drummer boy. Part of his job was to carry a small knapsack with him from camp to camp. Inside was the dreaded whip with its nine leather strips, each looped around two or three pieces of bone or sharp metal. The boy solemnly opened the knapsack and took out the whip.

"The cat" had been "let out of the bag."

The drummer boy did his work. It did not take long. The blood showed at the very first lash. Matthew tried to keep from screaming and almost succeeded—until the last two lashes. His arms were freed from the pole and he was marched away. The regiment was dismissed. Another day of war had begun.

At this point, General Washington led the bulk of his army across the river into New Jersey. He left militia men like Jonathan's, close to the end of their tour of duty, to guard the roads and keep an eye on the supplies, which were mostly the spoils of recent battles. General Lee arrived to serve as commander of these and other forces still on the New York side of the river. Washington had ordered Lee to join him in New Jersey. But

Lee and Washington did not get along; and, in fact, Lee was actively trying to get Washington's job. He found fault with every order, and in this case procrastinated simply to show his independence. Far down the line of command, Jonathan's men simply sat and waited. Lee's reluctance to bring this motley crew to fight in New Jersey had some basis beyond his stubbornness. He counted the men under Jonathan's command and sent an accounting to George Washington. Of the 460 men who could be accounted for in the regiment, he reported, only 174 were fit for duty. The rest were sick—or gone.

As December came, the men were discharged in groups and began the hundred mile trip back to New London. Jonathan passed along the money set aside to pay his men, giving it to his captains to make the distribution. Each citizen soldier received his wages, a dollar or two for "travel expenses," and a brief word of appreciation. General Wadsworth paid Jonathan his own wages, about two hundred and fifty dollars for six and a half months of service. Then an exhausted Jonathan Latimer gathered his belongings, mounted his horse, and set out for home.

General Lee still did not bring the remaining troops across the river, but he did cross himself. Rumor said it was to meet an attractive young lady at White's Tavern over in New Jersey. There he was captured by the British and made a prisoner. But Jonathan knew nothing of this; by this time he was well on his way back to home and Lucretia.

Everyone was gone by Christmas Day. There was not a single soldier left to guard the supplies.

Sergeant Witherel and the Pirates

Here and there the signs of twilight were multiplying on Station Camp Creek. Shadows were lengthening and the night sounds were beginning. All afternoon there had been stories of battles, of tragedies and triumphs, of great men and great deeds. But the grandsons were not finished.

"We want to hear more!" insisted teenaged Hugh, Robert's son, who bore the name of the famous Protestant martyr whose was burned for his beliefs long before the Latimers had crossed the ocean to the New World. Hugh Latimer may or may not have been their kinsman, but at any rate, they liked to think that he was.

"Tell us what happened after you came home from New York, Grandpa!" said the other boys, so loudly that Lucretia, still within hearing distance, gently shushed them.

In fact, the old soldier was weary now, and the memories themselves were taxing to him. Still, it would be interesting to hear how Witherel remembered what happened next.

"If that's what you're interested in, you ought to ask Uncle Witherel," the Colonel replied. "He was there, too, you know."

Tall and somewhat quiet and unassuming, Witherel was, like most of his family, a natural leader. Now almost fifty years old, he had always been a serious man, and a pious one. He was not the first-born of the Colonel's brood, but he sometimes acted the way firstborn sons are said to act, with a strong sense of responsibility and an eagerness to maintain the family's special way of doing things. Most of the Latimers were religious, but Witherel most of all. His closest friends were clergymen, his strongest sense of duty was to his church, and his personality leaned toward introversion, despite his long record of community leadership.

The fact was that he seldom talked about his confrontations with violence. He was uncomfortable in resurrecting the memories of bloodshed—though he had certainly seen his share. But as he had heard the others talking today, the memories had welled up anyway, and he might as well talk about them.

"Tell them about the days of the privateers," the Colonel suggested. "But keep it short; it'll be dark soon."

"Privateers? Grandpa? Aren't those the same as pirates?" Hugh's eyes widened at the prospect.

"I suppose so, Hugh," the Colonel replied. "Privateers capture other people's ships and steal the cargo. That's true enough. But in this case, most of the pirates were *our* pirates. You tell them about it, son." He gestured to Witherel to continue.

Witherel nodded and began his story.

"You have to understand what New London was like," he said. "It was a place dominated by the sea and by ships and by sailors. In fact, our own family grew up out of the sea, so to speak. Our ancestor Captain Robert Latimer came to these shores from old Ipswich in England back in the 1600's. A rough old seaman he was. He had his own boat, and he sailed the coasts of America on his ship *The Hopewell* from Boston to the West Indies, buying and selling. That's how he came to New London, and that's how my part of the story begins. From the time we were boys ourselves we saw the harbor of New London full of ships. And our friends were the sons and daughters of sailors and of the merchants who did business with them. There are lots of Latimers on the ships of New England, even to this day, even though our own family moved inland and left the sea-life behind long ago."

"I tell you this to help you understand what it was like to live in New London in those days of the Revolution. There were ships everywhere. Every day they came and went. Some came from all the way across the sea; some from other ports along the coast. Up and down Long Island Sound they sailed, to and fro from New England to the town of New York. And that's where the pirating came in."

"The British ships, full of soldiers or the supplies it takes to keep soldiers fighting, moved along our coast constantly. Sometimes they were so close we could see them, and see the enemy sailors minding the masts and hustling to and fro with their other duties. Sometimes we could see some poor American soldiers who had been taken prisoner, staring out at us, near to starvation. Whenever there was an exchange of prisoners, it usually took place in New London. When our poor Yankees were let off the prison ships they came ashore looking like ghosts, starving skeletons covered in sores, burning with fever and looking death in the face. Some died within hours after leaving their horrible prison ships; others begged someone to help them get back to their homes, hardly able to hold up their heads, let alone walk the necessary miles. Your Grandpa was often involved in the negotiations for these exchanges, and tried to do what he could for the poor prisoners."

"Sometimes the ships we saw were full of enemy soldiers who could have jumped off at any time and come after us with muskets and bayonets. New London lived in a state near terror for year after year."

"So the citizens of New London did what they knew how to do. We took our own ships out into the Sound whenever we could, captured whatever unwary British ship might fall into our hands, brought them into port, and unloaded their contents into the line of warehouses along our shoreline. Yes, I guess that's what pirates do. But what choice did we have? We couldn't let them pass; knowing they would soon be killing our boys in the battles General Washington and his army was fighting for us to the west. Our men became very good at taking British ships. We called the ones we captured 'prizes.' In just one month in 1779, our New Londoners captured eighteen English ships and brought them into New London's port."

Witherel preferred to say no more about American pirates, but he could have told the boys that privateering was a major industry at the time. American sailors scoured the seas by the thousands, their expeditions financed by businesses or individuals who shared the profits when their booty was sold on the market. Sometimes it was the government itself that financed these operations. No place was more profitable for privateers than Long Island Sound, so New London became the leading base for their expeditions. Among the main financiers were such friends of the Latimers as Nathaniel Shaw and John McCurdy. The citizens of New London knew that this activity put them, their houses, and their families at great risk of retaliation. That is why they lived in fear of a sudden invasion by British troops, once the Redcoats had had all they wished to suffer of such provocations.

"When your Grandpa and I got back from New York, we found New London in something like a state of siege," Witherel continued. "The British ships were up and down the Sound like a parade of dragons, ready to devour us. And they were very, very angry with our privateers, who were very, very good at capturing British ships. The State Assembly had been reluctant to send us off to New York because it left our harbors and shores unguarded. But they knew they couldn't afford to have enemy foot soldiers coming our way, too. So they had decided it was better to send your Grandpa and others back to the West to try to help General Washington keep the Redcoats out of our neighborhood."

"As Grandpa can tell you himself, he and his men felt they had done their duty, and they looked forward to coming home, planting their crops in the springtime, and enjoying some peace and quiet. But, of course, there was no peace and quiet in New London. There were constant alarms and cries that 'the British are coming'."

"Sometimes the alarms were a cold reality. We were no sooner home than we began to hear that only a few weeks before all of New London had been sent into a panic by the news that eleven ships could be seen, entering the Sound from the East, most of them men-of-war. Then more and more other ships joined them, 'til there were almost a hundred. They anchored out at Black Point, your grandmother Lucretia's home place. The Governor sent every militiaman he could find out to meet them, but they sailed away instead of staying for a fight. Everyone was still thoroughly shaken and talked about this in hushed and even terror-stricken tones.

We had hardly been home more than two months when almost twenty British ships showed up one day along the coast. You could see the names written on their sides: names like the '*Amazon*,' the '*Greyhound*,' the '*Lark*.' They anchored in plain sight just across the river near Groton, practically in New London's backyard. We thought they were there to burn down the town and kill us all and so once again there was terror and chaos everywhere. As it turned out, their real motive was only to steal everything they could get their hands on over on Fisher's Island. They took the pigs and the cows and the chickens, the potatoes, the maize, the hay, even blankets and bolts of cloth. They handed the farmers on the island a pittance, but we considered what they were doing nothing but looting. And that is just one example; there were lots of others."

"The big ship *Amazon* was particularly frightening. It lurked around the entrance to our harbor, capturing and destroying any local boats that tried to venture out into the Sound. We were for all intents and purposes under a blockade."

"We were hardly unpacked when the Council sent word out to Chesterfield that Grandpa was needed once again in New London Town. Of course, he was now the Colonel of the Third Regiment, but both he and his men were trying to keep their own farms in operation, so they had scattered to the winds. He read the orders to me, and I still remember them. He was ordered, the Council said, '*to draft and march 200 men of his regiment, to take post at New London, under such officers of his regiment as he should assign, with himself the chief in command.*'"

"He appointed me to be his Quartermaster, with the rank of Sergeant…"

"What's a Quartermaster?" young Hugh interrupted.

"A Quartermaster had to find transportation and food and everything else the soldiers need while they were on duty. It was a difficult job and a crucial one, and it made me feel a terrible sense of responsibility, I can tell you that," Witherel replied. "I knew that Grandpa was depending on me, and so were his men."

"Grandpa knew how important it was that his men could keep their farms in order and their crops planted and tended. So he let them stay at home as much as possible. A few had to do duty at the harbor and along the coast, keeping a lookout at all times. They took turns doing that. Of course, we didn't live in New London, but rather out in Chesterfield, seven or eight miles from town and the coastline. So we worked out a way to sound the alarm whenever the British ships showed up. One of the cannons in the harbor was to be fired two times, with an interval of two minutes. Everyone knew that meant that British Ships were close enough to threaten and that our militia were to drop everything and get to town right away. It also let all the townspeople know they should run for cover. Then, when the danger was past, a cannon was fired three times, with the same intervals. That meant it was safe now to return home."

"During that spring the cannon fired the alarm signal at least once every week, sometimes more than once. Time and time again we all dropped what we were doing at home and rushed to New London, ready to fight. But each time the ships moved on and left us alone. The cannons fired three times, signaling 'all clear,' and everyone came back to town. After a while, I must admit, we began to think that the alarm signal was just going to be another false alarm and we hated to leave what we were doing and set out for the harbor. We were lulled into a false security and eventually we paid dearly for it, but that's another story."

"Our first job was to organize the men into a construction crew and to work on strengthening the town's defenses, especially Fort Trumbull and the fort across the river at Groton. We were all painfully aware that if the British decided to land, we had very little to hold them back. The people had been trying to strengthen the forts, but almost all the able-bodied men were off fighting most of the time, so not much had been done. As you know, Grandpa has great skills as a builder, so he and his fellow officers set the men to work right away. But to tell the truth, there was not much talent for building among the men and not much enthusiasm, either. And besides, they wanted to get back to their farms. So the work wasn't the best, I'll admit. One of the fortifications was so meager that people called it 'Fort Nonsense.'"

"It's a good thing we did what little we did, all the same, because just a few days after we finished our work the British came ashore nearby at both Norwalk and Danbury and did some awful damage. That could have been us if the enemy hadn't seen us working and decided to go somewhere else to do their dirty work."

"Was Grandpap a pirate?" asked an excited Hugh, hoping that he was.

"Oh, definitely not," Witherel replied. "His job was on shore—to keep the British from landing and causing us harm, or, if they landed, to make them sorry."

"And he did a good job," Lucretia interjected, knowing that far more lay behind Witherel's statement than met the eye, or that could be adequately explained to a young boy. "For many years, although the British constantly threatened us, they didn't dare come on to our shores. That was because of men like your Grandfather who provided good leadership—and, of course, the courage of the young soldiers."

The Colonel smiled; even after all these years, she was quick to defend him. And what a great comfort that had been.

Lucretia was now fully engaged in the conversation. She turned to Witherel and said, "Son, if we are going to talk about privateers, we are going to have to talk about the Saltonstalls. And if we are going to talk about the Saltonstalls, we better tell the children about the letter from General Washington."

"Woman, it's almost dark! We don't want to sit out hear rehashing old matters from long ago and far away and meanwhile get eaten by mosquitoes!" The Colonel was smiling, but obviously not too happy with the direction the story was turning.

"Witherel is a man of few words," Lucretia replied. "He will tell the children what they need to know and get us inside in practically no time at all." She nodded to Witherel to continue, and so, of course, he continued:

"The Saltonstalls were a powerful family in Connecticut. Old Governor Gurdon Saltonstall started out as a minister in the church in New London and baptized a lot of Latimers. Then he became the governor of the colony for almost twenty years. His son, Gurdon, Junior, was given the rank of Brigadier General when the Revolution started, and your Grandpa had to serve under him for a while."

"Even though they were the same age—and your Grandpa was twice the soldier, and twice the man," Lucretia spoke with an uncharacteristic touch of vinegar. "But Mr. Saltonstall got his comeuppance, didn't he!"

"We'll talk about that," Witherel replied, winching, "but first we have to talk about the capture of the ship *Hannah*."

"So we are back to the pirates?" Hugh said, eyes again brightening at the prospect.

"That we are," answered Witherel.

"This story actually happened a few years later, after your grandfather returned from the Battle of Saratoga, but I think I'll tell it to you now, since we are talking about pirates, and about the Saltonstalls. General Gurdon Saltonstall had a son named Dudley. Because of the family's connections, he got himself appointed as a ship's captain—not a very good one, I might add. He was an unpleasant fellow and hard to get along with, to say the least. I won't get into all of that, except to say that when he made his big catch, it's hard to believe it was skill and not just dumb luck."

Witherel paused, thoughtfully, and whispered under his breath, "May the Lord forgive me for saying that."

"Dudley, whom we knew quite well, took his ship called the *Minerva* down around the southern side to Long Island to look for British ships bringing supplies to the Redcoat army in New York. He had already captured the *Arbuthnot* and its valuable cargo of tobacco a few weeks earlier. Now he had the good fortune of coming upon a true treasure trove. It was the great ship *Hannah*, bound from London to New York. She was full to the brim of valuable cargo of various kinds, worth more than $400,000 at the time. He forced her into New London port and watched with what seemed to me an excess of pride as the cargo was unloaded and stored in the warehouses nearby. Everyone was happy that day, but we would soon enough rue the day it happened."

"And that's enough of that," Lucretia interjected with an authoritative tone. "Someday the boys may hear the rest of that story, not tonight. But before they are off to bed, tell them about George Washington's letter."

The Letter from General Washington

Lucretia was a paragon of Christian virtue, but when it came to the Saltonstalls, her patience sometimes wore a little thin. For some reason, the Colonel did not feel so strongly although, from her perspective, he had plenty of reason to share her tinge of animosity. He and Gurdon actually worked together as community leaders rather well and, given the financial ruin the Saltonstalls had suffered after the War, he sometimes even felt a little sorry for them. And, of course, Dudley was married to one of the Colonel's cousins; family is family, after all.

It was probably their financial difficulties, already beginning to bubble up like a spring in the Chesterfield swamps, which had triggered the kerfuffle in the first place. Brigadier General Gurdon Saltonstall brought the Connecticut militia troops to New York in 1776, including the unit in which Jonathan Latimer served as an officer, as requested by General Washington. But they were late getting there; maybe because, as Gurdon said at the time of his appointment when it came to being a general he was "ignorant in the duty of the office in every respect but zeal."

Then, once he did arrive in New York, he was almost immediately struck down by some illness and quickly returned home, never to participate in the military again. This would have been understandable, had he not decided to send a bill to George Washington for his service, anyway.

Witherel continued: "One day in May, several months after your Grandpap and I had returned from New York, we were surprised that a letter arrived from General Washington himself, written from his headquarters is Morris Town, New Jersey. Actually, it was a copy of a letter he had written to Gurdon Saltonstall, in the fine hand-writing of his aide Alexander Hamilton. Now George Washington was a great man, and a gentleman in every way. But if you got him riled up, watch out! And when he got the bill from Mr. Saltonstall, he got riled up plenty. The letter, or at least parts of it, circulated freely in New London and it was a huge embarrassment to the Saltonstalls."

"The letter went something like this (I'm just putting it in my own words, you understand): 'I was surprised to get your demand to be paid for the New York campaign and for guarding the coastlines around New London. As I remember it, you were sick and went home right away, and someone else did your duty. I don't think the public ought to pay you several hundred dollars for work you didn't do. And I think the taxpayers will agree with me when I send the money to Colonel Latimer instead.'"

"Goodness me, that was a true embarrassment," laughed young Hugh, "but how nice for General Washington to think kindly of Grandpap!"

"All right, that is quite enough," the Colonel protested. "It's too dark to be out here and time for up young ones to sleep. Everybody up and in!"

The Colonel's haste may have had something to do with the gathering darkness, but it was more about the great personal darkness which the affair of the letter had brought to his life. It was not something he wanted to think about, and certainly not something to tell the children. What may have looked like a personal triumph to others was, in fact, an immense personal misfortune for the Colonel, and very nearly a major catastrophe.

It was all a dreadful misunderstanding. On the same day, he wrote the letter, George Washington had authorized a very large imbursement to "Lt. Col. Jonathan Latimer." This he had his assistant record in his account book as follows: "1777 April 28: To cash paid him by Wm. Palfry Esq., Col. Selden's balance of pay due the Regiment: $17,312." Palfry was the Pay-master General of the American Army.

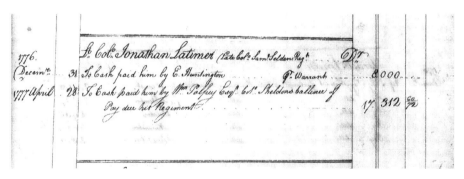

Fig. 6: The fateful receipt from General Washington

When the money had come to his hand, the Colonel thought immediately of his men: how they had to wait for months for the pay due them for their service in New York. He knew for a fact that the families of several were in desperate need, partly at least because the men had been away from home for many crucial weeks, facing the artillery barrages and bayonets of the British and Hessian soldiers on the Island of York. As we already know, he gave the money to his captains, and they gave it to the men.

Colonel Jonathan was very pleased—until he got another notice, after he was back in New London, this one from the State Assembly. Having heard of the distribution he had made, the notice said, the Assembly was obliged to remind the Colonel that it had advanced funds to the troops at the beginning of their deployment and that it expected to receive these funds back in full as soon as the Congress paid its promised compensation. Having taken over as commander of the regiment midst of the turmoil of battle, no one had thought to brief him on this decision, and he was totally unaware of what the State Assembly had decided to do. His heart began to sink.

And then the sentence that absolutely made his blood run cold: They were sure, they said, in the dispassionate prose of the day, that the Colonel understood that he was to send them the money right away, and if he had already given it out to his men, then he would just have to find it somewhere else. Since a dollar then, even a "Continental" dollar, was probably worth ten to fifteen times what a dollar is worth in our day, it is not hard to imagine the Colonel's alarm. Having to pay this amount from his own funds would surely have ruined him financially.

Unable to pay, and unable to get any relief from the State Assembly, which held the matter over his head like the Sword of Damocles, he was to live the next decade in constant anxiety.

FOUR: SARATOGA

Senator Foster

October 16, 1879
Schuylerville, New York

Had things happened a little differently, Lafayette Foster might have been the President of the United States. He had been elected President *pro tempore* of the US Senate in 1865. Six weeks later Abraham Lincoln was assassinated. The assassins had planned to kill Vice President Andrew Johnson as well, but the man picked to do the job had failed to act on his assignment. If he had done so, according to the rules of succession, Senator Foster would have replaced Mr. Lincoln in the White House.

While he did not become President, Lafayette Foster was nevertheless a distinguished politician, and that is why he had been asked to come to Schuylerville, New York to speak on a very special occasion. The little town had been called Saratoga in 1777 when it was the site of one of the most important battles of the Revolution. And now it was time to commemorate the one-hundredth anniversary of that great event.

Though he would have only a few moments to speak, the whole occasion set him to thinking about the hours he had spent as a boy, listening to his father spinning wonderful tales about the famous generals, the ferocious combat, and the surrender of the British Army at Saratoga.

It is Senator Foster's father Daniel who is the link to our story, because he is the man that Colonel Latimer chose as his adjutant the night before the Battle of Stillwater. He was the man who rode by the Colonel's side during the battle and its famous aftermath, and who knew things that only someone so close to events could have known. Already an old man when Lafayette was born, Daniel had been eager for his son to know about those legendary days of the Revolution, and the boy spent hours on his father's lap, listening in wonder.

Now an old man himself, Senator Foster's memory of those stories was vivid and powerful as ever. He rose from the desk in his hotel and rode out to the battlefield, where the local officials and workmen were busy preparing for the centennial celebration. He greeted them, but quickly walked on by, out into the green cultivated fields and thick woodlands. He paused to contemplate the site—stretching from Bemis

Heights, down along the river, a wild landscape full of deep ravines and forest covered hills, open fields only here and there. Reaching back in memory, he transported the words of his father out into the scene in front of him and imagined what it must have been like—one hundred years ago.

*

Despite the financial issues between Colonel Latimer and the State Assembly, he was nevertheless still their choice to lead the Third Regiment of the Connecticut Militia. As we have seen, once he was back home from New York, the Governor of Connecticut, John Trumbull, had also immediately called on the Colonel to organize a guard to intercept boats loaded with provisions for the British army off New London. This meant constant disruptions in daily life, because British ships might appear at any time, and one never knew what mischief they might be planning.

But then news came which called for even more dramatic action. The British General Burgoyne was rumored to be bringing an army of British, Hessians, Canadians and Indians down from Canada, marching along the Hudson River, apparently to join forces with the British troops who were occupying New York Island. If he succeeded New England would be totally cut off from the rest of the Colonies and left to the mercies of the Redcoats, who had many scores they would be happy to settle with the rebellious New Englanders.

Burgoyne must be stopped. There was no question about that. Washington was busy in New Jersey and Pennsylvania and couldn't come to the rescue. So the Congress appointed General Horatio Gates to gather an army and try to stop the invasion. The war-weary young men of New England were needed once again, as were their trusted leaders.

In May, 1777, the Assembly published this proclamation: *"Resolved by this Assembly that for the more effectual defense of this state on the Sea Coast & Frontiers and to prevent Invasions and Depredations of the Enemy there be forthwith raised two Battalions to Consist of 728 men in each Battallion including officers; in which two Battallions shall be computed the troops that are already ordered to be raised and stationed in the service until the first day of January next unless sooner discharged by the General Assembly or His Honor the Governor and Council of Safety."* Volunteers would be paid the same as regular Continental soldiers, but they were to provide their own *"arms, accoutrements, blankits and knapsacks."*

Governor Trumbull of Connecticut was worried; he was afraid these new troops would be sent away from Connecticut to fight elsewhere. He wrote to George Washington, telling him that he would prefer to keep these men at home, guarding New London. Otherwise, he said, "the advantages the enemy will have over us will be intolerable, to suffer them to get a footing at New London must be attended with very unhappy consequences." And to make matters worse, he said, so many arms had been taken to Boston and New York during the former alarms, and never returned, that the situation at home was getting desperate.

But stopping Burgoyne was vital, too, so two more battalions would have to be raised would go up the Hudson to meet him, regardless of the risks at home. This would not be easy. Most of the men who felt they were able were already in the militia. The only consolation seemed to be that the volunteers would only be asked to serve for two months.

The Assembly put an implied threat in their next proclamation. If there were not enough volunteers, the ranks would be filled up by an "indiscriminate preemptory draft," and no one without a reasonable excuse would be allowed to opt out. This meant that Colonel Latimer and his fellow-officer Thaddeus Cook, who were commissioned on August 21 to lead these two battalions, might well be faced with leading reluctant, even resentful troops.

Despite all this, within a week after he was commissioned, Colonel Latimer had 80% of his regiment signed up. They were mostly from Windham County, to the west of the Colonel's home. Unlike his earlier troops, most were not from families in his own neighborhood. As the time to march approached, many of these young men had second thoughts, and a good many simply refused to march when ordered. The governor and council responded to this by ordering that anyone not marching would be thrown in jail.

Leading these regiments was going to be a sizable challenge.

Latimer's Regiment, as the unit would be called, began to gather in Montville and New London on August 26. Some, from further away, would meet the main body along the route of the march. The Colonel was familiar with the long march which lay before them, more than one hundred and seventy miles of primitive, difficult trails winding through the mountains which lay between Connecticut and New York. Twenty years ago he had made this march more than once, as an officer in the army of His Majesty the King of Great Britain, sent to fight the French. He had to smile a bit at the irony of the situation.

But before the march could start there was one more very unpleasant matter to settle. Not only were many of the foot soldiers reluctant to set out on this assignment, one particular officer was reluctant as well. Captain Elisha Fox was a problem for the Colonel from several points of view. He had been drinking heavily. He almost certainly was leaning toward the Tories, despite his record of service in the patriot military. There were rumors that he had actually been writing letters to the British commander Lord Howe, hinting that he might go over to the other side. On top of all this, he was openly challenging his commanding officer, Colonel Latimer, and directly refusing to obey orders.

And to make matters far worse for the Colonel personally, Elisha Fox was married to the sister of Witherel's wife, Abigail Fitch. He would have to firmly separate loyalty to family from duty to country. He acted without any misgivings, however, despite the complications. Charges were brought before the Council of Safety, Elisha Fox was found guilty, and thrown out of the militia. Eventually, he would spend time in prison for his actions. There would certainly be some awkwardness at family gatherings in the future, but in the face of war, such things seemed too trivial to consider.

This particular unpleasantness behind him, the Colonel ordered the march to Saratoga to begin. Most of the men left from Montville, close to where the Colonel lived, or from nearby towns. It was an exhausting process, crossing rough terrain at the rate of fifteen to twenty-five miles a day; sometimes sleeping in friendly homes, barns or public buildings, but often in tents or the open air. At Hartford, the troops were issued provisions, such as they were, and after nine hard days of marching they were ferried across the Hudson River and arrived in Albany. It was September 13, 1777.

The reality of what was before them was underlined as they were issued handfuls of musket balls, which, for lack of a better place, many of the men simply dropped into their pockets. These little agents of death would, they hoped, find their final resting place in the body of some Redcoat or despised Loyalist. And may God guide those deadly little missiles which would come flying toward them from the enemies' side only into tree trucks and hillsides!

Ammunition in hand, the men continued their march six miles further to "The Flats"—a plantation of General Schuyler, relieved of his command and replaced by General Gates, but still doing what he could for the cause.

The next day, another twenty-mile march, and Stillwater. War had come to these now-exhausted Connecticut farm boys.

Daniel Foster had told his son the story of this march many times. As Senator Foster looked out from Bemis Heights across the lovely fields and forests, he imagined his father and his colleagues apprehensively pitching their tents in the American camp and wondering what the next few days would bring.

"The day we settled in the American camp," Daniel said, "word came that the British and Hessian troops, under 'Gentleman Johnny Burgoyne,' had started pitching their tents on the Saratoga Heights. They had arrived one day before we did. They were not far away—maybe seven or eight miles. It would not be long now."

"We were first introduced to the horrors in the form of small skirmishes carried out by Indians and Tories, who attacked our outposts and anyone who ventured far from the camp. God preserve anyone who fell into their hands! Their sole task seemed to be to terrorize us with their unspeakable cruelties toward anyone they could capture."

"It was about that time that I noticed Colonel Latimer taking some special interest in me. I saw him asking questions of two or three officers I had served under, and some of my friends—questions that caused them to look over toward me and answer him in uncharacteristically quiet voices. I had the definite impression I was the subject of their conversations."

"Meanwhile, we waited. All day on Wednesday, the 17th of September, we were kept in anxious readiness, our guns and ammunition by our sides, ready to march at a moment's notice. Colonel Latimer called everyone together and spoke to us in that gruff but fatherly way of his. He said that we should act like men, face our destiny with faith in Providence and confidence about our good cause, obey orders without any hesitation, and fight like a pack of hungry wolves! He had faced enemy fire many times, he said, and he was still here, was he not? So you must be confident that it will be the same for you. He spoke so comfortingly, and stirred our hearts so thoroughly, and looked so impressive in his fine colonel's garb, his shining French small-sword held aloft, that we all felt ready to follow him and to do our part."

"What we did not know, though Colonel Latimer did, was that General Gates had little confidence in militia units like ours, and did not intend to give us much opportunity for glory. We were, the General thought, untrained, undisciplined, and thoroughly unreliable. We might not have been surprised that when our orders came for the 18th, our contribution to the battle would be to repair the bridges between two opposing camps so that the 'real' soldiers would have a clear passage when the fighting started."

"Orders were orders, nevertheless. The day started early, and by midmorning I was busy helping to roll logs cut to shore up one of the bridges. Then a soldier whom I knew from back home in Franklin, Connecticut came up to me and spoke in a very official tone."

"'The Colonel wants to see you,' the young fellow said."

"Now I was not a novice, you understand. I was in my thirties, an officer already, and I had fought in several campaigns. I had reason to think I was chosen for some special duty. And indeed I was."

"When I arrived at the Colonel's tent he invited me in, smiling and looking surprisingly relaxed, given the circumstances."

"'Daniel,' he said, 'I've been watching you. You are a good soldier, respectful of authority, dependable, experienced, and brave. I'll give it to you short and plain—I want you to be my adjutant.'"

"I can't tell you how excited I was! My heart was pounding. I was to be the Colonel's personal assistant. This would mean I would be close to all the action, know the 'inside information,' see what a field commander did up close, and have some reason feel great pride in what I was doing."

"'Sir, you do me great honor and I accept this honor without reservation and with gratitude,' I replied, trying to sound as grave and mature as possible."

"'And I am very pleased,' the Colonel replied."

"At this point, a young soldier whose beautiful hand-writing had earned him a job as regimental scribe was summoned into the tent. He handed the Colonel a document he had already prepared. At the top were the words: *Jonathan Lattimer Esq. Colonel of the 2nd Reg't of Militia raised in the State of Connecticut now in the service of the United States of America.*' And then, in large letters: *'TO DANIEL FOSTER, GREETING.'*

"Next came this heady proclamation: *'Reposing special trust in your military skills and abilities I do hereby appoint you the said Da. Foster Adj't of said Regiment and I do hereby authorize and impower you to exercise the several duties of your said office of which you are faithfully to discharge according to the trust hereby reposed in you according to the American army.'"

"And at the bottom*: 'Given under my hand and seal in camp at Still Water this 18th day of September, AD 1777.'"

"The Colonel asked the scribe for a pen and signed the document: *Jona Latimer, Colo.'*

"'Go and get your things,' the Colonel ordered. 'You will move into my tent. And I suggest as soon as you are back with your gear you begin reading these orders from General Poor and General Arnold. This will be your Bible for the next several days.'"

"The first order I read set the course of the day. It came from Brigadier General Enoch Poor of New Hampshire. Our regiment had been attached to his brigade when we had arrived, and he would be

Colonel Latimer's direct superior. And General Poor's commander was to be General Benedict Arnold. The document ordered us to strike our tents at 3:00 o'clock a.m. the next morning, put them and our other personal gear in a safe place, and be prepared to march before sunrise, through the woods and directly at the enemy's encampment. These were chilling orders, indeed. They brought to mind the prophet Daniel marching into the lion's den. Obviously, there was going to be more to this for us than bridge repair."

The Fight at Freeman's Farm

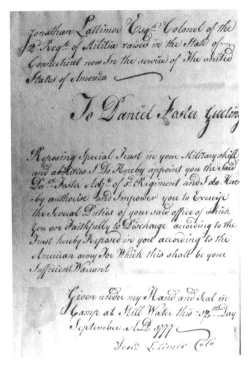

Fig. 7: Foster's Commission the Night Before Battle

Lafayette Foster walked across the clearing, only a few acres wide and deep, which had by now taken its place as one of those almost sacred fields for Americans, a place where America's destiny had been set on that September day in 1777. In his mind's eye, he could see his father, gazing into a distant memory, as if he were speaking to the horizon and to a congregation of the spirits of the dead.

"The morning of the 19th was hazy at first," he had said, "covered with fog, but then clear. The air was calm, and everything was blanketed with a layer of frost. Here and there you saw a man shudder, partly from the cold and partly from dread. We could hear the British doing what we were doing—lining up from east to west, getting ready to march into battle. The trumpets of reveille and the drums from both armies were echoing through the woods and hills and blending into a bizarre kind of symphony. We had struck our tents as ordered, gathered up our arms, and were ready to march. We took our place among the many regiments on the American left wing. There were militia men from New Hampshire, New York, Massachusetts, and of course the regulars from a host of the colonies; there were even tall frontier riflemen who had come all the way

78

from Virginia with Colonel Morgan. And over them all was General Benedict Arnold."

Lafayette remembered how he had reacted to this bit of information. Benedict Arnold! The traitor! What was he doing there and why was he leading those patriots whom the boy had been taught to almost idolize?

"You must understand, my boy, that in those days we thought of Benedict Arnold as a great leader, a courageous warrior. He was, though you may find it hard to believe or accept now, our favorite general. He was smart and he was fearless. If we had known what darkness there was in his heart, we might not have followed him so wholeheartedly. But if we had not followed him, we might have lost everything."

"When our scouts heard the movement of the Redcoats and saw them beginning to advance, they reported this to General Arnold. Our major general, Horatio Gates, always a cautious man, wanted to sit tight and let them come at us. But Arnold said we should go out and take them on— face to face. And that's what we did."

"It was ten o'clock before the fog had lifted enough to allow us to fight, and our scouts told us the enemy was three miles away and coming toward us. This was it. This was when a man had to pick up his gun and reconcile with his destiny and march into the day that might well be his last."

"Morgan's riflemen rushed ahead, and when they got close enough, the bullets began to fly. We began to hear the screams of men who had been hit and to see them fall into the grass. Soldiers running everywhere. Explosions. Shouts from the officers. Cursing. Desperate voices calling on God. Chaos."

"That's when we started to move up. Colonel Latimer moved back and forth among the companies, making sure the Captains were getting their men ready to advance. Some of our regiment hadn't even arrived on the battlefield yet, but most of us were there. The plan was to send wave after wave of reinforcements against the enemy, and we knew that they would do the same to us. New men were to be sent in about every half hour. We would have to wait a while to take our turn."

"As the morning passed, the number of men on the lines grew and grew. Guns and cannons were firing everywhere you looked. Men were dying everywhere you looked. Pandemonium was king."

"In the early afternoon, Colonel Latimer ordered us to move forward, into the swirling smoke. We were now about a mile and a half from where we had just spent an anxious night; there was nothing between us and those lines of firing muskets and fixed bayonets. But it was still not yet time for us."

"Things were going well. The enemy was falling back and our men were taking prisoners. We watched men fall in agony up ahead of us, men of both armies. We would soon be there ourselves."

"But about three o'clock the firing stopped and everything got very, very quiet. It was a strange sort of time-out. Both sides, exhausted, pulled back out of musket-shot range, leaving a strip of forest and the thin field called Freeman's Farm between them. We gathered in our lines at the place and in the formation Colonel Latimer had ordered. We were very quiet…waiting. We could hear the British officers barking out commands. We knew there was more to come."

"Half an hour passed; then another. There was only an occasional shot. The sound bounced echo-like around the trees and across the field. Little advance parties from both sides feigned attacks forward, testing the other side's resolve. Then, suddenly, everyone started shooting again. There was smoke everywhere. Too much smoke to keep the lines in place. The only order that could be obeyed was 'fire at will.' Once again there was chaos, but this time, though we were still a half mile from the front, the bullets were whizzing past us, artillery shells exploding all around us, and men dropping into pools of their own blood."

"Then a message arrived from General Arnold. The Colonel looked at it, drew his sword, and shouted, "It's our turn boys. Forward!" It took another half hour to get within firing range. It was only an hour now 'til sunset. I will say for our boys, untrained and terrified as they were, that they lined up like real soldiers, did not flinch, leveled their rifles, and fired away. We had our first taste of death. Six, seven, eight, nine farm boys from Connecticut fell into the tall grass and among the trees, never to rise. Two or three dozen more, not mortally wounded, nevertheless were crying out in pain and calling for help. Some said later that our two Connecticut regiments lost more men than any others, and even General Gates had to commend us. I have been told that we made an important contribution on that day, even if not much was ever made of it."

"All along the line our American boys were fighting furiously, and the enemy was gradually moving backward into the woods on the north side of Freeman's Farm. We were killing them in great numbers."

"Then, just as the sun began to drop behind the trees, the Hessians arrived. They were fresh and ready, and they had big cannons with them. We were horrified to see the shells fall among our men and sometimes tear them limb from limb. This was when one of Colonel Latimer's officers, Captain Clark—a good man, fell to the ground. He was found there after the battle, where he fell, sorely wounded, and taken back to camp. But two days later he died. I had been in his company before Colonel

Latimer made me his adjunct. We grieved for him and his poor family back home. But time was too precious to spend much of it on grieving."

"Finally, the combination of artillery and Germans was too much, and we had to fall back. Besides, it was now too dark to see to fight anymore."

The Second Great Battle

"There was no rest that night. We were all sure that as soon as the morning light allowed it, the Redcoats would mount another ferocious attack. Colonel Latimer's regiment had been scattered during the battle, and some were suffering the results more than others. Some were still so far behind the lines that they had not yet fired their weapons. But for most, night became a swirling mixture of respite and terror. Poor Captain Clark's men had the worst of it. Many were lying wounded on the ground. For some of them, it would be two or three days before they had anything to eat. Those who were closest to Freeman's Farm had the hardest night. They could hear wounded men from both sides crying out for help, or for some kind soul to put them out of their misery. They could see dark and mysterious figures moving around the field, unrecognizable, gathering up guns and plundering the pockets of both the living and the dead. Somehow these devilish creatures could move about freely, but if a soldier tried to go help his fallen comrades he faced almost certain death from snipers."

"The enemy was in worse shape than we were, though we didn't know that. They had no intention of attacking again until they could get themselves into better shape. And a good thing, too, because we were out of ammunition and supplies and would have been in big trouble had they come after us."

"The sun came up on September 20, and the predominant sound was still only the groans of the wounded. We spent our time caring for those we could, including the dying Captain Clark, getting ourselves reorganized, checking to see who had survived and who had not, and receiving new orders. We were able to load some of the wounded on boats and send them down to Albany. We were to strike our tents at 3:00 o'clock and get ourselves ready to fight again at any moment. This became the pattern for the next two weeks—strike tents, prepare for battle; strike tents, prepare for battle…"

"But the Redcoats did not come. Sometimes they sent Indians and Tories to harass us. We did our best to harass them as well. Sometimes we could hear scattered shooting. But that, bad as it was, was all. We waited."

"Both sides began to locate in almost the same spots they had camped before the battle at Freeman's Farm. It appeared that we were going to have to do the same thing all over again. September faded and October arrived, but the pattern of constant alarm continued. We were in range of cannon shot, but neither side made a move."

"General Gates now took control of the left wing of our army, with Poor, Learned, and Morgan under him. We were under Poor, and located on the heights, between the front line troops and Gate's headquarters. Notice I didn't mention Benedict Arnold. That's because General Gates had taken his command away from him, or at least made him so enraged that he resigned. There had been a terrible argument between them, and it was the talk of the camp."

"The fact is, though no one would say it out loud, we preferred Arnold to Gates any day. Gates stayed in his tent; Arnold got out in the thick and things and led like a real soldier. When the colonels found out what had happened, they sent a petition to Arnold asking him not to quit and telling him they had confidence in him as their leader. I know that sounds very strange now, but that's how it was at that time. Colonel Latimer signed the petition—I saw him do it."

"October 6 was Sunday, and of course we had church services in the afternoon. The preacher used the words of the old Hebrew prophet to encourage us: '*Return to the stronghold ye prisoners of hope; even today do I declare, that I will render double unto thee.*' We were back in the stronghold, all right, and praying mightily that the Lord would render to us double!"

"On the next day, we were sent out as a covering party between the enemy and our main camp. We had no provisions and soon got lost. Then we had to stay out all night in an ash swamp in the rain and cold, no sleep, and so close to the enemy lines that we couldn't even whisper to each other. We didn't get back to camp until 10:00 o'clock the next day— the day of the second great battle. As you can imagine, we were totally exhausted."

"The British had already been on the move. They were now less than a mile from us, sitting on the ground in a big wheat field with their weapons ready, waiting for orders to attack us. About noon General Gates sent orders to the officers, including Colonel Latimer, to get ready for action. Our job, along with our comrades in General Poor's Brigade, would be to attack the British on their left."

"The fighting started about half-past two o'clock. We were told to advance but to hold our fire and to keep completely silent. We marched in eerie silence, looking straight ahead, like souls of the dead rising out of Hades. We waited until the British were almost on top of us, bayonets almost in our faces. They were also shooting at us, but because we were coming up a hill they were missing—firing over our heads. Then our men suddenly let out a terrific shout and started shooting. The roar of the guns was deafening. The enemy soldiers began to fall in great numbers all around us. We ran ahead, right into the mouths of their cannons. Our men captured some of the guns, turned them around, and fired on the Redcoats with their own ammunition. I will admit that our enemies fought as bravely as we did—but we were catching a faint whiff of victory and that drove us forward."

Benedict Arnold

"About this time we heard again from Benedict Arnold. Strictly speaking, he was no longer our commanding officer and if fact, General Gates had pretty much shut him out of the whole affair. But he was not a man who lived by the rules, and he wanted to be a part of the action. He was furious about the way he had been treated and, some say, had been a little too busy with a handy keg of rum. He borrowed a small brown horse from one of the Connecticut men and rode off like a madman toward the battlefield. As he got closer, he rode right into the place where our men were waiting their turn to the front. He shouted to the first group he saw, "Say, boys, what's your regiment?"

"Colonel Latimer's, sir," they shouted back.

"Arnold smiled and roared, 'My old Norwich and New London friends…God bless you! Now come on boys; if the day is long enough, we'll have them all in Hell before night.' With that he galloped off toward the front at full speed."

"When he got there he simply took over three of General Learned's regiments, who shouted with obvious joy to be led again by their old commander. Off they went into the thick of the fight, following General Arnold. Then he called on the Connecticut militia units to follow him as well. And they did that very thing—gladly. He was, as usual, at the very front of the men he led. He ducked bullets on all sides with no sign of fear or concern for safety. But finally his luck ran out, and the bullets found their target, striking his horse and his legs at the same time. The little brown horse fell dead, and Arnold lay on the ground beneath the animal with serious wounds in both legs. Some of the Connecticut soldiers carried him back to headquarters in bad shape, but he had clearly won the day."

"Twilight was approaching, and it would soon be too dark to fight. Our regiment was next in line to reinforce the front. We had been held back because so many of our men had had no sleep or rest for more than twenty-four hours. Still, we were ready to go. But very shortly after we moved forward, orders came to cease fire for the day. We found ourselves disappointed and relieved at the same time."

Senator Lafayette Foster remembered that at this point in his story his father's face always turned somber and grey, giving him the look of a man who had just eaten something very sour. The Senator was walking across the wheat field now as the gentle night time winds pushed the vegetation back and forth. This was the only sound that disturbed the otherwise quiet vista in front of him.

On the night of October 7, 1777, the scene was far different. "When the fighting stopped," his father had told him, "we were ordered to drop where we were and to spend the night with our arms at the ready. When Burgoyne made his charge the next morning, as we were sure he would, we would bear the full brunt of it. Looking out over the wheat field, we could see it was strewn with the bodies of the dead or dying. The usual despicable camp followers were already there, plundering both the dead and the poor wretches lying on the ground in helpless agony. But we saw something even more horrible. Wolves and other wild creatures began to come out of the surrounding woods and feast on the flesh of the fallen soldiers. To this day I sometimes wake from sleep in my bed feeling cold and wet, terrified and full of revulsion—just as I felt that night. I can still hear the howling of the wolves."

"When the morning came we were ordered to march forward, fully expecting to meet fierce resistance from the Redcoats. But as we marched across the wheat field, the only red coats we saw were those of dead men, lying scattered everywhere. These at least had somehow escaped the indignities of the plunderers and the wolves. Realizing by now that the British had lost their enthusiasm for fighting us, and were retreating instead of attacking, we began to stop and bury the bodies, sometimes putting them by the dozens in mass graves. Sadly, we also found many Americans lying among them—and buried them as well."

"Burgoyne was all but surrounded, and we had him badly outnumbered, but he still would not surrender. Our job became preventing him from slipping away by blocking off his escape routes in every direction."

"Two days after the battle it started to rain, and the streams became swollen, the roads knee-deep in mud, and the temperature descending toward freezing. We were miserable, but not half as miserable as our retreating enemies. Still, Burgoyne would not give up. But many of his soldiers did. They were deserting and streaming into our camp in droves. Then we were told to stop firing and wait. We kept marching north to the little village called Saratoga, where we could stop the enemy if he tried to escape to the north. We waited for something to happen. Either the British would fight us again, or they would give up. We camped on Schuyler River, just west of the town and a little south of Schuyler's Mills, close to the Meeting House. We began to see envoys passing from their side to ours, then back again. We knew they were carrying messages, but what those messages might be, we did not know."

"In the midst of all this misery, something very good happened quite unexpectedly. Three big wagons drawn by teams of oxen drove up to our camp, led by David Trumbull, fresh from the General Assembly of Connecticut. When we uncovered the wagons we found, to our utter amazement, bag after bag of sugar, and, even better, five hogsheads of New England rum!"

"'Enjoy yourselves lads!' shouted Mr. Trumbull, a suggestion met with a loud "hurrah" from the troops. The Redcoats must have been perplexed to hear such a thing under the circumstances. The Colonel was smiling, but he called me aside and told me quietly to be sure that the jolly turn of events did not turn into dissipation. We were, after all, in the midst of a battle, and still faced with great danger."

The Surrender

"Finally, eight days after the battle, word came that Burgoyne had given up. The date was October 15. When the word began to spread through our camp, we could not help but shout for joy. But then, about nine o'clock the next morning, we heard that Burgoyne had changed his mind and his men were picking up their arms. General Gates sent him another message and told him he had an hour to put them down again or we would come after him. So he changed his mind once more and agreed to surrender. General Gates still wasn't sure he could be trusted, and so we had to sleep with our arms and be up at 3:00 am the next morning, ready to fight."

"But Burgoyne did keep his word. When we rose at 3:00 am we were ordered to parade. Then we waited until 8:00 am and paraded again. At the second parade, Colonel Latimer told us to strike our tents, load them up, and march as fast as we could to Headquarters at Saratoga. When we got there, we found that all the American regiments were gathering along the road just north of the Meeting House, lining up on either side. We took our place and stood at attention."

"The Sun had just risen and the morning fog lifted when we heard the British fife and drums and saw them coming, their flags flying—the

British in their red coats, the Hessians in blue and green. They were putting down their arms in a certain place, stacking them neatly, their faces full of the shame of defeat. We thought it was an honorable defeat, and so our men looked straight ahead or down at the ground as if to say, 'We know that pain, and we respect it.' We did not taunt them, but stood in absolute silence and tried to act like real soldiers and men of honor."

"There were thousands of them. It took them three hours to pass by, and we were very, very tired by the time it was over. At one point, however, we could hardly contain our enthusiasm when our own musicians struck up a lively version of 'Yankee Doodle Dandy.' The British had always made fun of this little song, and it must have pained them greatly to have to listen to it now!"

"We had beaten an army made up of experienced, hardened professionals, sent by the greatest power on earth to put us down. Some people say our victory was the turning point of the Revolution and is the key to our becoming a free people in a free nation. I'd like to think they are right."

"I didn't get to actually see Burgoyne hand over his sword to General Gates, but I'm sure Colonel Latimer did. And then General Gates invited all his officers to have a fine meal along with the British commanders. Wouldn't you love to hear Colonel Latimer tell what happened there, and what he thought of all those fellows!"

It was cold now, and late. Senator Foster pulled up his collar and moved across the old battlefield, the sounds of muskets and cannons and the voices of the victors and vanquished ringing in his head. Back in his room he dashed a few notes on a scrap of paper and lay down to sleep.

The ceremonies the next day were worthy of a triumphal procession in ancient Rome. More than three thousand people, many of them celebrities, marched to the battlefield to join additional thousands of spectators. There was the famous author George William Curtis; E. P. Howe, whose son would become the personal secretary and confidante of Franklin Delano Roosevelt; Horatio Seymour, former governor of New York who had run for President against Ulysses S. Grant, and a gentleman who was a grandson of General Schuyler himself. Curtis and Seymour gave long and eloquent speeches, and Howe read a *very* long poem written for the occasion by the poet Alfred Sweet. Senator Foster saw that the crowd was getting restless and the day was far spent. He was experienced and wise enough to know that brevity in circumstances like this would be recognized by the crowd as brilliance. And so he chose to simply tell a story about his father and Colonel Jonathan Latimer. It went like this:

"Among the numerous incidents that my father used to relate, which occurred a short time prior to the surrender of Burgoyne, I call to mind one that I will repeat. His regiment was ordered at a certain time to take up a new position. In marching through the woods to the post assigned them, they encountered a body of Hessians who were lying in ambush in their way, and who rose up suddenly and fired upon them.

"My father was marching by the side of Colonel Latimer. On receiving the enemy's fire, the colonel slapped his hand on his thigh, as my father thought in a rather excited manner, and called out, "fire!" The order was very promptly obeyed, and the order to form in line was almost simultaneously given.

"My father was marching with a musket, which he snapped when the order to fire was given, but from some defect in the musket-lock, it stopped at half-cock and did not go off. Most of the men by this time had changed their positions, and my father was left standing almost alone. He made up his mind, however, not to leave till he had fired his gun. He re-cocked it, took aim again, pulled the trigger and fired. He then took his place in the regiment, and after one or two more volleys, the Hessians retreated in disorder.

"On reaching their position, the regiment pitched their tents and encamped. My father occupied a tent with Colonel Latimer, and at night, when the colonel pulled off his boots to turn in, a bullet dropped from one of them on the ground. This led to an examination, and they soon found that his coat which had long pocket-flaps, reaching down on his legs, had a bullet hole through one of the pockets.

"In that pocket, the colonel had a large pocket-book quite filled with papers, and among them his colonel's commission. The bullet had passed through this pocket-book and was thus so deadened in its force, that on reaching the colonel's person it made only a slight indentation in the skin and dropped down into his boot. This served to explain the hurried manner of slapping his thigh with his hand when the first fire of the Hessians was received. The slight twinge which the bullet gave him was immediately forgotten in the excitement of the occasion.

"The commission was folded as it lay in the pocket-book, and when opened, it showed seven bullet holes through it. My father always alluded to that commission as one that a soldier would prize!"

The senator's brief tale was well-received, and he couldn't help but wonder how his father and Colonel Latimer, both men of modesty and lovers of simplicity, would feel about being the object of so much attention by so august an assembly.

He also wondered what had ever happened to that commission with seven bullet holes in it.

FIVE: ANNI HORRIBLES

A Shepherd-boy, who watched a flock of sheep near a village,
brought out the villagers three or four times by crying out,
"Wolf! Wolf!" and when his neighbors came to help him,
laughed at them for their pains. The Wolf, however, did truly
come at last. The Shepherd-boy, now really alarmed, shouted in
an agony of terror: "Pray, do come and help me; the Wolf is
killing the sheep"; but no one paid any heed to his cries, nor
rendered any assistance. The Wolf, having no cause of fear, at
his leisure lacerated or destroyed the whole flock.

—Aesop, 6th Century B.C.

The Road Home

Colonel Latimer's men were not to rest just yet. The day after the surrender at Saratoga, before the sun had shown itself, they were on the march
again, this time toward Albany. Word had come that the British, who
were occupying New York City, were sending troops to cut off the victo-
rious Americans and nip their pretensions in the bud. The Colonel's orders were to march relentlessly toward Albany, forty miles away, with no
breaks for rest. There was no time to prepare food and no opportunity
for sleep. This new British threat had to be intercepted and stopped.

As they made their way south along the river, the Colonel's men came
to "The Sprouts"—a series of treacherous channels at the point where
the Mohawk River joins the Hudson. It was now 10:00 o'clock in the
evening. Boats were not available, so the exhausted men had to wade
through the channels in the dark, at great risk. Somehow, they got across.

After a brief rest at Albany, they crossed the Hudson River and were
off again, marching on the east side of the river through Green Bush and
Kinder Hook. When they reached a place called Claverack the Colonel's
mind was flooded with old memories. Two decades earlier, he had
camped here as a young officer under General Phineas Lyman, preparing
to fight the French. This time there was welcome news. The British army
had turned back at the town of Esopus, thirty miles to the south. But
there was also bad news; the Redcoats had burned the town before leaving it. When Latimer's soldiers arrived along the river at the point opposite Esopus they could see the charred remains of the houses, churches,

and public buildings of the once lovely little town. Smoke was still rising from the ruins. The Colonel's thoughts ran back to the burning of New York City, only a few months before. What a terrible waste is war!

The men were very aware of the calendar now. They had signed up for two months, and those two months were finished. The immediate threat was over. It was time for them to go home.

On October 30 the regiment reached a little German town called Rhinebeck. Here Colonel Latimer called his men together and spoke warmly to them, expressing his admiration and thanks for their courage, their discipline, and their almost superhuman endurance. "Go home to your families now," he said, "And pray that our troubled land will soon see peace and prosperity."

With this, he packed his own gear, sheathed his silver-handled small-sword, and made off for Chesterfield, Lucretia, the children, and his beloved farm. A few days after his arrival back home, "Latimer's Regiment" was officially disbanded and became, for various reasons, a footnote in history.

Hard Times

The Colonel was given no time to rest. The situation at home had deteriorated dramatically while he had been gone. He immediately resumed his duty as commander of the 3rd Regiment, charged with keeping an eye on the British ships which were constantly threatening New London. The alarms were frequent but sporadic. They did not dominate daily life, but they so destabilized it that nothing ever seemed normal.

As for the town itself, and the harbor, other officers had the main responsibilities. There were forts on either side of the Thames River's mouth, Fort Trumbull in New London itself, and Fort Griswold (named for Lucretia's cousin Matthew Griswold) on the other side of the river in Groton; and then, of course, "Fort Nonsense"—the primitive installation on the high ground of the town, designed to help defend against an attack by sea. All these were under the command of other officers, but whenever they needed additional help, Governor Trumbull of Connecticut had told them, "call on Colonel Latimer for what may be needful in New London."

The citizens tried hard to keep their sons and fathers in the Continental Army, who were still off fighting to the west and south, in their thoughts and prayers. As the year approached its end, George Washington asked the people of the United States to celebrate a national day of Thanksgiving—the first for the new nation—to give thanks for the great victory at Saratoga. This would take place on Thursday, December 18.

In New London, of course much was made of the part played at Saratoga by the town's own young men, and of their leaders, Thaddeus Cook and Jonathan Latimer. The colonel did not enjoy this kind of thing and was somewhat embarrassed by the attention. But in his heart of hearts, he was at the same time very proud.

The citizens thought it would be appropriate to make a special effort to show their appreciation to the men still under arms, so they took up a collection for them. They gathered together cash (26 pounds, 12 shillings), and 17 shirts, 14 pairs of stockings, 4 coats, 7 jackets, 3 pairs of breeches, 2 pairs of drawers, 20 pairs of mittens, 1 pair of trousers, 7 pairs of shoes, 1 pair of gloves, 2 felt hats, and 2 dozen handkerchiefs. They had no way of knowing how welcome these things would be to their poor soldiers, often shoeless and at times almost naked in the cold winds.

The months rolled by. The alarms continued. Hostile ships were sighted over and over. The New London privateers continued to do their work. The British high commander General Clinton began to refer to New London as "a den of serpents." He was thinking more and more that something must be done to stop the American pirates and to root them out of their lair at the mouth of the Thames River.

Colonel Latimer had not only military duties but community duties as well, since he was still a Justice of the Peace. When some of the locals began to cut down trees on public land to use for building materials and firewood, he and his fellow justices wrote a stern order to them. They were to appear before the justices with a plan to pay the community for what they had taken. Otherwise, "they may depend upon being taken and prosecuted...which matter will be disagreeable to us as well as expensive to them." The matter would be "disagreeable" because the colonel and his colleagues knew how desperate people were getting as times got worse and worse. But order must be maintained, no matter how hard it was to survive under such stress.

One day in December, when a year had passed since the Day of Thanksgiving, a ship sailed into New London harbor bringing with it a terror even greater than the ominous enemy armadas passing up and down the Sound in full view. These had now become almost common. But this was a very different kind of vessel. Making its way down Long Island Sound from New York, it slowly turned into the mouth of the Thames and approached the docks of New London.

When the ship was close enough for the citizens on the docks to see its cargo, their blood ran cold. It was packed with wretched prisoners who had been held in New York City by the British and were now being dumped on New London. There were more than five hundred of them. At least there had been five hundred when the ship left New York. Two hundred of the prisoners were out-of-luck Frenchmen, caught up in a conflict not yet their own, the rest mostly American soldiers, prisoners of war. They were dying at the rate of fifteen or twenty every day. The dead were tossed one by one into the Sound, leaving a trail of emaciated corpses in the water.

As the gloomy line of figures stumbled down the gangplanks onto the dock the horrified New Londoners began to see that they were sick— very sick. The diseases were varied. Some were partially paralyzed. Some were fevered. But worst of all were those whose bodies were covered from head to foot with ghastly lesions and scabs—the demonic smallpox. There were voices demanding that these be turned back, or thrown into the river. But most called rather for Christian charity; humanity called upon them to do what they could. These put the new arrivals in buildings apart, with white flags flying over them as a warning. But someone had to care for them, and the pestilence was already transferring itself from the prisoners to the Good Samaritans among the people of New London.

For the next several months the New Londoners, already threatened constantly by the possibility of a naval attack, were also threatened by deadly disease and a growing shortage of the basic necessities of life. Nathaniel Shaw, a friend of the Latimers, a prominent citizen and ship-owner, sat at his desk in his stone house by the docks and wrote to the Marine Committee of the United States:

> We are in such a wretched state in this town by reason of the
> smallpox, fever, and famine that I cannot carry on my business,
> and am laying up my vessels as fast as they come in, for every
> necessary of life is at such an extravagant price that whenever I
> employ persons to do anything they insist upon provisions,
> which it is not in my power to give them.

A Plethora of False Alarms

The next year, 1779, seemed to be merely another copy of the two years before, except that if anything the alarms and the troubles grew more flagrant and intense. The United States Congress was more and more aware of the vulnerability of New London, and sent a detachment of its own troops there to help the local militia.

Hearts rose and fell as one threat after another emerged, some no more than swirling rumor, some very much real. In March scouting ships arrived in port with a very disturbing report. There were, they said, a fleet of vessels, twenty or more, heading from New York east on the Sound. And two great warships, one with sixty-four guns and the other with fifty, were on their way to meeting them, coming on the south side of Long Island. And that another fleet of twenty-six ships was gathering at Sag Harbor, less than thirty miles away. And that the British commander General Clinton had already left New York and was gathering a huge army at Southampton—even closer to New London. As if to confirm all this, some seaman saw ships gathering in Gardiner's Bay, almost within sight of New London. And worst of all, the enemy frigate "Renown" could definitely be seen anchored just at the mouth of the River Thames. All this could only mean one thing—New London was about to be attacked by a mighty British invasion force.

As always in such cases, the alarm-bells began to ring, and signal fires were lit (it was already almost dark); a ship in the harbor fired two measured cannon-blasts—the signal for all able-bodied militia men to rush to the defense of the town. Colonel Latimer received orders from his General, John Tyler, and passed them along to his men:

> Whereas I have received orders from General Tyler to see that the Rigment under my command equipt to march to the post at New London in a moments warning compeat in arms & ammunition three days from then According to orders you are hereby ordered to see that your company is equipt with arms and ammunition for three days duration and to hold themselves in readiness to march to the town of New London without delay when the alarm is given.

Day after day they waited. A week passed. Nothing. One by one the ominous fleets that did in fact exist (some were mere phantoms) began to move, but in different directions. There was no invasion. Ironically, the British General Clinton was in the area because he had heard rumors that the Americans were about to attack *him*. And thus does constant stress, enforced by rumor, flower into needless panic.

On June 25 it happened again. Fifty vessels, seven of them warships, were so close they could be clearly seen by the lookouts along the western shoreline. The signal guns were fired in the harbor. Everyone watched with dread as the fleet anchored off Plum Island, just across from the old Latimer and Griswold lands at Black Point. Militia men appeared from everywhere, including Colonel Latimer's charges. General Tyler's whole brigade was there, drawn up for battle, full of enthusiasm and ready to fight. The British ships were now in sight. But then, instead of turning toward New London, they sailed straight to the west toward New York, and out of sight.

General Tyler gave a nice speech to the troops, offered them his thanks, and sent them home.

Less than two weeks later the whole drama unfolded yet again. Word came of a fleet on its way from New York through the Sound. The impressive enemy frigates "Renown," "Thames," and the warship "Otter" were seen near New London. This time the threat was real, but it was New Haven the enemy was after, not New London. The British did land on nearby Plum Island and Fisher Island, plundered them and burned everything they could not steal. Then they moved on. General Tyler's regiment stayed for three weeks, Colonel Latimer's men once again among them. They went home without firing a shot.

Meanwhile, the sailors of New London continued to enhance their reputation with the British as a "den of serpents." During this time of constant false alarms, the New London privateers managed to capture eighteen British ships, along with their crews.

The question was, when will the enemy have all of this annoyance he can endure?

The Colonel continued his civic duties, now on a greater stage than ever before. He was selected, along with Gurdon Saltonstall (despite their earlier difficulties, the two men were once again good friends), as New London's representatives to a "Convention of Committees" in Hartford. Deputies, including many major political figures and economists, had gathered from five states to discuss the darkening financial situation, the rampant inflation, and the possibility of putting price controls into effect. The report of the convention was sent to the Continental Congress, where it was read to the assembly of famous persons making up that august body.

Jonathan Latimer was at the height of his career. A war hero, a leader of men, even a statesman of sorts, he was now a major figure.

The confidence he inspired can be seen in a glowing letter which Dr. Simon Wolcott, a New London physician of the distinguished Wolcott family, wrote to his friend Thomas Shaw, Nathaniel Shaw's brother. Wolcott was in Boston serving as an army surgeon when he heard of events in New London. His judgment of Colonel Latimer approaches the rapturous.

Friend Thomas:

I think as you write in your last post that New London shall & will be defended if the same fire that seems to have taken hold of your pen and does universally pervade the breasts of our Connecticut heros. I know it to be a truth. I often think I see that old veteran Col. Lattimer in his military best collecting his regiment in military array. Then dismounted with his shoulder to a carriage wheel that has thundering cannon for its load, he straining like Hercules to lift it from the slough. Then in mighty counsel seated planning for the public weal. By Heavens, Tom, you must be safe under such guidance.

Your Humble Servant to Command, Simm Wolcott

The Wolf Did Truly Come at Last

September came to New London, and despite their many trials and tribulations, the people tried to maintain some modicum of order in the midst of swirling uncertainty and constant apprehension. The people of New London were not of one mind. For some, independence was a cause worth dying for. For others, it was an unthinkable outrage. The town and countryside were torn apart by these conflicting sentiments, and it seemed that for every patriot there was a counterbalancing Tory—someone not to be trusted. Beneath the surface, not far beneath, there smoldered a growing hatred between neighbors. For every bold patriotic rhetorician, there was nearby some silent loyalist—watching.

The harbor was alive. Ships went out into the Sound almost every day to hunt for enemy vessels to capture. The warehouses along the docks were packed with the contents of pirated British ships. Workmen were busy unloading the valuable cargo of the great ship *Hannah* as she sat helpless in her captivity. All along the coastline guards watched for danger, or at least were supposed to be watching.

But no one had noticed a whaleboat being rowed in the darkness from the direction of Sag Harbor, across the Sound. Nor did anyone see the vessel land at Crescent Beach. Several passengers jumped out into the shallow waters and moved ashore. Obviously familiar with their surroundings, they set off with great haste toward a certain house a short distance away. It was the house of the well-known Tory Elisha Beckwith. Beckwith welcomed his visitors and invited them to a meal Mrs. Beckwith had prepared and set for them before the warmth of the fireplace.

Beckwith was far from being the only citizen of New London who did not approve of the war for independence and sided with the enemy, of course. But he was one of the most notorious. By means of these night-time trysts, he had been keeping the British well-informed of events in the area.

The boatmen got to the point of their visit quickly: "Our ships have already left New York and are on their way. It is time to put a stop to what is happening in New London. We think we have the right people to do the job. Now we need to be sure we have picked the right time."

"Where are your ships, and how many do you have?" Beckwith asked.

"They are assembling now, just across the Sound. We have been bringing them in under cover of night. They will be no more than ten miles from New London. When they all arrive, there will be at least thirty-two vessels. The rebel coast guards are sure to know something is up by the time all the boats have arrived. But if we can move into the harbor in darkness, we'll have them finished before they even realize what's happening."

"How many men?" Beckwith asked.

"Sixteen hundred."

"Surely that will be enough," Beckwith said. "Particularly when you consider that the guards and the townsmen are not happy with all the recent false alarms. They literally have let down their guard. I hear them talking. They grumble a little more each time they hear the two alarms fired from the harbor. They get a little less quick in response each time—a little less convinced anything is going to happen. Furthermore, the two forts on either side of the river, Fort Trumbull near the harbor, and Fort Griswold over in Stonington, are poorly manned, poorly equipped, and ripe for picking. The militia units have mostly scattered back in the countryside, and won't be happy about coming back to town. And you have to understand that these people are tired and many of them are sick. Things have not been going well for them."

"Good! Perfect!" the visitors responded. "Now we need to go over the map of the harbor and the town once more. Tell us the weak spots and the things to watch out for. And tell us which houses and shops are owned by our friends and which by our enemies." Beckwith was more than happy to comply. He answered all their questions.

He had one more question himself. "What sort of soldiers are you sending?"

"Mostly British regulars," they replied. "But you will be pleased to know that there are also three loyalist units and a nice pack of Hessians.

We don't know which of these will get the greatest pleasure from slitting a few rebel throats and starting a fire or two!"

Then, as they were rising to leave, Beckwith gestured for their attention. "There is one more thing," he said. "Remember this; it will be quite valuable to you: To the citizens of New London, two cannon shots signify 'Come quickly—we are being attacked!' But three shots signify, 'All clear—just stay where you are!'"

"We will remember," their leader responded, casting a knowing smile in Beckwith's direction. Having what they had come to get, the visitors moved back out into the darkness, boarded their hidden craft, and rowed back across the Sound.

The British plan was to strike rapidly, in the middle of the night, and to destroy the forts and the wharves, with their full warehouses, and to be gone before the locals could even get their defenses organized. Thus would this annoying thorn in the side of His Majesty be permanently removed.

At first, everything went just as planned. Inhabitants along the coast had begun to see all the ships the day before the attack—how could they not? But when word was sent into town, no one paid much attention. No particular precautions were taken. This kind of report had been made many times before and had resulted in much unnecessary preparation and panic. This fleet would sail on by, just as the others had sailed on by. The citizens of New London went to bed in confidence that tomorrow would be a day like any other day.

During the night the wind shifted and came blowing directly out of the mouth of the Thames. The British couldn't get their big ships in and had to wait until morning. So much for hitting rapidly in the dark and stealing away; they would have to land in daylight.

It was only a minor inconvenience. The landing would be made in two places: on the shore just west of the lighthouse at the river's mouth for troops going into New London, and on the shore just east of the river for those headed for Fort Griswold on the east side of the river. About eight hundred men in each place; most of the Hessians and Tories on the New London side of the river.

The sun rose on a rather warm September 6. New London awoke and began its usual routines. Colonel Ledyard, commander of the town's fortifications and the soldiers who manned them, made his usual rounds. He found the defenses insufficient, but no more so than usual. Then very disturbing news began to arrive from along the coast. The big fleet was not sailing by New London after all. It was turning north toward the town, and approaching the mouth of the river. By 9:00 am the ships were less than 3 miles away. By 10:00 am the transport vessels had landed and troops were spilling out of them.

Meanwhile, 8 miles away, out in the meadows of Chesterfield, the Latimers were preparing for a September day on the farm. There were apples ready to pick and vegetables to gather in. There was Indian corn and squash waiting to be harvested. The whole family was busy with this project—crops ready for harvest can't wait. Then, just a few minutes past 10:00 AM the serenity of the bright rural morning was interrupted by two far-off cannon blasts—distant, muffled, but unmistakable: the distress signal from New London Harbor.

"Did you hear that, Papa?" Fifteen-year-old Joseph Latimer looked up from the mounds of squash vines.

"I did indeed, Joseph…"—the Colonel was interrupted in mid-sentence by another unmistakable sound, the roar of a third cannon shot.

"Praise the Lord," Lucretia, who was passing by with a bucket full of apples, said with a great sigh. "The 'all clear' signal. Another false alarm. Everything is fine."

The Latimers returned to their harvesting. Joseph, looking to the east, thought he saw smoke rising in the distance, over toward New London. But he couldn't be sure, and turned back to picking squash.

The Inconceivable

In New London, the third shot brought grinding dismay among the citizens. It was obvious that the invaders knew the code and had been able to deceive the hundreds of militia men in the outlying countryside. What happened at the Latimers' was happening far and wide, as far away as the cannon shots could be heard. "All is well" was the message the third shot conveyed. "Go back to your daily tasks." Only the guards posted along the shoreline could see that the third shot had been fired from one of the British ships.

The people of the town responded with undiluted panic. Families rushed to gather up their possessions, their money, and their furniture. Many took these precious things to the house of Pickett Latimer, Jonathan's cousin, whose place seem far enough outside the town to the north to be safe from the invaders. Then the women and children, carrying everything they could, some with babes in arms, began to flee into the surrounding woods, many shouting and crying out in near terror. Some were thoughtful enough to pick up some bread or biscuits; most were not. The most fortunate were able to keep their families together and to find shelter in nearby farmhouses. The able-bodied men grabbed their rifles and stayed behind to attempt a defense, though there was no one there to organize or lead them. The old and infirm could only stay in their homes and hope for the best.

Though Colonel Jonathan and his family lived several miles away in the country, there were many Latimers living in town, the Colonel's brothers and cousins: Pickett, Amos, Henry, Samuel, Richard, Peter, Robert, Charles... Charles, Jonathan's brother, held the rank of Ensign in the Colonel's regiment, and it was his duty to inform Jonathan of any alarms or emergencies in New London. But he, like so many, unable to see the source of the third blast, had been deceived at first by the duplicitous signal. By the time he had gotten a clear sense of the danger, secured and saddled his horse, and ridden off toward Chesterfield, the British troops were already all over the town and busily destroying everything in their path.

Colonel Jonathan's second in command was a local lawyer named Joseph Harris. It was his duty to handle any emergencies that might occur on the New London side of the river, and to send for the Colonel as quickly as possible if he were needed. But Harris had almost no military experience and fell into panic when he saw what was happening. He lived on Town Hill, a mile and a half from the town center, and had been rudely awakened by the alarm guns. The confusion he felt as he sprang from his bed never really left him and he began to scurry around aimlessly and mumble almost incoherent orders. Colonel Ledyard told him to send for Colonel Latimer immediately. For some reason, it took him two hours to get word to Charles Latimer to go for his brother Chesterfield, and even then the orders were so muddled that Charles had to take matters into his own hands.

Harris was not able to organize men to try to stop the British before they came to the town, though he did send some men more or less in their direction without any clear orders. When they came under fire, Harris rode off toward the north. Some of the leaderless militia men began to gather on the high ground of Town Hill, watching the British force moving up Town Hill road, through the quiet farmland south of the town center. Harris' orders were again confusing and contradictory, and the town's defenders were wandering from place to place, not sure where they were supposed to gather. Then, at least according to one witness, he told the men he had a very bad headache and that they would have to take care of themselves. He told them to abandon Fort Nonsense, which stood on Town Hill. Then he quickly rode away.

But when the invaders got within range, the townsmen who could see them began to shoot. Some of their musket balls found their mark, but instead of slowing the enemy down it merely enraged them, adding personal revenge to their motives for destroying the town. The British commander began to deploy his troops with such precision that it seemed he knew his way around New London like a native. Some of his troops went after Fort Nonsense, some Fort Trumbull, some onto the main streets of the wharf and business districts in the town center. The Forts quickly fell, and many of the New London men rushed to boats and crossed the river to help at Fort Griswold, little knowing that decision would carry most of them to their doom. Those who stayed in the town fired their muskets at the British from behind stone fences, trees, and buildings.

When the commander of the invasion force rode to the top of Town Hill to survey the scene, the defenders could finally see who was raining fire down upon them.

There, astride his horse like some ancient conqueror, dressed in a fine British general's uniform, sat Benedict Arnold.

"It is one thing to betray the secrets of your country to the enemy, as we now know Arnold was doing," one embattled defender said to another New Londoner at his side, "but it is quite another to come to a town inhabited by your childhood friends, down the streets where you played games with them as children and cut them down like a field of Indian corn."

Then the burning began. First, those houses from which guns were being fired by the locals. Then, the systematic burning of the warehouses and businesses in the center of town. Arnold directed that the hundreds of men on the other side of the river begin their attack on Fort Griswold. Then he led some of his men northward, around the west side of the town. One party was sent up to Colchester Road, so that they could come back toward the south, closing off the town center in both directions. To the utter dismay of the townsmen, this meant that the first house in their path of that of Pickett Latimer—the house full of the most precious possessions of so many of them. Within minutes everything in the house was consumed in a ball of raging flames.

Benedict Arnold rode up the incline and into the old burial ground beside the church, knowing that it was a good place to see the town below, and Fort Griswold across the river. He sat on his horse among the gravestones. He glanced at the inscription on the grave stone closest to him:

HERE LYES YE BODY
OF CAPT ROBERT

LATIMER WHO
DIED NOVEMBER
27, 1728
AGED 67 YEARS

"Colonel Jonathan's old grandpap!" he mumbled to himself.

Out in Chesterfield, Captain Robert Latimer's grandson was only now receiving the gruesome news from New London. His brother Charles and his own sons mounted and rode away to the neighboring farms, gathering every able-bodied man they could find. This was a time-consuming and not-very-successful process. By the time the Chesterfield militia was on its way, it consisted of less than two dozen men. And the town of New London was already mostly reduced to ashes.

The Colonel arrived about noon, coming down from the north, and found Harris in a serious state of panic. Jonathan gave him orders to go to the rear, where he could do no more harm, and then began to establish an orderly line of defense at the north limits of the town, drawing on his decades of experience as a field commander. New defenders were arriving, and Colonel Jonathan hoped that he could at least stop the progress of the invaders, and maybe even launch a counter-attack. Harris soon disappeared altogether and was not seen again until the British were gone.

As Benedict Arnold surveyed his ignominious work below with a long spyglass, some locals, hiding behind walls in the area, got a good look at him. He was short, dark-complexioned, muscular, and in all rather handsome, just as they had remembered him from better days. His expression was determined and his jaw fixed. There was no sentiment to be found there, no sign of feeling for the old friends whose lives were being so devastated by his selfish ambition and arrogant pride. And this was a man who had once seemed a hero to them!

One by one the houses of those who had served in the American army, or who were known to have participated in privateering were quickly put to the torch. Some of them had known Arnold since childhood. Gurdon Saltonstall's lovely home was enveloped in flames. The line of stores and warehouses was disintegrating; the ships in the harbor blazed like firebrands. The *Hannah*, still full of valuable goods, was set on fire and then sent adrift. She slowly floated out into the river, a huge burning torch, and sank in a whirl of steam. Stores of gunpowder in the warehouses began to explode, creating an uncontrollable firestorm.

By the time Colonel Latimer arrived with his small band of men, riding in from the north along the Colchester Road, the British had had their way in the town for over two hours. One of the first sights to meet the Colonel's eyes had been the charred remains of Pickett Latimer's house, filling the air with smoke. Groups of sullen townsmen stood near the road, speaking to one another in low, angry voices. Their ire, irrationally but perhaps understandably, seemed directed more at the Colonel and his companions that at the British.

"Welcome to what was once our town," someone called out in sarcasm. "Sorry you came late to the entertainment!"

Further down the road, toward the docks, the smoke and flames rose together in breath-stealing clouds. Collapsing roofs and walls produced a chorus of crashes like muffled thunder. The British troops on the west side of the Thames had already finished their work and were loading themselves in landing boats and heading back to their ships. The scattering of men-in-arms who had tried to harass the invaders began to appear from behind stone walls and the few remaining buildings. Like the men at Pickett Latimer's house, not all of them were happy to see the Colonel. This made him very sad, of course, but he saw no practical gain in trying to explain what had happened. He simply sat on his horse, absorbed or ignored the taunting abuse, and began to try to bring order to the situation, shouting orders in his gruff, but reassuring, cadence.

By now a hundred men or so were in the neighborhood, and some of them wanted to rush down to the docks and shoot at the departing Redcoats. The Colonel rode back and forth among them, shouting orders for them to stay where they were. He knew that these orders would be misunderstood by some as well, but he had learned during his long years on the battlefield that it is the responsibility of the leader to save his men from needless slaughter and never to send them on adventures driven by emotion rather than prudent strategy. As hard as it was to accept the truth, the damage was done, and there was now nothing to be done about it except to care for the wounded and pick up the pieces.

Across the road from Pickett Latimer's house there lived a man named Thomas Fitch, a man known for his Tory sympathies. He had in fact been caught near Black Point bringing sheep to the British soldiers for food. Some men from the town rode up, overcome by the thirst for revenge, agitated and filling the air with curses.

"Where is that damned Tory!" they shouted. "Bring him out to us!"

The Colonel ordered his men to guard Thomas Fitch with their bayonets. He would have no part in a lynching. Thomas Fitch would have his day in court and receive his just deserts. But those who have just lost their homes and possessions are in no mood for reasoned justice. The Colonel seemed to them to have become more their enemy than their friend and protector. They retreated, muttering insults at Thomas Fitch, Benedict Arnold, and even Jonathan Latimer.

Massacre at Fort Griswold

While Benedict Arnold looked down from his position among the graves of the old burial ground in New London, yet another tragedy was unfolding across the river at the fort named for Lucretia Latimer's cousin Matthew Griswold. By the time that Colonel Jonathan arrived among the charred ruins along the docks of New London, this other bloody tragedy had almost played itself out. Many inhabitants of the neighborhood had answered the call of Colonel Ledyard to defend the fort—thinking they might even be able to drive the British back to their ships. Arnold ordered his troops on the other side of the river to call for a surrender; and if the defenders would not surrender, to take the fort by storm and cut them down with swords and bayonets. No quarter would be given. Then he thought better of the project and sent another messenger to stop the attack. But it was too late; the battle had already started.

At his headquarters on the north edge of town, the Colonel began to see small boats from the tiny village of Groton, which lay next to the fort, making their way across to New London. The boatmen bore faces contorted with horror and grief, and eyes washed over with evil images. They clamored in competition to bring him the chilling news of what had happened, shouting all at once.

"The British have taken the fort," they said. "And they have shown no mercy. Our young men could be heard crying for quarter, having given up their arms and standing before the enemy defenseless. And the answer was to slaughter them like sheep. Colonel Ledyard was run through with a sword—some say it was his own. The ground is soaked in the blood of our people. The bodies lie mangled, covered with soil and blood, almost unrecognizable. It is too horrible to capture in human speech!"

But by now the British, with their Tories and their Hessians, and several dozen prisoners, were crowding back into their ships and moving off toward the mouth of the river and the waters of the Sound. There would be time during the trip back toward New York for them to wash off the soil and blood of New London.

The Colonel spent the next several days in town, bringing order out of the chaos. Militia companies from many surrounding areas were arriving by the hour, filling the debris-strewn streets with mostly undisciplined busyness. They were too late to provide anything militarily useful. But they could be mobilized to help the poor townspeople hunt for a surviving possession here and there, or to feed the aged and the children and find a way to protect those now homeless from the Fall chill.

The Colonel tried to think only of the challenge directly before him, but other thoughts kept pressing upon him. "If only those in the town who had been responsible for notifying him of the attack had done their duty! And if only that unspeakable third cannon shot had not…"

He longed to be back in Chesterfield where he could unburden his soul to Lucretia, as he had done so many times before. With her, he did not have to play the role of a stone-faced man of arms. A fifty-seven-year-old pillar, unshaken and unshakable. She would understand the torrent of conflicting feelings rushing to and fro in his mind.

A few days past and the militia units began to drift away, seeing little more they could do and needing to tend to their own farms. The Colonel found himself sitting in the darkness of his Chesterfield home, the only light coming from the big fireplace. Lucretia came into the large front room carrying a bowl of hot cider—a large one.

"Here you are, Jonathan," she said. "This will warm your spirit and relax your weary soul and body."

The Colonel took a sip and began to speak, looking into the flames and speaking as though he was in some other, far-off place.

"There will be a court-martial, Lucy. You know there will be a court-martial. Someone must be held accountable for all the sadness and loss. The people will demand it. The British are gone; there is no way to assuage the need for revenge against them. It must fall on those of us who bear arms. I have seen this drama played before. I have served as a court-martial judge myself. It is what we must expect."

"But Jonathan, what more could you have done?" Lucretia protested. "You were there as soon as humanly possible. You brought order to the chaos. You refused to give in to useless and dangerous impulse, as the hotheads wanted."

"But these are people who had suffered great loss. They cannot be blamed for surges of dim-wittedness," he responded, with a mixture of sadness and disquiet.

"You are a good and wise man, my Jonathan. You have been a respected leader of our people for decades. Who could possibly wish you ill or blame you for the events in New London?"

The Colonel paused and then turned his eyes from the fire and into the eyes of Lucretia. "There will, in fact, be those who wish me ill, and those who will turn their wishes into deeds. There will be a court-martial. We can do no more than wait."

And while they waited, another heartbreaking personal tragedy befell them. Just over ten years before, during the relative quiet of the pre-Revolutionary years, Jonathan and Lucretia had welcomed their twelfth child and their tenth son. They had named him Daniel, in honor of the Colonel's illustrious ancestor Daniel Wetherell. The name Daniel would persist in the family for many generations. But the baby was weak and sickly, and barely survived. As a decade passed, Daniel remained small and prone to illness, thin and sallow-eyed. A few weeks after the burning of New London he became so weak that he could not stand, nor eat solid food. His little body, already showing his ribs and joints, continued to waste away. On November 27, 1781, he died, holding his mother's trembling hand. There was nothing now to do but lay him down in the Chesterfield Cemetery with his sister Lucretia.

As she stood beside her husband on the quiet hillside, Lucretia whispered to herself, "Suffer the little children to come unto me, for of such is the Kingdom of God." And saying that, she turned once again to the land of the living. Another scripture came to her mind, "Sufficient unto the day is the evil thereof."

Shamefully Negligent

Months passed, and the Latimers waited. They had all heard the whispers whenever they went to New London Town. There were many true friends, who assured them of loyal support. But there were also watchful and determined enemies, preparing to strike. As was customary in such cases, government and militia officials were inviting accusations from eye-witnesses and interested parties who felt themselves harmed by the actions of the militia during the tragic events in New London and Fort Griswold or who believed they had seen militiamen acting dishonorably.

Governor Trumbull appointed a panel of judges to investigate the charges brought, led by an experienced jurist, Brigadier-General Roger Newberry of Windsor. The judge-advocate would be Hezekiah Bissell, of Windham. The Colonel had known and worked with these men for many years. They knew his record and his reputation well. That, at least, was good. He was also relieved to hear that among the members of the panel of judges were Dr. Joshua Downer, a respected surgeon, along with his son, Avery Downer, also a surgeon, both of whom had been present during the burning of New London and the massacre at Fort Griswold and had seen everything that happened as they were attending to the wounded. Surely they could be counted on not to be carried away with the emotions of the moment.

The Colonel was not the only man facing this ordeal. The list of the accused was long and included many officers. There were two colonels and two lieutenant colonels. There was a major, three captains, a lieutenant, and an ensign. But there were also plenty of citizens of New London who would be present, and whose seething anger could only be purged by seeing someone pay for what had been done to them. Someone…anyone. That was not so good. The accused had few rights in military trials, and sometimes such trials were used to show that the leaders were exercising firm discipline and to calm unrest among the populace. The Colonel had seen George Washington himself order the troops to watch as deserters were tried, convicted, and shot—all within a few minutes' time. No appeal. No hesitation.

And then there was the humiliation. Colonel Jonathan had been notified that the court-martial would take place on Tuesday, August 20, not in New London itself, but rather across the river in Groton, near the site of the massacre. The family went to church, as usual, on the Sunday before. The next day the Colonel packed some necessities in his saddlebags and rode into New London Town. He knew that if he waited, he would be visited by militiamen sent to arrest him. The idea of riding into town as a prisoner was more than he could bear. He would put off the inevitable arrest to the very last minute and make his status as a prisoner as inauspicious as possible.

He spent the day on Monday reviewing the charges made against him. As a high-ranking officer, he had had the right to see these charges several days ahead of time. He spoke to as many old friends, military colleagues, soldiers in his units through the years, and even the well-known local gossips, as he could find. The situation was clear. Most New Londoners liked and admired the Colonel still, and felt the charges were unjust. Many were willing to speak in his defense if the court decided to let them do so. But there were a few who were out for blood. He must be prepared to hear himself demonized in unspeakable ways before his old friends and his family.

Before Lucretia, for instance. Especially Lucretia.

He was thankful that his father had left this world and would not have to hear this.

Others would come before the court before him, but he knew that the awful words in the charge would be no less harsh for him than for them:

> You are hereby charged with being shamefully negligent in your military duty when called to, and in actual service, and for breach of military law in not leading your regiment forward, and pre-

venting the enemy from sacking and burning the town of New London, on the 6th day of September, A. D. 1781."

The prosecutor then spelled out the charges in detail:

1. The Colonel did not lead his regiment forward and thus did not support the inhabitants of the town in their attempts to repel the enemy.

2. He did not attempt to prevent the burning of houses and stores by the enemy.

3. He did not prevent the wanton plundering by the soldiers which occurred in the town.

4. He allowed his men to remain in the hills, "strolling and unimbodyed," in full view of the enemy.

5. He did not support the inhabitants in the north end of the town as they bravely tried to fight.

6. He did not pursue and attack the enemy at the favorable moment when they were retreating and boarding their boats.

7. He set up his rendezvous point where it actually helped the enemy instead of hindering him.

At this point, there was a very happy turn of events for the Colonel. The President of the panel of judges, General Newberry, stood and said, "I believe it would be wise to hear the charges against Lieutenant Colonel Joseph Harris Jr, and his rebuttal of them, before proceeding with Colonel Latimer's case."

The Colonel knew full well that it was the ineptitude, and perhaps even cowardice, of his second in command, Joseph Harris, which lay behind the charges being made against him. The man had been out of his depth; he was no soldier, and he had gained his rank without ever engaging in actual combat. Those who had promoted him to such a rank also had to assume some of the blame, surely.

Although, he thought to himself, if Harris had made not a single mistake, the outcome would still have been a very sad one, and perhaps not much different.

Lt. Col. Harris was an articulate lawyer from a prominent family, and he put up a spirited defense of his actions. But brilliant rhetoric can take one only so far. He admitted that Lt. Col. Ledyard, who would later lose his life at Fort Griswold, ordered him "to immediately procure some suitable person to send express to Col. Latimer" to tell him that an attack was underway. These orders came early in the morning, but for some reason he could not explain, it was two hours before he actually had someone on his way to Chesterfield. In the meantime, he had given a series of seriously flawed orders, and the situation was out of control. One witness after another told what they had experienced under his command. His orders were confusing and his system of internal communication was non-existent. What few men that were available were wandering aimlessly around the town, uncertain where to go or what to do. Then, when the time came to confront the British forces, he was suddenly nowhere to be seen. When he ran on to a group of local militiamen, he told them that he had a terrible headache, could not even sit on his horse, and they would have to fend for themselves.

Finally, when Colonel Latimer arrived on the scene, he saw the bedlam Harris had created and sent him to the north of the town, away from the action, with orders to organize the men there. They would not follow his orders anymore, however, and once again there was chaos. Unable to succeed in what the Colonel had asked him to do, he simply disappeared again.

Once the court and the spectators had heard the witnesses and the defense given by Lt. Col. Harris all the charges made against the Colonel could be seen in a new light. Lucretia and his children were already showing signs of immense relief and were nodding to each other as the picture of what had happened emerged. The Colonel had said little to them about what had happened and had retreated into a painful silence for the last several months. They had never lost their confidence in his integrity, bravery, and brilliance as a commander, but his silence had not made it easy for them.

Several witnesses spoke in his defense, and one or two townsmen made highly emotional speeches of accusation, blaming him in general terms for their very real misfortunes. When the time came for him to speak, he was well aware of his limitations as an orator. He was a man of few words, simply constructed sentences and ideas simply put. In an age of flowery and indirect communication, he tended to say what must be said, and only that, and then be done with it. He would do the same on this day. Anyway, he could tell that the panel of judges was leaning heavily in his favor, and the testimony from and about Lt. Col. Harris had helped immensely.

"Honored Gentlemen," he began, "one does not spend upwards of forty years on the fields of war without developing some sense of what one must do as a soldier and a commander of soldiers. There must be a clear plan, growing out of years of experience even if sometimes applied in haste. There must be clear commands, easy to understand and practical to execute. There must be a willingness to stand with the men in danger, inconvenience, and risk. There must be an understanding of the emotions of combat—fear, rage, trust in one's comrades. These are the ideas and actions which have guided me since the days of the war against the French and Indians, the fight for New York, the fields of Saratoga. And I assure you, gentlemen, these were the ideas and actions which guided me on September 6, 1781."

"I count seven charges against me. They all have to do with my decisions after I arrived in New London. Many mistakes were made at the beginning, before my arrival, some of them fatal. I would like to think that had I been present, things would have been different. You have heard and know well yourselves why I was so long in arriving. There was no negligence, certainly no cowardice. I came without any hesitation the moment the word reached me. I could not prevent the burning because the flames were uncontrollable even before my arrival. I came on the scene with a mighty army of twenty-two men, mostly farm boys, and found the defenders of the town confused, disheartened, and leaderless. I did what any experienced commander would have done, setting up perimeters, organizing assets, stabilizing and consolidating our pitifully small but brave band of defenders."

"I did not lead these men into the maelstrom along the docks or make senseless and futile attacks on the hundreds of invaders roaming our streets, plundering, burning and killing, because a good commander does not lead his men into certain death. He evaluates the situation, and he does what can be done. Good soldiers can always distinguish between bravery and reckless foolhardiness. To spill blood needlessly and uselessly is more akin to murder than to military brilliance. Firing a few shots at the backs of a retreating army of over a thousand men might satisfy the soul at the moment, but makes no military sense. I hope I do not seem self-serving or arrogant when I say that what was needed on that fateful day was cool and rational thinking, sympathy for the dead and sympathetic care for those suffering pain and loss."

"I have explained to you why I did what I did. I leave my fate in your hands."

There was a long silence. The judges retired to a private room and returned after a few minutes. General Newberry held a small scape of paper in his hand, which he raised to a spot where his aging eyes could properly focus on the sentence. He read it in a loud and clear voice, so that the people, who could hear little of the actual dialogue during the trial, could hear it plainly.

"The Court, upon due consideration of the whole matter before them, is unanimously of opinion, that Colonel *Jonathan Latimer* is *not guilty* of neglect of duty as charged against him, he therefore, by the court, is acquitted with honor."

Jonathan's brother Daniel, who had been brought before the court for "not seasonably forwarding intelligence to his colonel of the expected approach and attack of the enemy," was also acquitted—the facts now being clear.

Elisha Beckwith, who bore so much real responsibility for the tragedy at New London, was arrested and held in custody briefly in Hartford. But somehow, in the chaotic aftermath, he was unwittingly released. By the time that Colonel Latimer was undergoing the humiliation of the court-martial, old Mr. Beckwith was living safely and comfortably with his family in faraway Nova Scotia.

The Colonel would allow no celebration. There was nothing to celebrate, he told his children. He had been shamed before his community and things would never again be the same. There would always be certain darkness, buried deep in the hearts of many of the people of New London, when his name was mentioned. The pain of this was far greater than the pain of a musket ball, or the point of a bayonet.

An End to War

The general gloom was broken for a few days when Jonathan and Lucretia's son Charles married his sweetheart Mary. And then, a few months after the court-martial, the long war against the British Crown came to an end by means of negotiations and treaties signed far from the "heaps of rubbish, ruinous and forlorn" (as an observer described them) which littered the streets of New London. In the fall of 1783 word came to the Colonel, who was pleasantly and quietly tending his farm in Chesterfield, that the British were leaving New York Island where seven years ago he had been thrust into the leadership of a defeated regiment. The new United States rejoiced as General Washington rode back into Manhattan in a triumphal procession, down the very road the Colonel had traveled in the other direction, leading his tattered Connecticut farm boys in their retreat.

"I would have enjoyed being there," he told Joseph and Nathaniel, the youngest of his surviving sons, as they worked together repairing fences. "But I am much more content being here." He said no more about it.

One day, a few weeks later, Lucretia came in from the garden to find the Colonel sitting at his desk in the half-darkness that always pervaded homes like theirs, even in the daytime. In front of him on the desk was a sheet of paper and beside it an inkwell and quill pen. And across the front of the desk was something else—something which immediately took Lucretia's eye. It was the old small-sword, its ornate silver decorations bathed in a mixture of sunlight and shadow. She was familiar with this scene. It was part of the liturgy by which the Colonel had time and again answered a call to arms. Lucretia's heart beat faster. "Surely not again," she whispered to herself.

Then she saw that he had written a message to someone on the sheet of paper and was waiting for the ink to dry. When he became conscious of her presence, he picked up the paper, turned and handed it to her without a word. She moved to the light of the window and read:

To the honorable General Assembly of the State of Connecticut:

Having had the Trust & Confidence of this Assembly by being Honored with the appointment to the Command of the 3d Regiment of Militia of this State almost from the beginning of the late long and tedious War, and now that peace and tranquility is restored to my Country, I flatter myself your Honors will readily accept this my resignation, and allow me to retire from the burden of this Office. With great respect,

Your most obedient & Very humble servant.
Jonathan Latimer

"I am sixty years old," he said, answering her unarticulated question, "and the war is over."

"But you have always been a soldier. It has been thus almost forty years. It is said that men find their identity in their vocation, and yours has been to be a soldier. Perhaps it is time for your grateful fellow-citizens to make you a general, not to accept your resignation." She made this remark because she thought it would please him, not because it represented any wish of her own.

"Men become generals because they belong to the ruling class, or because they are afire with personal ambition, or because they see war as a game to be played and won. I have never been quite a part of the first of these categories, and have never desired to be in the other two."

"But you have always been a leader of men," Lucretia protested.

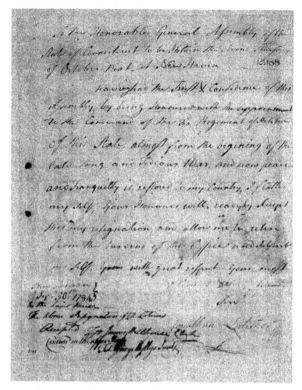

Fig. 8: The Colonel's resignation letter

"Only when the call of duty demanded it," he replied. "It is time to put away the sword." And this he quite literally did, walking slowly from the room and climbing the ladder into the attic, where he gently laid the weapon in an old chest of mementos once belonging to his father, full of relics of things past.

There was, unfortunately, one piece of unfinished business. The State Assembly had never freed the Colonel from a sort of vague liability in the matter of the money he had paid his officers after the battle in New York so many years before. When Colonel Selden had been taken prisoner by the British and died in their custody, and Jonathan had been thrust into leadership, no one had told him that the State wanted a considerable share of the funds provided by the Congress for officers' salaries to help them pay government expenses instead. These expenses were keeping the government itself constantly on the verge of bankruptcy. For all these years they had kept him on pins and needles, never freeing him from the threat of taking away almost his entire estate but never acting on the threat either.

He had hoped against hope that the matter could be settled before he retired from the militia. The time seemed right. Lucretia's cousin, Matthew Griswold, had recently been elected governor of Connecticut. Perhaps he could do something. But, sadly, no action was taken. Still filled with uncertainty, Jonathan Latimer had resigned his military commission and left off soldiering for the first time since his youth. But the unfinished business remained unfinished.

Anni Horribiles—Years of Horror

For every step forward there seemed to be another in the other direction. By this time, among the graves next to the church that stood on land the Colonel had provided as a gift to the community, were those of three of his beloved children. First, it was little Lucretia, her mother's namesake. She had left them before the Revolution—only nine months old. Her short, frail life signaled the end of childbearing for her grief-stricken forty-three-year-old mother.

Like most wives of her day, Lucretia had spent most of the previous two decades pregnant.

Fourteen pregnancies.

There would be no more.

And then, seven years later, little Daniel was gone—ten years old and never really strong enough to survive.

And then it was their son Nicholas, struck down at the cusp of manhood—twenty-two years old. This may have been the hardest loss for Lucretia to endure; Nicholas had survived all the hazards of childhood, only to be carried away just when he should have been ready to be a man. Nicholas died in 1785, a year in the midst of this cluster of years so full of momentous events, some of which formed the family's future, it is true, but as they lived them, mostly dark and better forgotten.

At almost the same time Jonathan and Lucretia were losing Nicholas to the angel of death their oldest daughter Borodell came to her mother with distressing news. Her swashbuckling husband Eusebius had stunned her with a shattering announcement. He had decided to leave New England to go seek a fortune in someplace called the Cumberland—in a primitive village called Nashville, or Nashboro, or some such name.

"Mother, I have no idea where Eusebius got this notion or what has attracted him to this God-forsaken place. It seemed to come from out of the clear blue. I know he has been discontented and fretful of late. He has been talking about how evil the times are here, and how few are the opportunities for men like him. And you well know it that he has always been inclined to such thoughts. I have tried to reason with him. I have pled and I have wept. But there seems to be no room for any discussion."

"It is the lot of women," Lucretia replied gently. "They watch their men go away into the mouth of danger and destruction, as I have done so many times, or they follow them on their quests for who knows what."

"But…" she paused for a moment, "follow they must."

This place called the Cumberland was so foreign to the worldview of New Englanders that it might as well have been in the land of the Turks —or on the moon. Even on modern roads, it is a voyage of over a thousand miles. But in those days it was also a journey fraught with a thousand dangers and hardships. Their children would be with them, of course, none yet in their teens and the youngest not yet four years old. For Borodell, who bore a distinguished name passed down for six generations from the days of the Mayflower and Oliver Cromwell and not yet thirty years old herself, it would be a journey with tragic consequences; the family she left in New London would never see her again. Jonathan and Lucretia were about to lose yet another child. The goodbyes were poignant enough, even without the knowledge of their finality.

And as if this were not enough, only a few weeks after Borodel's departure poor Abigail Fitch, the young wife of the Colonel's son Witherel, died after the birth of her second son. Death in childbirth was almost commonplace in those days—but no less full of anguish for those who loved such ill-starred young mothers. Her grave was added to the growing number of Latimers in the little cemetery in the churchyard which the Colonel had given to the community of Chesterfield during the days of the Revolution.

And beyond the human tragedies the community in which the Latimers had played such an integral part was struggling for its very existence. If those patriots who endured long hardship to build for themselves a new country thought that victory would bring Utopia, they had another think coming. New London had been devastated by the British in the last days of the War. The burning was only part of the tragedy. The port, once full of ships from Europe and the Caribbean, providing wealth for their captains and their investors, and for the merchants of the city, stood virtually silent and unused. New London's own ships and seamen had been devoted to the War, serving as privateers. Their trade connections were lost. Many of the ships themselves were captured or destroyed. Those who had sailed them were scattered and many simply never returned. The merchants, like the Colonel's old war-time associate Gurdon Saltonstall, could not regenerate their businesses. One after another, they fell into bankruptcy. The giant warehouses along the docks, those which had not been burned to ashes, stood empty and useless. The ships which remained had no place to go and lay disintegrating beside the docks. The shipyards where they had been built in the days of prosperity were deserted. There were attempts, here and there, to get things going again. But the road would be long and hard, and the results uncertain.

The traitor Benedict Arnold, Colonel Jonathan's "old Connecticut friend," had not only burned away the basis for the city's commerce and prosperity, but also dozens of its homes. All of this had happened only three years before the particular *annus horribilis* we are now describing, and the ashen ruins were still very much in evidence. The streets on which these fine homes had stood were literally disappearing beneath an undisciplined carpet of grass. These ruins pressed upon the Colonel with particular poignancy and only added to the melancholy of personal loss.

Their town and their lives in ashes, the people of New London began to leave. There was no reason to stay and plenty of reasons to go. Many veterans of the War, and others whose homes had been destroyed, were moving to a new area far to the West in what was called the Northwest Territory (and what we call the state of Ohio). Among them were the sons of Jonathan's kinsman Pickett Latimer, and other relatives as well. The lands they received, because of the source of their distress, became known as the "Connecticut Firelands."

"Passions Unrestrained in Childhood": The Execution of Hannah Ocuish

Then something happened in New London so macabre, so steeped in aching horror that it seemed to gather together all the other horrors of these evil times into one pathetic symbol.

Despite the parade of tragedies, the Colonel continued to do his civic duty. Year after year he was appointed Justice of the Peace in New London County—the primary position in local government. In 1786 the State Assembly created a new township, Montville, and he was chosen to serve as moderator for the traditional town meetings, calling the people together by posting an announcement on the doors of the meeting house.

It was not a time of total despair. There was another happy family occasion when Jonathan and Lucretia's much-loved son Nathaniel—the youngest of their surviving children, married a distant cousin, Mary Latimer. Nathaniel was special—tall and handsome, an obedient and dutiful son, he had given them much joy. Their minds were lifted from the darkness for this wonderful assurance that the earth's order was not entirely gone awry. If they had known Nathaniel's future, there would have been no joy even in this event either.

And, of course, the wedding could hardly wash away the stains of the last few months in New London, nor the somber events that lay ahead. One event cast a particularly distressing pall over the people. It had started on a Thursday in July, when a passerby noticed a dead body lying near the path a short way from the town of Norwich, not far from New London.

It was a small body. Heavy stones were lying on its arms and legs. The passerby turned the corpse face up and gasped in horror. It was a child. A little girl. Her head and body were mangled; her limbs were broken. But she was recognizable—particularly in a place where everyone knew everyone else. It was Eunice Bolles. She was six years old.

Suspicion of murder quickly fell on 12-year-old Hannah Oculish, a Pequot Indian girl well-known for her anti-social behavior. At first, she denied the deed, but when the officials made her look at the body, she dissolved in tears and confessed.

"Please forgive me," she pled, "and I'll never do such a thing again."

The citizens of this part of Connecticut lived in relative serenity with the two native tribes they had gradually replaced there—the Mohicans and the Pequots. Their concern for the natives lay more in the spiritual realm than in everyday life, of course, given their Puritan roots. It was an honest concern, nevertheless. Everyone agreed, however, that Hannah was a poor, lost soul. Her mother was an alcoholic and had abandoned her. She survived by becoming a servant in the home of a white family. Already at the age of six, she had beaten a white child in an attempt to steal a necklace from her. The other children were afraid of her. She had, said the authorities later, "a degree of artful cunning and sagacity beyond many of her years."

In her confession, Hannah told how the summer before little Eunice had "complained of her in strawberry time…for taking away her strawberries." Seeing Eunice walking alone from school one day Hannah attacked her. She knocked Eunice to the ground and began to pound her fists against the little girl's face and neck and chest. She pounded until Eunice lay absolutely still. A dark, sinister rage rose up in her, like some demon from the world beneath her feet. It clinched her fists and propelled them toward the object lying before her. Then she beat Eunice's limp body even more, expelling her youthful rage in a rain of crushing blows. The little girl was no longer breathing. The life had gone out of her. Hannah covered her victim's body with rocks so that people would think a wall had fallen on her.

The verdict of the court was swift. Hannah was to be hanged.

President Stiles of Yale College sent a young seminarian, Henry Channing, to represent him at the hanging. Reverend Channing strongly agreed with the suitability of the punishment. It is true that he visited the girl in prison, but his pastoral counseling consisted mostly of severe warnings that her soul was in danger if she did not repent.

On January 20, 1787, the day of the execution, Rev. Channing stood before the crowd of witnesses and preached to them and to Hannah, as was the custom of the day. He exhorted the crowd to learn from what they were about to see the cost of parental indulgence. He warned them to observe how "appetites and passions unrestrained in childhood become furious in youth; and ensure dishonor, disease and an untimely death."

Far from comforting her, he said to the terrified young murderess: "Hannah!…The good and safety of society requires, that no one, of such a malignant character, shall be suffered to live, and the punishment of death is but the just demerit of your crime: and the sparing you on account of your age, would, as the law says, be of dangerous consequence to the public, by holding up an idea, that children might commit such atrocious crimes with impunity."

The young girl shook in terror on the gallows. The Sheriff of New London put a rope around her neck and hanged her until she was dead. Thus, as one witness remarked, was the child Hannah "launched into the eternal World."

As for the Reverend Mr. Channing, his message proved so powerful and impressive to the spectators that he was immediately called to become the permanent minister of the Congregational Church in New London, the church where the Latimers had been baptized for generations. President Stiles of Yale preached the ordination sermon.

Jonathan and Lucretia said nothing about all this, not even to each other. But deep within both of them, it was as if a bitter draught of poison had been poured upon their very souls.

"What have we become?" Lucretia asked her husband, not long afterward.

"What has our world become?" he replied.

All the Property of Which I Am Now Possessed

Somehow Colonel Jonathan and his sons were keeping their heads above water, despite the persistent threat of financial disaster surrounding them after the Revolution. The threat was real, constant, and seemed to be closing in. The Latimer family, pillars of the community since the founding days of the colony, seemed, as did so many of their neighbors, to be descending into a financial abyss.

As early as 1784, with the War barely finished, the first humiliation appeared. There, for all to see, was a notice in *The Connecticut Gazette* that land belonging to the Colonel's brother Amos Latimer would be sold to pay "state and town taxes" that are "now due and uncollected." But even more humiliating were the trials of his brother Robert. Robert lived in the fine house on the main street of New London, built for him by his and Jonathan's father, whom we have already known as a wealthy and influential citizen of New London who had died at the beginning of the Revolution and left all his sons a comfortable inheritance. But the time and place were working against them all. Robert's debts escalated as the War continued. Then came the public embarrassment as he was charged before the law for passing a counterfeit bill which, he assured the court, had been given to him by his relative-in-law Amasa Learned. Learned lived in half the house Robert's father had built for him on Main Street and was a rising political star. He would go on to be a member of the Constitutional Convention of 1787 and a distinguished member of Congress.

Though innocent of any intention to do wrong, Robert, unlike Learned, was descending further into disgrace. He was forced to sell his house to Thomas Shaw who, along with Amasa Learned gave it to the local congregation as a parsonage—thus establishing themselves as patrons of the Church. Robert fell further and further into debt and in the same year Learned was laboring over America's new Constitution, Robert found himself in debtor's prison. The State Assembly noted "that by various misfortunes he has become unable to pay his Debts, has no Property, and is now confined in Gaol at New London for Debt." Probably because of his family's prominence, the Assembly agreed to let him out of prison, provided that he turn over all his possessions to his creditors—except the clothes on his back and a few pieces of furniture. *The Connecticut Gazette* carried his humiliating statement, "delivering up all the property of which I am now possessed...to and for the use of my said creditors."

Matters were even worse for the Colonel's cousin Nathan Latimer. There were the same public notices in the newspaper about unpaid taxes. But there was also a fight. Neighbor Samuel Beckwith came and confiscated furniture from the mill operated by Amos and Nathan, along with other family members. Nathan knocked down Beckwith's fence and turned his cattle onto Beckwith's property to eat his grass. A fistfight ensued, complete, said the official report, with "violent hitting and kicking." Nathan ended up in jail—partly for the fight and partly for his debts. Even after he was released, his troubles continued. Not long afterward

Nathan put a notice in the paper announcing that his wife Ann had "eloped from his bed and board" and that he was not responsible for her debts.

Anni Horribiles, indeed.

SIX: BUSHNELL

Eusebius Bushnell

Nashville, North Carolina
September, 1789

It was a Thursday in mid-September, 1789. Griswold Latimer stood in front of the house, admiring the first color beginning to show itself in the surrounding forest. He noticed a figure walking quickly along the narrow path to his simple cabin. The figure was still far in the distance, but easy to identify.

It was his brother-in-law, Eusebius Bushnell.

Eusebius, as we know, was the husband of Griswold's beloved older sister Borodell, named for the grandmother the Latimers all adored. Eusebius and Borodell had been the first members of the family to arrive in the Cumberland. Now there were three of the Colonel's children here, all in or near the rough little village of Nashville: Borodell, Griswold, and Griswold's older brother Witherel. The settlement was little more than a rude clearing deep within an ocean of dark forests and cane breaks. All three of the Latimer siblings bore names which were strange to their Scotch-Irish neighbors, but names that held deep meaning to them because they reflected the grand old families of their heritage in colonial Connecticut. Even stranger to the locals were their curious Yankee accents, so different from those of the men from the southern mountains who made up most of the population of this ragged frontier.

Eusebius and his family had been in Nashville for several years now. The journey from New England to the Cumberland had been long, viciously tiring, and very dangerous. Borodell had arrived weak and sick, but nevertheless charged with caring for the children and making a new home in the wilderness. Eusebius was vigorous and enthusiastic, animated by the possibilities for wealth and influence here in the forest. He left family matters almost entirely in Borodel's hands and began to survey the opportunities before him. There were fortunes to be made for entrepreneurs like himself, provided he remained focused and did not allow himself to be distracted by domestic details—or other such relative trivialities.

The Cumberland Latimers were well aware of the complex preparations being made in far-off New England by the rest of the family. They had been busy for months, preparing for the arrival of the Colonel and his family in Tennessee. It would not be long now before the center of the Latimer clan would shift from the comforts of Chesterfield and the traditions of Old Connecticut to the hard realities of the boundless Cumberland. The only remaining impediment—the humiliating judgment against the colonel for the funds he had mistakenly paid to his men years before during the Revolution, was being swept away by an action of the Connecticut State Assembly. He had been completely exonerated and could now leave his ancestral home with honor. As for the family, there was excitement, anticipation and, yes, also considerable anxiety.

In addition, Griswold was preparing to marry his sweetheart Molly, a lovely child of the great forest who had lived so much of her life here that she could imagine no other place to be. Already in his mid-20s, he was ready to become a family man with a loving wife and children and to have a place of his own.

Despite the distance between himself and the approaching figure, Griswold could see that something was wrong. Eusebius' face was grey and his steps uncharacteristically erratic and uncertain.

What could be the matter this time?

Eusebius lived his life with high drama, and his activities in the Cumberland so far had led to one crisis after another. Griswold suspected that his brother-in-law was in deep financial trouble, despite his prosperous outward *persona*, a look he had always carefully cultivated. He suspected this because of certain off-hand but anxiety-saturated remarks Eusebius had recently been making to him. Griswold was the one person Eusebius seemed willing to confide in. Just why he did this was something of a mystery. Griswold's older brother Witherel might have been the other candidate for a shoulder to lean on, but Witherel was a formidable character with an exceedingly strong sense of morality and an ample residual dose of New England Puritan values. He could not be counted on for much sympathy for Eusebius' foibles and self-induced calamities.

The fact is that in these formidable characteristics Griswold was not that different from his brother. Maybe Eusebius confided frankly with him as the lesser of two evils, younger and perhaps less worldly wise. Or maybe simply because he had no one else.

He certainly could not speak candidly to his wife Borodell about his troubles. It was too humiliating after all that she had already endured to support his hazardous behavior and perilous gambles. She had given up a genteel life in New England where her family and his had firm roots, even though there were already several children, two of them quite young. The family had set out for the Cumberland in 1784, at the very height of the "killing times"—when families, including wives and children, were regularly meeting horrible deaths at the hands of marauding Indians, both along the route and after their arrival.

During the years previous to the coming of the Bushnells the Chickasaws, Cherokees, and Chickamaugas had struck the settlers with deadly force again and again. Only sixty-three of the one hundred and thirty-one of the earliest settlers who tried to settle permanently around Nashville were still alive by 1784. To live in this place was to face the constant risk of hunger, kidnapping, loss of home and possessions, and death itself. The only friends available were those poor souls into whose consciousness were burned the memories of beloved parents, siblings, and children hacked to death with tomahawks, their hair torn from their heads, their bodies left for the ravenous appetites of the beasts of the forests. People were only safe when they gathered behind the strong walls of log forts, and sometimes not even then.

Strictly speaking, Tennessee did not even exist as yet; there was only the vast wilderness still called "Western North Carolina," or, "The Territory South of the River Ohio." This place was, as someone had described it, "the back of beyond."

And besides all this, Borodell was never very strong, and had fought one illness after another since arriving in the great forest.

But for Eusebius, it was a time and place of great promise. His eyes were wide with the prospects of wealth. Back in New England, there was little chance of building a fortune in the days following the Revolution. One could hope for little more than subsistence—and even that would be a struggle. But here the possibilities seemed without limit for a man such as himself—well-educated, multi-lingual, smooth-talking and physically vigorous.

Especially when it came to land speculation.

It was the land that brought Eusebius to the Wilderness. His interest was not in cultivating the land, however. He had no desire to own and operate a great plantation. Farming had never appealed to him. It was the opportunity to buy huge tracts on credit and sell them at great profits that brought him here. Soldiers of the Revolution had been receiving land grants by the hundreds. And in the case of officers, particularly high-ranking officers, these grants might consist of many thousands of acres. Most of the land went to men who had little interest in settling their families in the dark forest among bloodthirsty natives. They were willing to sell their grants for a pittance, and the land speculators were willing to buy (often on credit) and quickly sell again to those who were willing to take the chance—especially the incoming hordes of desperate Scotch-Irish and German immigrants who longed for land of their own.

It was a situation perfectly aligned with the talents and inclinations of a smooth-talking entrepreneur like Eusebius. Within a few weeks after his arrival in 1785, he was busy witnessing and signing documents. Day to day expenses could be covered by buying and selling needed commodities, including slaves. Slavery had not been uncommon in 18th Century Connecticut, and Eusebius had no qualms about the concept, though he knew that some of his relatives, including his wife, did.

As a man of some education and culture, with experience as a surveyor, Eusebius was soon a candidate for government appointments. By December 1785, Eusebius was one of three Commissioners who was assigned to examine the claims of soldiers and sailors residing in the district. This position gave him access to a great deal of inside information. It was a perfect position from which to begin land speculation. He got himself a partner, William Dobbins, a respected surveyor, and began to make a series of daring and risky moves.

Land speculation on a large scale required capital or credit—lots of it. On August 30, 1785, Eusebius had taken on a huge debt, and somehow convinced Elijah Robertson, the brother of General James Robertson, the dominant figure of the time and place, to co-sign the note. Even a man with Eusebius' ample bravado shuttered when he looked at the small piece of paper with such huge implications (and problematic grammar):

"I, Eusebius Bushnell of Davidson County, NC, is firmly bound to Elijah Robertson for forty thousand pounds."

Over two million dollars in today's currency!

In 1787 Eusebius volunteered to go as an officer with General Robertson to fight the Chickamaugas, and no doubt to fortify his business relationship with the Robertson family. This expedition was prompted by the desire the Robertsons felt for personal revenge. In the late spring of that year a marauding party of Indians, warriors of Chief Doublehead, had been hiding along the path beside Richland Creek when Mark, the General's brother, came riding along. He was returning from a visit to his brother's house. The warriors ambushed Mark and mercilessly killed him in broad daylight. General Robertson was filled with rage. Without waiting for permission from the Governor he put out a call for volunteers to go after the killers. A hundred and thirty men volunteered, among them Eusebius.

The band of settler-soldiers stealthily followed the warriors to Blue Water Creek, then all the way down to the Coldwater, where they took the Indians by complete surprise. As they ran for their canoes, the warriors were easy targets. Eusebius joined the others in pouring a hail of bullets upon them. They fell like flies—fourteen Cherokees and six Creeks—and some Frenchmen, too—traders who were with the Indians to encourage them to stir up trouble and found themselves caught at the wrong place at the wrong time.

"Serves the Frenchmen right," Elijah had snarled.

The party returned to Nashville, thirst for blood assuaged, and Eusebius felt confident that the Robertson's would someday want to return the favor he had done them. And perhaps they would be lenient on the matter of the big debt. And in any case, he was confident that he would soon be a wealthy man and the debt only a memory.

The next few months were also full of adventure. During the summer and fall of 1787, Eusebius and Dobbins began to buy up land warrants by the dozens from Revolutionary War veterans, making heavy use of the borrowed money. These purchases, mostly lying along Stones River, amounted to many thousands of acres. Not everyone was happy with his activities, or with his way of doing business, however, and Nashville was a place in those days where disagreements tended to have physical consequences. One day three fellows, named James Hickman, Thomas Bradford, and Joseph Brooks, showed up at one of Nashville's several taverns where Eusebius was making a sales pitch to a potential customer. There were angry words, pushing and shoving, and Eusebius found himself tossed, unceremoniously, headfirst, into the street. Bystanders heard the torrent of invective from both sides, but the issues seemed too complicated for a mere observer to understand. Eusebius suffered considerable embarrassment and therefore brought the matter before the court. The three of assailants were charged with disorderly conduct by the Davidson County grand jury. Whether this was the result of measured justice, or whether it illustrated Eusebius' ability to cultivate friends in high places we cannot know. And we can only guess what the fight was about.

To make matters worse, Eusebius also fell afoul of Jacques-Timothée Boucher, Sieur de Montbrun, or, as he wished to be called in America, Timothy Demonbreun.

When James Robertson had come to found Fort Nashboro in 1778, he discovered that Timothy Demonbreun had already been there for many years. He had come down from Canada in 1760, first to Kaskaskia on the Mississippi, in what is now called Illinois, and then into the deep Forest to French Lick, where Nashville would eventually be. He was there to trade with the Indians. His habit was to stay in the Cumberland during the winter and spring, then take a load of animal pelts back to Kaskaskia in the summer. He was an unabashed and impenitent bigamist with a wife and family in Illinois and another in the Cumberland. Presumably, the family in Kaskaskia had a house, but the one in Tennessee lived in a cave—at least until other white men came and built a town.

Eusebius thought it was amusing that Demonbreun had fought for the French army in Canada, while his own father-in-law, Colonel Jonathan, had fought on the British side. At some point, he conjectured, they might have even been shooting at each other. It would be interesting to hear them talk about all that. But he would say nothing about it, either to the Canadian or to the Colonel, once he arrived. Better let sleeping dogs lie.

He quickly adjudged Demonbreun's value as a conduit to take his own activities even further afield. He convinced the tall, dark, wily Canadian, whom the Americans had appointed to be Lieutenant-Governor of the Illinois Territory, to make some connections for him up the river in Kaskaskia. Maybe something would turn up there to help him climb out of the increasingly deep financial hole he was digging for himself.

He headed up the river to see what might develop. His sons Ezra and Matthew, both mere boys under the age of ten, accompanied him. They found the town of Kaskaskia in the Illinois Territory to be a sad little place inhabited by about two hundred men and a potpourri of women and children bearing differing percentages of European and Indian blood. Even Nashville seemed more civilized.

The father and sons arrived in August, just in time to put their names, along with those of several dozen other Americans, on an imposing agreement with Bartholomew Tardiveau, Esquire, whom they grandly entitled "our agent at Congress," promising the man a healthy reward for using his contacts in the national capital to secure grants of land for them in that region. Unfortunately, in Eusebius' case at least, nothing ever came of it. This was neither the first nor the last of that assortment of schemes which Eusebius watched ascend, full of promise, and then crash.

"While you are up there in Kaskaskia," Demonbreun suggested, speaking in the rough and corrupted French of the frontier, "look up that wily countryman of mine, André Fagot. You will find an acquaintance with him worth your while."

Fagot was a merchant and a militia officer, and he wasn't hard to find. He was the sort of fellow who is constantly insinuating that he has a delicious secret which he would be happy to share with you if the occasion ever arises. And this was the sort of thing that held great appeal for Eusebius. He decided that it would not be hard to cut through all the obfuscation and discover what Fagot was all about, and to somehow benefit from it.

He did not discover the truth about Fagot right away, but eventually it became plain to him. Fagot, as a Frenchman, was deeply entwined in the complex world of intrigue up and down the Mississippi, where English-men and Frenchmen and Spaniards tried to play the Indians and naïve Americans off each other to the benefit of their respective sovereigns back in the Old Country. And even though he was a Frenchman, Fagot was also a spy and agent provocateur for the Spanish. The fellow in-trigued Eusebius, but although the Frenchman's manner and even his lifestyle appealed to him, he knew that wisdom called for circumspection where Fagot was concerned.

"But who knows what the future might bring?" he thought to himself.

The trip was essentially a bust. Eusebius and the boys returned to Nashville no better off than when they had left. When he heard this, Demonbreun had lost his patience, swore with robust sincerity, and de-cided to sue Eusebius for one of the many debts he had hoped to cover with the fruits of this Yankee's Illinois adventure. And, alas, the judgment went against Eusebius. He had to come up with seventy-nine dollars and five shillings to satisfy the rather intimidating Gallic frontiersman—not an easy task, given his present circumstances.

Far worse was yet to come. Nothing seemed to be going Eusebius' way. Sales were not meeting expectations, and possible buyers were becoming far too well informed about the Indian atrocities. The huge debt to the Robertsons became more and more a millstone around his neck.

But at this precarious moment, a way out of his difficulties seem to drop down out of Heaven.

Conspiracy

As 1788 began, the random Indian attacks and brutal killings continued. The people in and around Nashville lived in constant fear of sudden and horrible death. The smallest and least significant tasks of the day were filled with life-threatening risk. Something had to be done. Over and over again General Robertson and his associates had petitioned the govern-ment of the United States to help them. Had they not fought in the Rev-olution, willing to give their blood for the life and freedom of this new nation? Did justice not call for reciprocity?

A meeting was called in Nashville, late in the night, and ideas were whispered about that had the sound of treason. Eusebius had made sure he was invited to this meeting, though Griswold and Witherel made just as sure that they were not. A decision was made—one which was to be kept as an absolute secret among those who were in the meeting. A delegation would go south to what is now Alabama to the Creek Chief, the half-breed Alexander McGillivray and make a bold, and some might say traitorous, proposal to him. McGillivray, or *Hoboi-Hili-Miko*, as his people called him, was the son of a Creek woman and a Scottish trader. He had chosen to cast his lot with his Indian relatives, as such half-breeds often did. He quickly rose to leadership and had been working hard against the Americans from the time of the Revolution on. His allegiances changed from time to time. At the moment he had formed an alliance with the subjects of the King of Spain.

The exasperated men of the Cumberland hinted strongly to McGillivray that they might be willing to declare themselves subjects of the Spanish King and align themselves with the Indians, if the attacks would stop and if the Mississippi would open up for trade for them all the way down to New Orleans. If he could make this happen he could even have a lot in Nashville and build himself a house there, they said.

James Robertson followed up with a letter to the chief which had more than a trace of treachery in it:

> In all probability we cannot long remain in our present state, and if the British, or any commercial nation which may be in possession of the Mississippi, would furnish us with trade and receive our produce, there cannot be a doubt but the people on the west side of the Appalachian mountains will open their eyes to their real interests."

Hardly anyone who was a part of this intrigue really wanted to separate from the new nation and fall back into the system they had fought against so valiantly only a few years before. But maybe, they thought, when word of the depth of their desperation got back to the Congress of the United States, as it certainly would, their government would do something to help them.

Word of these developments soon reached the Spanish authorities. Letters began coming to the leaders in Nashville from the Spanish governor, full of promises should they decide to transfer their allegiance to his sovereign. One such letter came to Eusebius' creditor Elisha Robertson. Eusebius watched all this as something of a new-comer and outsider, but nevertheless concerned to be sure he came down on the most advantageous side of the affair. Then one day, as he walked the muddy paths between the log buildings in the village of Nashville, carrying on his frantic business, Eusebius saw a familiar face.

"Monsieur Bushnell, mon ami très bon!"

"Monsieur Fagot! André!"

The dashing young fellow dismounted and threw his arms around Eusebius in the manner of a Spaniard or a Frenchmen—certainly not the kind of greeting comfortable for a New Englander. "Just the man I'm looking for!" he almost shouted. This was not quite the truth. He was actually looking for the Robertson brothers, and the young lawyer Andrew Jackson, and several others with more political clout than Eusebius. He had been sent as an agent for the Spanish to dangle various attractive proposals before the Cumberland settlers to see if they would actually change sides. All this was a very dangerous game, and Eusebius was about to find himself in the middle of it.

Fagot's proposition for Eusebius was simple and straightforward: side with Spain and you will soon be rich. Help us make Tennessee Spanish, and you will be rewarded with fabulous grants of good land and lucrative trade arrangements in New Orleans. The Frenchman had no idea how good his timing was. Perhaps Andy Jackson and James Robertson were only playing a game themselves, trying to scare the United States into helping them by flirting with the Spanish and their Indian friends. But Eusebius was in big financial trouble, and his needs were more straightforward. He needed to be free of that cursed little note he had signed that put him in debt to the Robertson's to the tune of forty thousand pounds.

"What you offer has a certain attraction to me," Eusebius said, trying to sound calm and a little hesitant. "But of course I'll need to know details." The two men enjoyed a cup of rum at one of Nashville's many taverns. Fagot wrote several nice letters to various Spanish officials, introducing Eusebius and suggesting that he be given certain favors. He handed the letters to Eusebius. Whether Fagot actually knew the persons to whom the notes were addressed, we cannot know. But it required little effort to write them, and one never knows what might come of such a thing.

This pleasant afternoon conversation was nothing more than a diversion for André Fagot. His real objectives required time with men like Elijah Robertson, with whom he quickly worked out an arrangement. He would use his contacts along the river and among the French and Spanish authorities to represent the Robertsons, should they ever require it. Elijah saw advantages in this alliance; one never knew when one might need representation in Kaskaskia, or Natchez, or even New Orleans. For his part, he would assure the Spanish authorities that the leaders in the Cumberland were eager to move their loyalty to someone who would actually help them. As for the Congress of the United States, they were very far away and occupied with other matters. This august body had shown itself apparently uninterested in some rustics in the Wilderness, living in log cabins and wearing buckskins, he would say.

Marketing the Wilderness

As a new year dawned, Eusebius and his partner Dobbins began a frantic attempt to dispose of all the lands they had acquired with borrowed money—preferably at a profit. Eusebius, who had a natural gift of clever and persuasive speech, decided to do some advertising. On September 5, he sent a packet of letters back to Connecticut, reporting to the family on events in the Wilderness. Borodell sent a note to her mother and sisters. Along with these family matters, Eusebius addressed the question of immigration to the paradise of the Cumberland. He enclosed a letter addressed to the editor of the *Connecticut Gazette, New London Edition:* "As the following short description of the county where I now live may be a benefit to many of my friends and acquaintances, I am induced, being an old customer, to request a publication of it in your paper. I am your's, etc. E. Bushnell."

The article was printed in the *Gazette* in November, and reprinted in several other New England newspapers. Of his new home, Eusebius said, "it is a most beautiful country, consisting of gently rising hills and extensive plains, watered with large rivers." Not many roads, he admitted, but easy travel by water. "The soil exceeds my highest expectations," he enthused. Every kind of crop will "flourish exceedingly." The temperature is so good that you can simply turn cattle loose in the woods in the winter and come back to gather them up in the spring, finding that some of them will now weigh a thousand pounds. "The water is good, and the air very healthy." And though it used to be difficult to come here, "Happily for us, we have a new road open to Holston River, which will be a very good wagon road." New England pales in comparison to the Cumberland, he said. "One day's labor in a week here is as profitable as the labor of a week with you." And "while you are beating the snow feeding your cattle," and standing by the fire "burning on one side while freezing on the other," "we can get out and plow, even in the middle of the winter."

What Eusebius failed to mention is that settlers would also find themselves surrounded by very angry Indian marauders who were quite eager to chop them up with tomahawks and tear off their scalps. And the "wagon road" was still very much a pipe dream.

Never-the-less, before the article even appeared in the paper, his brothers-in-law Witherel and Griswold Latimer were already on their way to the great Wilderness, eager to begin a new life. Eusebius and Borodell could hardly wait for their arrival. For her, this would mean a reunion with her beloved brothers and perhaps a respite from the constant strain, even terror, of daily existence in the forest.

Eusebius, despite a tinge of guilt, kept thinking about how his brothers-in-law would be prime customers for one of his real estate deals.

Witherel, Eusebius well knew, had some money. After all, before he headed for the Wilderness, Witherel had sold the fine farm in Connecticut which his father had given him. He was, at the time, stricken by grief and ready to flee from the scenes of personal tragedy generated by the familiar landscape around Chesterfield. There, almost a decade ago, he had married Abigail Fitch, a member of a distinguished local family. There had soon been a child, Daniel Fitch Latimer. It had been a difficult pregnancy, but Daniel was a fine, sturdy boy. Four years passed before the next pregnancy and it, too, was difficult. Much more difficult. The child, a second son, was born in October 1785. They named him James Luther.

Abigail did not survive.

The gravestone stands to this day, though crumbling with the ravages of time, in the old Chesterfield graveyard near where the Colonel had built a house for his new bride so long ago. On the stone is a weeping willow, skillfully carved in bas-relief, and underneath, the words: "In memory of Mrs. Abigail Latimer, wife of Mr. Witherel Latimer, who died Oct. 22, 1785, aged 31 years." Thus Witherel became a young widower, with two small sons.

When the family gathered in the little cemetery next to the meeting house, on land they had given to the community some years earlier, Witherel had already made up his mind. He would not—could not—stay in New England.

This had happened only a few months before Eusebius and Borodell, along with their children, had withdrawn into the great Forest of the Cumberland. They had been driven by entirely different motives than Witherel, of course, but all these events were gradually moving toward a momentous decision, one that involved the whole Latimer clan. Perhaps they should *all* go. Or at least those who needed, for one reason or another, to begin a new life.

When the Colonel mentioned this outrageous idea to Witherel, at first half in jest, Witherel immediately took a firm hold on it.

"I'll go see what Eusebius is up to," he told his father. "And if the prospects seem good, I'll send for the whole lot of you!"

He was surprised, but also pleased, when the Colonel replied, "Do it, Witherel. You do it." The Colonel was often very private about his own thoughts and feelings. Though his face showed nothing, he could not keep his mind's eye from peering down on that crushing moment when he had appeared a prisoner before a judge, and his Connecticut friends, and been cut to the heart by unreasonable accusations. And besides, Goodness knows, the times were hard and the prospects dim in New London. Maybe it would be best to simply fade away into the wilderness.

Witherel's voice interrupted and rescued the Colonel from this unwanted bundle of thoughts and emotions. "And I'll take Griswold with me. He's got nothing to lose, and he needs a little adventure."

"Yes," replied the Colonel, "that's also a very good idea."

It took several months for the grief-stricken Witherel to make all the preparations necessary to leave his old life behind and try to make a new one in the Wilderness. The last task would be to sell his fine farm, a cherished gift from his father, but too full of painful memories. He decided to put an ad in the *Connecticut Gazette* to try to find a buyer:

To be Sold on reasonable Terms,

A FARM, containing about eighty or one hundred acres of choice land; on which may be cut annually about 14 tons of good hay, with a good proportion of plowing and pasturing, with a dwelling-house and saw-mill thereon, and will be augmented with about two hundred acres, which is under good improvement, with a dwelling-house and barn thereon. Said Farm is situated in Montville, near Chesterfield meeting-house, and about eight miles from New London city. For particulars, enquire of WETHEREL LATIMER, living on the premises.

A quick sale followed. Fortified with the funds from the sale of his farm, Witherel and his younger brother Griswold set out on the long and dangerous journey to the Cumberland. The hardest part of it was leaving his two young sons, one of them still an infant. Lucretia and the Colonel would take good care of them, of course. They were far better off here. But to lose them, as well as Abigail, was painful beyond words.

In the very year that Witherel was winding up his affairs in New England, the legislature of North Carolina approved the building of a road between the south end of Clinch Mountain in east Tennessee and the town of Nashville, through what would become, almost ten years later,

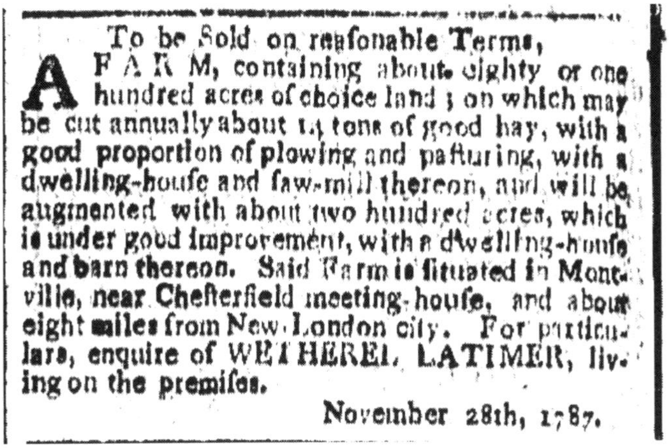

To be Sold on reasonable Terms, A FARM, containing about eighty or one hundred acres of choice land; on which may be cut annually about 14 tons of good hay, with a good proportion of plowing and pasturing, with a dwelling-house and saw-mill thereon, and will be augmented with about two hundred acres, which is under good improvement, with a dwelling-house and barn thereon. Said Farm is situated in Montville, near Chesterfield meeting-house, and about eight miles from New-London city. For particulars, enquire of WETHEREL, LATIMER, living on the premises.

November 28th, 1787.

Fig. 9: Witherel sells his farm

the State of Tennessee. On the last leg of their long journey, Witherel and Griswold would travel along this primitive path which the long-hunter Peter Avery had hacked from the forest. The road was not much to look at. Avery and his two companies of foot soldiers had cut a ten-foot swath through hostile Indian lands and done a little leveling here and there. Most people called it the Holston Road. It was too narrow and rough for anything but people riding horses—or walking—not the "wagon road" that Eusebius had promised. But it was better than nothing.

It was also very dangerous. The North Carolina legislature provided two companies of militia of forty men each to escort travelers on the road and keep careful guard over them. Witherel and Griswold volunteered for this duty. The first group of settlers to use the road departed on September 25, 1788, the second group a few weeks later. Witherel and Griswold escorted this second group, along with a tall, impressive fellow from Waxhaws, South Carolina, who had some plans of his own. He was about Griswold's age. A newly minted lawyer, he had gotten himself appointed as Prosecuting Attorney of the Western District. The Latimers would often have dealings with this young man in the years to come. So would the great tribes of Indians in the Wilderness. So would the United States of America. His name was Andrew Jackson.

When they arrived in Nashville Eusebius was there to greet them. It was fall, and a slight chill was already in the air. The trees in the huge surrounding forest were again showing their first color. Although they had done enough investigating to have very modest expectations, they were still stunned to find the town consisted of only a few stores, an inordinate representation of taverns, two churches, a distillery, five or six framed and hewn longhouses, and twenty or thirty log cabins. Equally stunning was the fact that the Indians were still terrorizing the settlers and killing them, men, women, and children, in the most ghastly fashion, and with distressing regularity.

The brothers had hardly unpacked their horses before Eusebius was offering Witherel a land deal. Witherel had no way of knowing, of course, what a financial mess his brother-in-law was in.

"I have an opportunity for you that you can't afford to pass up," Eusebius effused.

"But I've not even found a bed, yet!" Witherel protested.

"Here in the Cumberland you have to move quickly. He who hesitates is lost!" was the reply.

Witherel was a careful man, not given to hasty choices. But he was a newcomer and had no reason to doubt his brother-in-law's good intentions.

"So, tell me about this wonderful opportunity," he said, a wry and somewhat skeptical smile on his lips.

"It's almost the same size as your farm back in Connecticut. Two-hundred and twenty-eight acres of prime land on Stones River, right next to Major Blount's grant lands. It'll be worth a fortune someday." Eusebius countered Witherel's smile with a broad, very earnest one. He had picked up the tract only a few weeks before from a veteran named Isaac Hill. He could, he felt, sell it in good conscience to his kinsman for a quick profit, since it was *true* that it "would be worth a fortune someday." Just *when* that day would come was another matter, of course, especially given the fact that anyone who tried to actually occupy land along Stone's River would live in mortal danger from bands of murderous young Cherokee braves.

"Fifty-seven dollars, Witherel. That's all. Two Hundred and twenty-eight acres. That's twenty-eight cents an acre, for Heaven's Sake. Think what it would cost back in New London County!"

Witherel bought the land. The deed was dated less than 24 hours after his arrival in Nashville. But he bought it with eyes wide open. He had talked about the situation in the Cumberland with his fellow travelers on the Holston Road enough to know that this tract could only be justified as a long-term investment. In order to set himself up for a living, he would need other land as well, nearer the safety of the forts and blockhouses around Nashville. In the meantime, he would do his brother-in-law a favor and do a little business with him.

Witherel found a place to live on land belonging to David McGavock just across the river from the town, not far from the Kentucky Road that led up toward where the town Gallatin would eventually rise, and near enough to several forts and blockhouses to provide some safety in a crisis. Then he was able to buy a piece of nearby land right on the river and only one mile from Nashville. This tract he purchased from Martin Armstrong who was the biggest land-speculator of them all. He was pleased that he had turned one piece of land in Connecticut into three in the Cumberland—with money left over.

Witherel and Griswold spent their first winter in the Cumberland getting settled in and beginning to make preparations for the arrival of the Colonel and his entourage. Back in Connecticut, the situation was dark and foreboding. These were the *anni horribile*. Those who could were leaving. Those who stayed were struggling; some were ruined. The scars of war still disfigured and stung the heart like scorpions.

On April 30, 1789, George Washington was inaugurated in New York City as President of the United States of America. The Colonel himself remained a pillar of the community and was again appointed by the State Assembly as a Justice of the Peace. The joyous news from New York provided some validation for the long years on the field of battle. He had played his part in creating a new nation with new hope and freedom. He had more than once served at Washington's side.

But, on the other hand, his brother Robert had only recently been released from debtors' prison, defeated and humiliated. Cousin Nathan Latimer's troubles, personal and financial, were just beginning to leave their embarrassing stain on the family's reputation. And a cancer continued to grow deep in the Colonel's own heart. Not a physical cancer, but a deep, painful wound he felt when those who whispered around seemed to be whispering about him. And when those who were his faithful friends might be kind enough to his face, he thought, but at the same time be carrying hearts full of doubt about him. In some irredeemable way, they might be thinking that he was the cause of their misery.

"Lucretia," he said to his stalwart companion, "you know that my heart is heavy. Nothing will ever be the same here. I cannot shake off the memory of being brought before my friends and colleagues as a prisoner. A prisoner!"

"But John, you were completely exonerated. Your friends have not lost their confidence in you, and the people in our neighborhood still look to you as their leader."

"Maybe," he replied.

The Wilderness Claims a Victim

"Griswold," Eusebius spoke too loudly as he approached his brother-in-law's cabin, even for the distance between them, almost as if crying out a warning.

"Borodell is dead..."

Poor Borodell Latimer Bushnell was dead. The words bit like Cumberland frost. Griswold shook his head in disbelief. His beautiful older sister, who had mothered him back in their fine home in Chesterfield, as older sisters did in those days. She deserved much better than this. He vividly remembered the day she and Eusebius had left Connecticut for the Wilderness. He remembered that her eyes were full of tears, even though her husband assured her that the parting was only temporary. In fact, however, when she turned and waved to the large family gathered to see her off, it was the last time most of them would ever see her. That was the cruel fact of it. Why could the Good Lord not at least give her a few more months, so that she could see her parents and family one more time?

Griswold literally dropped to his knees and his eyes filled with tears. Eusebius, seeing this, fell beside his brother-in-law and sobbed uncontrollably. His distress was partly grief and partly naked guilt. His ambition and greed had carried her away, he thought to himself. She could have been enjoying the cool green fields of New London, her children playing among the stacks of hay, riding their ponies through the lovely woodlands...but he had brought her here. A beautiful and bountiful land, it was true, but a dark and bloody one. An alien one.

Griswold looked at the man weeping beside him with a mixture of pity and anger. It was difficult not to lash out with accusations and recriminations. But he held himself back with that tight New England self-control he had learned from his father and grandfather.

"Eusebius, you cannot blame yourself," he said, perhaps not with quite the level of conviction he was attempting to convey. "It is the will of the Almighty."

"You'll have to help me, Griswold," Eusebius sobbed.

"Of course I will," Griswold replied. "Shall I call Reverend Craighead to arrange a service?"

Thomas Craighead was the first minister to arrive in the settlements and was a man highly respected by the Latimer brothers. Their own grandfather, George Griswold, had been a minister in Connecticut and both men had some understanding and some opinions when it came to Theology. This set them apart from most of their neighbors, who gave religion a nod from time to time, but mostly saw the world in a decidedly non-theological way.

Craighead lived nearby and preached in a little stone church built on his land near Mansker's Station, close to the road that led to where Gallatin would be, six miles from Nashville. The building also served as the first academy for the town. There Craighead spent his weekdays teaching a few children in the traditional way—introducing them to Latin and Greek and the Bible. He was, after all, a graduate of Princeton and saw himself as a harbinger of civilization here in the Wilderness.

Witherel's place was quite nearby. Though church attendance was not mandatory on the frontier as it had been in Connecticut—far from it— the brothers often went to hear his sermons and knew him well.

"Yes, yes. Of course, of course," Eusebius said in a very distracted sort of way. Griswold could see there were other things on his brother-in-law's mind, despite his honest grief.

"I'm going to have to leave the Cumberland. Right away," he mumbled. "I pushed it too far, Griswold. I owe a lot of money to a lot of people. And to make it worse, I talked Elijah Robertson into co-signing for a huge loan. I know now I'll never to able to pay him back. I'm on the wrong side of the Robertsons. You know well enough how powerful and influential they are. And if that's not bad enough, how could I face the Colonel when he gets here? I just can't do it. He will come to this wilderness and find his daughter dead and me in hopeless debt. It might kill the old man. I need to get together some cash and get out of here. And I need your help."

He said nothing at all about André Fagot and his proposition.

Griswold was stunned, and he felt a deep anger rising within him. How could Eusebius be focusing on his own troubles at a time like this? "You know I won't do anything illegal for you, Eusebius. There are limits to what a person can do, even for family. And to be thinking about saving your own skin while your poor wife and my poor sister lies dead is lower than low. What is it you want from me?"

"Well, Griswold, as I say, I've overextended myself a bit—and I think prudence calls for me to try to make a second start. Someplace else." Eusebius had once again taken on his smooth, salesman *persona*. "I need to turn everything I can into cash. I need to do that right away. I was just hoping you could help me out by buying all the stuff I have stored out at Colonel Hays' house."

"Colonel Hays!" Griswold thought to himself. "I hope to Goodness he's not gotten sideways with Colonel Hays as well." And to make matters worse, that young lawyer whose acquaintance Griswold and Witherel had made on their perilous trip to the Cumberland, Andrew Jackson, had taken a shine to Colonel Hay's sister-in-law Rachel. She was married, but to a wife-beater. Jackson made no secret of his interest in her. And Andrew Jackson was spending most of his time as public prosecutor bringing legal action against people who were not paying their debts. Back in July, Eusebius and Griswold had served on a jury together in a trial in which Jackson was the defense counsel. They knew well what he was capable of doing.

Eusebius was desperately looking for ways to raise quick hard cash. Among the possessions he had recently acquired were three slaves—Phil, March, and Yarro. Yarro's name was African, and betrayed the fact that he had personally suffered the terrible passage across the Atlantic in a slave ship. Eusebius had thought the three would be useful on his imminent journey to the South. Now that idea seemed hopelessly impractical. The situation being what it was, these three were now more a liability than an asset, unless they, too, could be transformed into cash. He offered them to Frederick Stump, one of Nashville's earliest settlers and an infamous "Indian killer." But Stump was a wily fellow, knew that Eusebius was desperate, and offered so little that there would be no profit made. And he would only take two of the men. "Well," Eusebius reasoned to himself, "at least cash will travel better."

Eusebius wanted one hundred and twenty-five pounds for the stuff at the Hays place, including some rather fine furniture, and he persuaded the long-suffering Griswold to hand over the money before he let a second shoe drop.

"There's something else," he said, uncharacteristically tentative in his tone. "It's the children. Obviously, I can't care for them as a widower, and anyway I'm going to have to pursue some business matters away from Nashville. And who knows when those matters will be settled? Of course, the boys can come and live with me soon, but what about the girls? What can I do with them? I just don't know…"

The children: Hannah, Clarissa and Ezra, all teenagers; and little Matthew, only eight years old. Griswold's sense of Yankee honor and responsibility would not let him do otherwise, so he heard himself saying, "Don't worry. I'll see that they are cared for." Something within told him that would mean becoming a surrogate father, but what choice did he have?

"Oh, and one more thing. I hope you are willing to take Power of Attorney for me, so you can settle whatever business matters come up here in Nashville." Agreeing to this filled Griswold with more dread than had any of the other requests. Who could tell what financial quagmires might lie hidden away in Eusebius' shadowy affairs?

"We will have to send word back to Chesterfield. The family will have to know this sad news before they set out on their own journey," Griswold said.

He was shocked, and once again felt the anger rising in his heart when Eusebius replied, "Griswold, I'm sure you won't mind to write the letter. I just couldn't…" The sentence stopped, since even Eusebius could not think of an excuse for what he was doing. It would be the heart-wrenching duty of Griswold and Witherel to find the words to tell the Colonel and his family that Borodell would not be waiting for them when they arrived in the Wilderness. They could only hope that the letter would arrive before the family left Connecticut. Letters sometimes took months. Sometimes they never arrived at all.

And as for Eusebius, the Latimer family was never going to hear directly from him again on any subject. He was about to disappear.

The funeral took place at Rev. Craighead's little stone church next to the road to Sumner County. The preacher's words were comforting, but Borodell's children were understandably devastated. Not only had they lost their mother, but their own futures were very much in doubt. Eusebius had assured them that he would soon have their situation sorted out but, as much as they loved their father, they had learned to take such assurances with a grain of salt. Witherel and Griswold both felt that combination of grief and anger that would plague them for a long time to come. Borodell was put to rest in a grave near the church, one of the first graves in what would eventually become a huge city of the dead. Her grave was, as was almost always the case at that time, unmarked and eventually forgotten.

Eusebius felt the need to hang on to whatever cash he could get together, so instead of paying the minister for his services, he gave him his fine leather bound dictionary. Rev. Craighead was very pleased indeed. Books were rare in the Wilderness, and a dictionary would be invaluable to the scholars in the little school he taught in the meeting house during the week.

Now Eusebius had to move quickly. There were papers to sign, deals to complete, arrangements to be made. Much of October was taken up with these activities. He said little about his plans to anyone, but it was obvious he had formulated what might today be called a withdrawal strategy. His plan involved leaving the United States of America and becoming a subject of the King of Spain.

The implications were immense. Spain was wrestling both France and the infant United States for control on the continent west of the great Mississippi River. Part of the Spanish strategy was to encourage the deprecations of the Indians. To go over to the Spanish side, or the French side, for that matter, was treading very closely to treason. It might well mean that Eusebius could never expect to be accepted as an American again.

Flatboat to Natchez

But his decision was a surprisingly common one. Eusebius Bushnell made it his business to keep up with current events, political and otherwise. The important news for him was not the inauguration of George Washington, but rather an order by the king of Spain that his agents (like Eusebius' friend Andre Fagot) should encourage the immigration of Americans into the vast areas the King's agents controlled in Louisiana. Kentucky was full of people who had arrived in that state too late to get the land they wanted and needed. Such people were ready to move on, and the offer from the King of Spain was hard to refuse. So hundreds of them began to load their families and possessions into flatboats at ports along the Ohio River and float from there into the Mississippi and then down to the Spanish fort at Natchez, a few miles north of New Orleans.

This movement was in full swing by the time Eusebius had finished his preparations to leave the Cumberland. One way or another, he had managed to put together enough cash to get by on, and maybe even begin another round of land speculation without the inconvenience of the troublesome debt that hung over him in Nashville.

After the funeral, Eusebius left Nashville as unobtrusively as possible, kissing his children, whom he sincerely loved, despite appearances otherwise, and shaking the hands of Witherel and Griswold a bit too enthusiastically for the taste of either of them.

"I'll be in touch," he said with a smooth earnestness, not really knowing himself whether he was telling the truth.

He had little trouble finding a boat at the docks of Nashville that would take him down the Cumberland River to the Ohio. In a few days, the currents carried he and his fellow-travelers to where the Cumberland emptied into the Ohio. Here Eusebius and his remaining servant debarked. As he looked out into the broad Ohio River, he could see an almost constant stream of flatboats headed toward the Mississippi, filled with eager settlers from Kentucky. These cumbersome vessels were very hard to control, and the river turned them frontwards and backwards and sideways as it chose. Nevertheless, he was able to get the attention of the leader of a convoy of six boats floating quite near the shore, one of which seemed to have some space for more travelers.

"Headed for Natchez?" he shouted.

"We are."

"I'll pay to join you," Eusebius shouted again.

Without a word, the convoy's captain ordered the boats to the riverbank. The one with some space belonged to a man named Elisha Winters, himself on his way to settle in Spanish Territory. He welcomed Eusebius and the slave aboard, pleased with the unexpected extra income.

The journey down the Mississippi was relatively uneventful, and in a few days Natchez appeared in the distance, high on a bluff on the left side of the mighty river. The travelers could see a fort on the bluff, made of wood and earth, surprisingly small. Over the fort flew the flag of Spain. The flatboats were pulled on shore at the foot of the imposing bluff where a group of stores and houses, hardly more sophisticated than those in the Cumberland, lined a small strip of flat shoreline. This "town" of Natchez was obviously no more than a station on the way to the fabled city of New Orleans. It belonged entirely to the river. Most of the people in the convoy of flatboats had arrived at their destination, however. They would be looking for land on which to build themselves a new life. Eusebius was encouraged. He would, he thought to himself, soon be doing his best to provide them with what they wanted.

The date was June 22, 1790. In only a few days Borodell's family in Chesterfield would begin their long and perilous journey to the Wilderness. She would not be there to greet them. Nor would Eusebius.

His head was full of plans and ideas for his new life. But first, there was the two hundred foot bluff to climb, following a very narrow, very steep path. At the top, the new arrivals were required to report to the commandant, who was, to the travelers' surprise, not Spanish, but rather a Frenchman named Carlos de Grand-Pré. The new commandant, Manuel Gayoso, set to replace de Grand-Pré, was there as well, already at work laying out a town on the bluff in the Spanish style. Thirty-four city blocks had been plotted. In the center, there would be a grand plaza with a fine church named San Salvador.

The sound of the place was an absolute Babel. People were speaking Spanish and French and German and several varieties of English—with accents so different that those from London and Cambridgeshire could hardly understand their much less sophisticated Scotch-Irish fellow-settlers. And a plethora of native languages and dialects besides.

Eusebius licked his lips in anticipation. He had arrived at exactly the right time, in exactly the right place. In his pocket were certain important papers—letters for various Spanish authorities given to him by Fagot, introducing him as a man to be given every consideration.

Actually, these documents were not necessary. Though he did not know it, the officials already knew very well who he was and what value he might be to them. The Spanish had a sophisticated network of spies and other informants and information moved rapidly up and down the river.

When the commandant's aide wrote down his name in the book in which every arrival was recorded he spelled it "Eusebio." Eusebius was, after all, a sort of Spaniard now.

SEVEN: JOURNEY

The Minister's Daughter

Chesterfield, Connecticut
Spring, 1790

It is not easy to turn the eyes away from scenes of childhood, the warmth of long-time friends, the graves of parents and grandparents, the familiar, the expected, the enduring. Lucretia Griswold Latimer made her five-mile pilgrimage though the gentle woods and farmlands from Chesterfield to the graves of her own parents, lying next to the little church where her father had ministered for many decades. The little building had no steeple, no bell, no porch, and no paint. The hand-hewn wood from which it was constructed had turned greyish silver and its beams and pilasters bore the century-old hatchet marks of its builders. She did not go inside, but the interior was perfectly familiar to her—the ancient pulpit where her father had stood for decade after decade, looking out at the small congregation and the several doors all open to let in the cool breezes. The women in her memories were wearing little black bonnets held in place by long pins, or plain linen caps, and some wore short red-hooded jackets. The men all seemed to have fine pocket handkerchiefs with checkered decorations, and great shoe-buckles made of steel. She could almost hear the voices, singing Old Hundred or some other venerable hymn exactly as it had been sung for centuries. At her father's funeral they had sung,

> Time, like an ever rolling stream bears all its sons away,
> They fly, forgotten, as a dream dies at the opening day…

Reverend George Griswold, said a contemporary, was "an excellent Christian of ye primitive stamp," one who was "extremely temperate in all things." What this meant in practical terms is that Lucretia has been raised in the strictest of the old Puritan traditions. She was a model of New England womanhood and lived comfortably within the restrictions and limitations of those traditions without particularly noticing them, and with no particular expectation of change.

At the same time, she was a woman of uncommon talents and strength of character, a product of a father who wielded the Sacred Sword of the Word, but was himself raised in a family of those who with equal comfort wielded the scepter of power, belonging as they did to the very top-most rung in colonial society. Her grandfather had been the governor of colonial Connecticut. Her cousin, Matthew Griswold, had headed the Council of Safety during the Revolution and had finished his term as the second Governor of State of Connecticut only a few years before. Her relatives were graduates of Harvard, her mother's father one of the founders of Yale. Her kinsmen had for generations presided on judicial benches and towered over the halls of commerce, living on fine estates with lovely gardens and libraries full of imposing leather-bound books. Two of her cousins would find a place among the most powerful and wealthy businessmen in New York City, helping to build what would be-come the center of the world of commerce.

As she stood in the graveyard, random thoughts of her childhood wafted by like the gentle winds in nearby trees: She did not remember her mother Hannah, who died "of a quinsy" at age thirty-seven when Lucre-tia was only three years old. But she had grown up hearing stories about her wealthy and powerful grandfather, Judge Lynde, a founder of Yale, the school where her own father had studied. Then there was the visit, when she was only ten years old, of the famous preachers George White-field and Gilbert Tennant, and the incredible events that followed. Her father's sermons were, like those of his contemporaries, rather formal, the language stilted, written out in a tiny hand on scrapes of paper and read with head bowed. But during the height of the excitement, she re-membered that those sermons suddenly began to cause the knees of his audience, mostly young people, "to smite one against another" as one witness had said. "Great numbers cried out aloud in the anguish of their souls. Several men fell as though a cannon had been discharged, and a ball had made its way through their hearts. Some of the young women were thrown into hysteric fits." She could not know that she would be seeing similar scenes in the Wilderness not too many years hence.

The great revival in her father's church was followed a couple of years later by even stranger events. On March 6, 1743, one of the revivalists convinced his followers that they must "burn their idols." Hundreds of the kind of books that Lucretia had learned to love were tossed in a great pile on Christopher's Wharf in New London and set on fire by crowds of hymn-singing citizens, intent on purging their world of its wickedness. Not yet satisfied, they set about to start another bonfire, this one fueled by petticoats, silk gowns, pretty caps, fans, necklaces, and red heeled shoes. Fortunately, someone convinced the earnest citizenry that this was a step too far and at least a remnant of the wardrobes of the women of

New London were spared. Twelve-year-old Lucretia had watched all this with wonder and confusion.

Despite the extreme emotions of what historians were to call the "First Great Awakening" which struck her father's church like a mighty rushing wind, her home continued to be full of books. The dinner table, surrounded by a host of brothers and half-brothers, sisters and half-sisters, was a place for serious and intellectual discussion. From time to time there were Niantic Indians there as well since her father took great interest in the native peoples' welfare, both spiritual and temporal. He had encouraged these bedraggled survivors of past injustices to become members of his church, and some of them did so. But by this time the natives she met seemed beaten and pathetic to her, and she was inclined mostly only to pity them.

Despite his Puritan underpinnings, the Reverend George Griswold not only allowed his daughters to learn to read but encouraged them to pick up the great books around them and read whichever ones they might choose. He was for his children a model for the life of the mind, having given his salutatory speech when he graduated from Yale in 1717 in respectable, if not perfect, Latin. The dons of the college thought well enough of it to give his hand-written copy pride of place in their nascent official archives, where it resides to this day. Her well-honed literacy and her considerable social skills would serve her marriage well. Married at the tender age of sixteen, she took on the *gravitas* of a home-maker with maturity beyond her years. Colonel Latimer, often gone off to war, left her the responsibility not only of their home, but of the documents that must be signed, and the business decisions that must be made in his absence—something truly unusual in those days.

Now many of her childhood friends were leaving their homes just as she was, from Lyme, from Montville, from New London. Like her, they had known only New England. And though they had lived through tempestuous times, there had been a kind of predictability about life in communities rooted in these hills and forests, and along these rivers, for almost two centuries. And though they, too, were finding it necessary to leave now, their situation seemed different to her than did her own—less traumatic. They were going in great groups together. And not so far away as were the Latimers—mostly over into New York State and what would eventually be called the Western Reserve in Ohio. There would be so many of them, and they would take so much of their New England ways, that some would call their destination "New Connecticut."

The Cumberland, on the other hand, where the Latimers were headed, might as well be on the moon.

There was another graveyard pilgrimage to be made. Lucretia returned home first, to the lovely two-story house where she and the Colonel had spent all the years of their marriage, the place where all of the thirteen children had been born. From there, it was a very short journey to the burial place of little Lucretia and her brothers Nicholas and Daniel. She touched each stone and whispered goodbye. She would never be able to perform this simple act again.

But at least there was a grave, and a gravestone, and a place—something firm and stable for the grieving memory. For her beloved daughter Borodell, there could be no pilgrimage—only tears. The letter from the wilderness had come only a few weeks before, along with other letters with information about the road, and the land in the Cumberland, and the things that needed to be done in preparation for the journey. The note which had cut open her heart was a mere scrap on which a grief-stricken Witherel Latimer had written only this:

The Lord has chosen in his infinite wisdom to take our dearest Borodell into his own dwelling place, where He shall wipe away all tears from her eyes; and there shall be no more death, neither sorrow, nor crying, neither shall there be any more pain. Sorrow not as those who have no hope.

This Witherel had written, and nothing else.

Preparation

The family of Jonathan and Lucretia was a large one, and many complex decisions had to be made. Who would stay and who would go? What could and could not be taken on such a formidable journey? When should they leave, and by what routes?

The Colonel felt a strong responsibility to provide for the future of his children. They must take personal responsibility for their lives and fortunes, but they must all be given what people in another age and place would come to call a grubstake. That was what he felt as father and patriarch of the family. There were eight living children. Three of them had already left for the Cumberland: Borodell, Witherel, and Griswold. Two of these were, as far as the Colonel knew, already well taken care of. He would have to wait a while to know what had happened to Borodell's family. His two oldest sons, George and Jonathan, Jr., would stay in Connecticut, on land given to them by the Colonel. They would own and run the Latimer Mills which should provide a good and comfortable life for them. There were four additional sons. Two, Charles and Robert, were in their 30s, married, with young children. Charles' wife was pregnant. The youngest two were still in their 20s; one, Joseph, still single, and one, Nathaniel, married, but without children. That left one daughter, Hannah, the oldest of Jonathan and Lucretia's children, married to Daniel Rogers, a member of one of the old and respected families in New London. She and her husband were in their 40s but also eager to begin again in the Wilderness. Finally, there were the two sons of Witherel by his lamented wife Abigail, Daniel and James, known by the family as Dan and Jimmie, both under ten years old—left with Lucretia and Jonathan when their father and Uncle Griswold had departed to "spy out the land" in the great forest. There would be more than twenty persons in all, several of them young children, some mere infants.

The Colonel was an old man for the times—almost sixty-seven years old. His wife was sixty. But he had led hundreds of men on marches of hundreds of miles during the wars. He had learned the necessary logistics and learned them well. He was confident that he could get this little caravan to its destination—more than fourteen hundred miles from their Chesterfield home.

At best, he estimated the trip would take fourteen to fifteen weeks. This meant that it would be important to leave in late spring at the latest. Waiting any longer would mean winter travel during the most precarious part of their journey—the last few hundred miles. Surely, even with the women and small children, and a fair amount of luggage, they could average a hundred miles a week. Jonathan not only had a great deal of experience in moving groups great distances, but he also had the advantage of the experiences of Witherel and Griswold, who had sent messages to him reporting on their own journey to the Cumberland whenever they could. Mail was excessively slow in those days, but it did eventually get to those to whom it was addressed. At least most of the time.

It might not be possible to complete all the complicated business arrangements in the time that was left, particularly the sale or distribution of his extensive land holdings around New London. But George and Jonathan, Jr., could deal with whatever needed to be done on that score. Deciding what to take along was particularly difficult, both to the head and the heart. Many prized family possessions would have to be left behind. One does not simply say goodbye to dearest friends, but also to those inanimate objects that carry with them all that is left of events and lives borne away by time—wonderful pieces of furniture from colonial days, letters and documents full of meaning and remembrance from loved ones long gone, dishes and lovely silver objects from the kitchens and dining rooms of the family homes. Long family discussions and negotiations were necessary, almost always ending in tears in some quarter. This process could have gone on for months, but finally, the Colonel simply put on his old tri-cornered hat, at least figuratively, and pronounced his orders in the old military fashion. He sent for his eldest son, George, who had served in the Revolution and knew about military discipline, and who, anyway, would not be making the trip. He said that George should meet him at the house he had built with his own hands more than half a century before, the house where he and Lucretia had lived all their lives together. It was soon to be George's house.

George thought this summons had something to do with the transfer of ownership. He was greeted at the door by his father and ushered into the front room, and seated at the desk. There he found quill and inkstand, and a stack of bits and pieces of paper, torn from the unused bottoms of other documents—as was the custom of the day, even for important matters. Paper was, after all, a rather rare and precious commodity. He prepared to write.

The Colonel began. "*State of Connecticut. Regimental Orders.*" George looked up, rather startled. His father smiled. "Just write what I say," he ordered. "To the Latimer Family of New London. Pursuant to the decisions hitherto made, you are required to bring your company of able-bodied persons and have them equipped and ready to march whenever they may receive such orders, most likely on Thursday, two weeks hence. They are to bring such provisions and equipment as has been determined by the officer in charge, no more or no less. They will be ready to march no later than 6:00 am. Signed, Jona Latimer."

"Make copies for each family," the Colonel said, "and deliver them immediately. That should move things along!" The smile broke into laughter. George laughed, too, but he felt a twinge in his heart all the same.

The next two weeks passed quickly as each family busied itself with last minute tasks. Then the day arrived; a day of glorious sunshine, the green meadows in full summer growth, the livestock happily grazing. It was the sort of day when all seems well in God's world. But the Latimers knew that it was best to ignore the beauty before them. It was better to dwell on memories of the crushing cold of mid-winter here in New England when the toes and fingers ache and the fields and livestock are covered with blowing snow. The waters of Long Island Sound are blue and the breezes warm today. Better to think of the icy chill that will replace those breezes in only a few weeks, and the raging waves splashing on the sandy beaches with such force as to threaten life itself, should anyone get too close. There were memories of idyllic childhood, lived in lovely houses on prosperous farms. Better to think of how little opportunity there would be here for such a life for their children.

The time of departure was full of tears. This journey was so long, the resulting separation so immense, that everyone knew the goodbyes were almost certainly final goodbyes. This is why letters from the Wilderness in those days often began by saying, "I know I will never see you again until we meet on that sweet, eternal shore…" Most of those who made this kind of journey made it only once, and there was not even a phantom hope of ever returning.

Lucretia, who had grown up in a home where the words of the Holy Book permeated day to day life, often found words in that place for her own feelings. She remembered her father's sermon about the patriarch Abraham, how he set out with his family for an unknown land. The Biblical words seemed almost made for this moment. She recited them to herself, *soto voce*:

> Abraham, when called to go to a place he would later receive as his inheritance, obeyed and went, even though he did not know where he was going. By faith he made his home in the promised land like a stranger in a foreign county; he lived in tents, as did his sons Isaac and Jacob, who were heirs with him of the same promise. For he was looking forward to the city with foundations, whose architect and builder is God.

She looked at her husband of almost half a century, hair as white as the clouds above them, but still full and glowing like silk. He still stood tall and looked like what he was, a leader of men. She mentally surveyed his handsome children and grandchildren, tall like him, and extraordinary in so many ways. How proud of them she felt! Ready to go they knew not where, to be like strangers in a foreign county, to live in tents, to look for a city with foundations. And all these things were true of her as well— perhaps even more true of her. She allowed herself only the briefest of tears. She was not tall like the Latimers—father and sons, but she was nevertheless their rock. She would be for them in this thing what she had always been for them.

Exodus

On the Great Wagon Road
Summer, 1790

Now it was time for the Colonel to draw on all those years of marching soldiers across the untamed terrain of a new land, finding food and lodging for them, and encouraging them in the face of challenges which sometimes seemed to move from merely difficult to impossible. Armed with years of experience, and the valuable advice from his sons Witherel and Griswold, who had already made the trip under even more difficult circumstances, he had planned this journey with the same care he had used as a leader in the days of the Revolution.

It seemed best to divide the fourteen hundred miles they would travel into four segments, each with its own distinctive characteristics and challenges. The Colonel took his quill pen and a scrap of paper and wrote:

1. New London to Philadelphia—The Post Road.

2. Philadelphia to Big Lick, Virginia—The Great Wagon Road

3. Big Lick to Knoxville—The Wilderness Road/Holston Road

4. Knoxville to Nashville—The New Holston Road

Timing was very important. The family must leave by late spring or early summer so that the whole journey could be completed during good weather. Traveling as they would be with small children and much luggage meant that getting caught by the storms of winter would spell disaster. And besides, they would need a few weeks of reasonable weather to get settled after they arrived.

"So," the Colonel thought, "let us say twenty miles a day, five days a week as an average. Fourteen hundred miles, more or less. Fourteen or fifteen weeks. The cold winds might well begin to catch us by mid-October. We need to leave by July 1. July 1 it will be." Such a schedule was optimistic, to say the least, and would require skillful planning, great discipline, and no bad luck.

"We'll give it our best," he thought. "We are a sturdy crew."

The weeks of preparation followed. All business obligations must be handled. Friends must be consoled. Old favors and old grievances rectified. Some things bought and some things sold. This was no ordinary trip. All the good-byes were likely to be the final ones on this earth. They would not be easy.

At last, the day of departure arrived. Reverting once again to his military past the Colonel insisted that everyone line up for muster. There was Lucretia, of course. Then their oldest child Hannah, wife of Daniel Rogers with her husband and their five young children, including one named Jonathan and one named Lucretia. Next came Charles Latimer and his wife Mary (several months pregnant) and their two young children. Next, Robert Latimer, a student of Nathan Hale, his wife Lucinda, and their four young children. Then the ill-fated Nathaniel and his wife Mary (also pregnant). Finally, Jonathan and Lucretia's unmarried son, Joseph, and the two sons of Witherel, both under ten years old, who had been living with their grandparents since their widowed father had left for the Cumberland.

The Colonel took note of the totals: eleven adults, thirteen children, and two more on the way. He had often felt the weight of responsibility for the lives and well-being of others, but never with quite the intensity that he felt that weight now. He was ripping up two generations of his family from roots which were very, very deep—stretching back to the old ship Mayflower herself. It was like a violent Atlantic hurricane tearing the oaks of New England from their ancient moorings.

And yet he sensed surprisingly little apprehension among them. The future that could be expected here in the woods of New England—with its broken economy, painful personal memories, the loss of loved ones, a culture crippled by war and uncertain of its power to rejuvenate itself—provided little competition with the unknown but promising future in the vast wilderness beyond the mountains. There, everything would be new again. Everything once again would be possible.

The first stage would, of course, be the easiest by far. The Post Road that ran from Boston to New York was perfectly familiar to the Latimers. Most of the adults had used it, or at least the first few miles of it, to visit family and friends in the neighboring towns of Lyme and Saybrook, and even to go as far as Hartford to the West. The road passed through beautiful villages, with towering steeples and fine houses, and lovely New England forests and fields which had been carefully cultivated for more than a century and a half. That is not to say that the road provided a particularly pleasant experience itself. A few years before the Latimers' journey travelers would have (and did) use words like rough, stony, uneven, or worse, intolerable or most miserable, to describe their journey here, but things were somewhat better now. There were, nevertheless, still several rather treacherous ferry-points to cross, and it still took two days to get from New Haven to New York, and several more to reach Philadelphia. The challenges were good practice for what was to come.

Once Again to Arms

The Colonel and several of the Latimer men had followed this road to the battlefields of New York during the Revolution and, in the Colonel's case, the French and Indian War as well. His little army of emigrants this time consisted of sons and sons-in-law, daughters and daughters-in-law, and a fine brood of grandchildren, along with four wagons piled high with precious possessions and provisions, tents and tools. There were horses, more than a dozen, and...guns.

It would not be prudent to speak of it now, except perhaps to the older, more experienced of the men in the family, but the analogy between this band and the soldiers he had led in the past was not a merely romantic one. He knew full-well that before the journey was over the guns might stand between them and absolute disaster. He was comforted by the fact that not only he, but several others in the family had known the sounds and fury of combat, and had fired and been fired upon in the heat of battle. Letters from Witherel and Griswold in the Cumberland were not full of flights of fancy like those of Eusebius had been. They had not hidden the almost daily horrors they had seen when, as sudden as lightning, the Native Americans had time and again unleashed their fury on those who were invading their ancestral hunting grounds. There was no need for guns on this rather nice road along the shores of Long Island Sound. The guns had been silenced here almost a decade ago, and peace reigned. But not so, further along.

It would have been more comfortable to go to New York by boat, as the Colonel had done a number of times, but the large amount of baggage the Latimers had with them made that too expensive and impractical. And the presence of a string of Inns and Taverns along the way meant that they would not yet have to set up tents to stay the night—a process that would become commonplace soon enough.

By following the Postal Road, the Latimer grandchildren would be able to experience what so few of their contemporaries, and certainly none of their future friends in the wilderness, could even imagine. They would always remember that they had seen the two greatest American cities, New York and Philadelphia, with their own eyes. Who else in the primitive and far off Cumberland would be able to boast of such a thing?

The Colonial gave the old familiar "forward march" signal. The horses were urged ahead. The wheels on the wagons turned on their axles, creaking under the weight. The children, conditioned by old Puritan discipline, wanted to shout, but instead only whispered excitedly. Apprehension could be seen only in the eyes of the wives, looking back and forth between their chattering children and their determined husbands, whose own eyes were only on the road ahead.

Under the Flag of Spain

Meanwhile, only about a week before the Latimers left their homes in Chesterfield, Eusebius Bushnell arrived in the new town square of Natchez, breathless from excitement and the difficult climb up from the banks of the river. He had turned his assets all into cash, a considerable bag of large gold coins that had been freshly minted somewhere far to the South. On the coins was a portrait of Carlos IV, his big nose and high forehead prominent in profile. Old Carlos seemed to be smiling, slightly. Perhaps this was a good omen. On the other side of these coins, Eusebius read the inscription: HISPAN. ET IND. REX ("King of Spain and the Indies").

"Are you a settler or a visitor?" the government official had asked him when he entered the government house which stood close to the bluff overlooking the river.

"A settler," he confidently replied.

He had intended to show the official his letters from André Fagot, but it didn't seem necessary. He would keep them for a more auspicious moment. He could not know that Fagot was as unknown in Natchez as he and would prove to be of no further use to him.

The Cities

There was traffic on the Post Road from the first day in the form of large, lumbering stage coaches, some plain and some positively elegant. The coaches ran regular schedules from Boston to New York—the nation's largest city, and from New York to Philadelphia—the nation's second-largest city. Soon they became commonplace and the Latimers hardly noticed them anymore as they approached from ahead, and passed them from the rear. There were many other people on the road as well, some back and forth doing business, and some leaving forever for the south and west, just as the Latimers were leaving.

The first stage of the journey, from Lyme, where the Latimers picked up the Post Road, to the fabled city of Philadelphia, would cover something over two hundred miles and would take two weeks or so—the first two weeks of July. The road along the coast was fairly good by the standards of the time, and everything progressed as planned. When the party crossed over onto the Island of New York, the Colonel and those sons who had fought in the momentous battles there, quietly reminisced among themselves, and sometimes told the wide-eyed children stories of the Revolution. Intent on their own dramatic adventure, the Latimers passed through New York without taking particular note that the Congress of the United States, meeting there, was in the process of deciding to make a mosquito-infested swamp down in Virginia, steamy and thoroughly unpleasant, the site of the new nation's capital. Congress would name it after the new nation's newly elected president, George Washington. All this, of course, was of little relevance to the Latimers. Their thoughts had escaped to places far beyond the great chain of mountains that divided the thirteen new states from the vastness of the great forest.

A few days later the Colonel's brood arrived in Philadelphia. Now came the second stage of the great journey. The Colonel led his family toward the west, into the fertile farm country of southeastern Pennsylvania, where the dominant language was German. The New Englanders had dealt with Germans before, but not on the friendly basis they found here. It was the ferocious Hessians that came to mind when Germans were mentioned in Connecticut. Horrible stories came back with the New England farm boys who had faced the Hessians in battle. The Colonel had had many fights with them, of course. It was a Hessian bullet that had cut the holes in his military commission at Saratoga. They were the ones, said the returning militia men of Connecticut, who had killed defenseless soldiers in the Battle of Long Island, soldiers who were merely trying to surrender to them—plunging bayonets into their chests as they pleaded for their lives. The Latimer children frightened one another with such stories as their party set out of the Great Wagon Road down among the fine farms of the "Pennsylvania Dutch"—as these particular Germans were called.

But soon they learned that the fearsome Hessians, certainly those who had stayed after the War and become Americans themselves, were also simply farm boys, forced into wars they did not understand and cared nothing for. And that they were actually mostly God-fearing and frightened victims of the avarice of their leaders—German and British alike. In lovely Pennsylvania towns like Lancaster and York, the citizens looked up from their work in the fields at the immigrant wagons passing through and shouted *Gute Reise!* or *Die besten Wünsche für die Zukunft!* Have a good trip! Best wishes for the future!

Along the Conestoga River, the family stopped to replace some of their wagons with better ones built there, with their fine cloth coverings and metal reinforced wheels. There were negotiations on price, finally an agreement, and handshakes all around. These wagons would serve them well as the roads became more and more steep and rocky and muddy and full of treacherous and unexpected hazards. Because they were so long, twenty feet or so, and so tall, ten feet, and could carry such a heavy load, almost all the Latimer's oxen and horses were required to pull them. But there was room for most everyone to ride in the wagons, except those who rode the remaining horses to serve as scouts and guides for the family.

The days became routine after a while. The travelers rose very early, long before sunrise, and moved ahead. In mid-afternoon, they stopped, cared for the animals, prepared a big dinner, and set up camp for the night. From the very beginning, the Colonel insisted that they camp like soldiers, establishing a perimeter, appointing guards, and listening carefully to the night sounds. For a while, those eerie cries in the forest would be merely packs of wolves. Disconcerting, but no real danger. And the popping and crunching sounds signaled nothing more than a raccoon, or some other small beast, making its way in the darkness. But before the journey was completed such sounds might be the signals of marauding Indians, circling the camp. That would be another matter altogether. So someone had to stay awake and watch, no matter how exhausted they might be from the challenges of the day.

Sometimes the wagons broke down and had to be repaired. Sometimes the rivers were flooded and almost impossible to cross. Sometimes food supplies ran low when the next supply station was still a long way off. Sometimes someone got sick, especially the children.

"We will somehow manage," Lucretia would say. "We always do."

South to the Shenandoah

Toward Virginia
July 15 through August 26, 1790

The heat of July bore down on the travelers, with its attendant pests—mosquitoes, flies, fleas—buzzing and biting. The Latimers turned their wagons south and west. Soon Pennsylvania became Maryland. The journey had already taken them through five of the thirteen colonies which had become the "United States of America." The older members of the family, who remembered the days before the Revolution, could not help but think how once these states had been like different countries to them, separate and independent, tied together only by the long chords which stretched out to all of them from the Mother Country across the sea. Now, as they traveled further and further from their homes, everyone they met was, like them, simply an "American"—even those who spoke Dutch or German. This was a new world, and it took some adjustment in one's way of thinking about it.

The trip through Maryland was a relatively short one, and soon the famed Potomac River appeared before them, and beyond it, Virginia. They joined a surprisingly large number of fellow-emigrants crossing the Potomac at Watkins Ferry. Two weeks ago they had been in Philadelphia; it seemed an eternity.

Now the path followed a lovely steam called the Opequon to the portals of a beautiful Valley. The gentle hills became a fertile plateau. The fields were bright green. On one side were the tree-covered Appalachians replete with chestnut trees, and oaks, and maples, and hickorys. And beneath the massive trees, the dogwoods and rhododendrons. On the other side, they saw the mysterious heights of the Blue Ridge Mountains and heard the sound of little shallow creeks and tiny waterfalls.

Shenandoah!

The Latimers soon found themselves moving down the main street of the lovely little town of Winchester, Virginia. The Colonel could not resist shouting a command for the little wagon train to stop, taking care to pull aside so as not to impede other travelers. He had never visited Winchester, but he felt strong ties to the place. This was the town of Daniel Morgan, his fellow colonel and comrade in arms. And those tall, handsome sharpshooters who had played such a dramatic role in the Revolution. The siege of Boston. Saratoga. Freeman's Farm. Bemis Heights.

"Look around you, children! Look at those fellows standing over there. Some of them probably carried their long rifles into battle next to my own men from New London. What marksmen they were. Think of it!"

"And this is the home country of General Washington himself. He is the one who built that Fort you saw as we came into town—for the French and Indian war. And he spent his youth surveying the land around here. I expect we'll see more signs of him again before long."

These thoughts energized the aging colonel and excited his wonder-filled grandchildren. With so much to see, and with the tales he could tell them, the tedium and discomfort of the long weeks on the road faded away—at least for a while.

The scenery around them was incredibly beautiful. But this was no empty wilderness. The countryside was dotted with well-tended farms and lovely houses. There were trading posts so well placed along the way that travelers were never in danger of running out of supplies or food. The trek through the lush green valley was almost pleasant, though everyone was working hard to keep on schedule and see that order prevailed. And bugs, of course, will be bugs.

There were towns. Towns like Harrisburg (another week had passed) and Staunton and Lexington (yet another week). Lexington was especially interesting to the colonel since it had been named by Tom Jefferson him-self, along with others, to commemorate the Battle of Lexington. The colonel's thoughts went back to that wild ride toward the other Lexington with his fellow militiamen to see if they could help their friends in Mass-achusetts. So long ago. The road ran directly through the town, and the Latimers stopped, despite the admonitions not to fall behind schedule, in order to taste the good food available at the famous tavern there.

Now the road turned west, taking the travelers further and further from the familiarities of the sea. Their forebears had come to this land in ships and had lived in a city of ships for generations. There would be no more ships.

South and West of Lexington the valley began to close in, the moun-tains closer and closer to the travelers on both the left and the right. And there, in front of them, there came into view something so spectacular that the lot of them simply stopped at once in amazement, without any order to do so. The great natural bridge, hundreds of feet tall, owned at one point by Tom Jefferson, and surveyed by Washington himself, could cause one to wonder if his eyes were deceiving him.

"Take a good look, then it is back to the wagons," said the Colonel. "We must keep moving."

On to Fincastle. The Great Wagon Road was now following the course of the Roanoke River, which would furnish the Latimers a way through the mountains and into the new world to which they were going. At a place called Big Lick, they crossed the Roanoke River. Here the road split and the family watched as most of the travelers who had been with them as they passed through Virginia went to the left—on south to the Caroli-nas and Georgia. The Latimers would be taking the road less traveled, off to the right, toward the West, rough and increasingly dangerous, to-ward the Cumberland. They were more than four hundred miles from Philadelphia and more than six hundred miles from their home in Con-necticut. The summer was slipping away.

The Great Wagon Road was now becoming the Wilderness Road. The fine farms and well-supplied inns along the Shenandoah would be giving way to a wilder and wilder scene. The great trees of the endless forest seemed to be closing in. The road was narrower. Signs of civilization far less evident. A dark green, ominous tangle full of unseen hazards, un-known sounds, uncertain footing. Sometimes, on the high ridges, they could look down and across an impenetrable and seemingly endless panorama of trees, packed together like a huge carpet as far as the eye could see. This primeval forest was broken in the lower places by even more impenetrable cane breaks and here and there a grassy meadow. The children looked at such scenes with a combination of wonder and dread. What secrets did this mountain vastness hold? What was out there?

Soon there would be Indians. Not the pathetic, defeated, dispirited creatures of Connecticut, subjects of pity and the spiritual concern of Lucretia's tenderhearted father, but rather angry sons of the forest, full of hatred towards the hordes of intruders descending upon their ancient hunting grounds. These were a people thirsting for revenge and the blood of the travelers whether they might be man or woman, or even babe in arms.

Before them, and to either side, the massive mountains loomed above like the walls of some Celestial City. At the foot of the mountain range, they stopped for a night at the tavern of a hardy woman named Mrs. Kent, who greeted them with kindness. The next day they pushed ahead. And soon before them, yet another rushing river appeared—almost suddenly. Another river to cross. The New River, it was called. The waters were cool and clear. Beyond it, the heart of the wilderness.

Ingles Ferry

The river was broad, but the travelers' had the great advantage of using the famous Ingles Ferry to get across. The Latimers were warmly greeted by William Ingles, who was in the midst of building himself a fine new house near the river. His men helped the family, along with several others, to load their wagons and themselves onto the ferry.

"There are a lot of folks waiting at the tavern on the other side, eager to meet you, Colonel," he said. "And my mother would love to sip some coffee with you, Mrs. Latimer."

Apparently, the Colonel's reputation as an officer of the Revolution was particularly appreciated by the rabidly patriotic settlers in the region, as it would be time and again along the journey. As the Latimer wagons rolled off the ferry on the western shore, something of a crowd was already gathering, made up mostly of old timers, themselves veterans of the War, who wanted to shake the Colonel's hand. He was surprised by the attention, having always had only modest regard for his contributions to the Revolution. The grandchildren, on the other hand, were practically exploding with pride as they saw the honor paid to their Grandpap. The trip across the river was exciting for the Latimer children, but even more exhilarating was the opportunity to jump off the wagons and enjoy the cool breezes and grassy meadow near the tavern in the company of other children following the same path to the wilderness.

A woman appeared before the entrance of the imposing log building known as Ingles Tavern. Her hair was white, her skin darkened and wrinkled by six decades of exposure to wind and weather.

The famous Mary Draper Ingles.

"Mrs. Latimer—how nice to meet you," she smiled. "Come and sit a while. We have things to talk about."

Mary had come from the genteel colonial world herself, a native of Philadelphia. She was almost exactly the same age of Lucretia, though she looked very much older—the wilderness having taken its toll. Her two families, the Drapers and the Ingles,

Fig. 10: The Crossing at Ingles Ferry

had created the first English-speaking settlement west of the Alleghenies in the days before the French and Indian War. While still in her twenties, she had been captured by the Shawnees and dragged up the New River into the wilds of Kentucky and beyond. Then she had escaped and somehow had been able to travel over eight hundred miles back to her family—a story which had become a part of the legendary lore of the wilderness. Widowed now, she presided over the Ingles' enterprises—the tavern, a general store, and a blacksmith shop.

Lucretia Latimer was exactly kind of woman that Mary Draper Ingles liked. And in fact, they did have much to talk about, despite the very different turns their individual lives had taken. Mary looked at Lucretia's still-delicate features, her poise and obvious education, her apparent affluence, with clear admiration. And Lucretia, in turn, admired Mary's strength, her courage, and her intimate knowledge of the wilderness into which Lucretia was being thrust in the declining years of her own life. There was, indeed, much to talk about. It would be a dialogue between two very strong women.

"Shall we call ourselves Mary and Lucretia?" Mary asked. "I know you have been accustomed to more formality, but such customs tend to fade in the wilderness."

"Mary it shall be," Lucretia replied. "I am a woman of your age, but I am like an infant now, learning how to live in another world. I know there is much that I could learn from you."

"And I would be thrilled to hear of the world from which you have come," Mary said. "Your coming is itself a great puzzle to me. I remember something of the cultured world of Philadelphia—though the details have long ago vanished. But this wilderness has been my home since I was a girl of sixteen years. And I am sure you know that as a young woman I was torn from even this bit of civilization and forced to live among the savages, and then to make the tortuous journey back to this place."

"And your children were taken from you and raised as Indians. Everyone knows your story, Mary, and everyone holds you in awe because of it. I cannot even imagine the pain."

"Well, even those events were long, long ago, and I am now an old woman in the world to which I belong. But you, also a woman of mature years (forgive me for saying so), have left the gentle world of New England and come to this place—this dangerous place—when other women might look forward to a life of retirement in places familiar to them, and among old friends. Why have you done this?"

"There are many reasons, and the explanation would take a long time," Lucretia answered. "But suffice it to say that I am here because Jonathan is here, and because my family is here. This is the destiny of wives and mothers, is it not?"

"It is indeed."

Meanwhile, the Colonel and his sons were busy making preparations for the next leg of the journey. The greatest challenges—by far—were ahead of them. As he saw his wife, starved for friendship, in a lively exchange with Mary Ingles, and his grandchildren, running and shouting with pent-up energy on the pastureland adjoining the compound, he felt something almost like dread, mixed with something almost like guilt. The next weeks would not simply be exhausting or difficult—they would also be dangerous.

"It's a pity we can't afford to stay a little longer," he said to his son Robert, who was standing beside him at the entrance to the stables. "But the trees are turning, and Fall will too soon be Winter. We must keep moving."

There were goodbyes, the one between Mary and Lucretia particularly poignant, and the Latimers and those with them set off once again into the forest. Soon the road, barely wide enough for their wagons, was once again swallowed up by the verdant vastness. The trees reached out over the roadway, turning it into a dark green tunnel. There was no way of knowing what lay in the woods on either side of the road, and there was no way to go but forward into the unknown which lay ahead of them.

Forts, Stations, and Blockhouses

As the road skirted the North Fork of the Holston River, it followed a beautiful but in fact increasingly dangerous valley. From here on the supply stations began to look more and more like fortresses. These structures varied, but most of them were similar. They were designed to give the immigrants a place to resupply, but also a place of refuge, where they might feel safe, at least for a few hours. Almost always there was a strong palisade made of upright logs and a "blockhouse."

The blockhouses had two floors, each with a large room. The upper floor had portholes or "loop-holes" in all four sides, looking out in all directions. These, it was clear to see, were designed to give defenders a clear shot at attackers. The upper story was the larger, and over-hung the lower one, making it very difficult for an attacker to climb up. There were always large numbers of travelers camped in the woods around the blockhouse. It would be their refuge, should trouble arise before they went on their way. There was good reason for such caution. Just a few months before the Latimers' arrived the Indians had once again started raiding the homes of the settlers in the area, sometimes with terrible results.

As they passed through the forest tunnel leading from Mary Ingles' place, the travelers approached Fort Chiswell, called by most everyone Fort "Chissel." There Mr. McGavock, who had built the fort, shared his very valuable knowledge and experience with the Latimers and several other travelers who had fallen in with them as the forest became more foreboding. There were dozens of grim-faced militia men living in the fort and guarding the narrow roadway, all of them aware that the countryside was stained with blood and that danger still lurked in the think cane breaks and dark forests.

These men were busy at the moment dismantling the courthouse that stood at the fort since the seat of government had moved to a new place a few miles further on called Wytheville. But they were also ready for battle should the need arise. The travelers could not help being disquieted by the presence of so many soldiers. Their presence was proof positive that they had reached the borders of the great wilderness. Here would begin the roughest part of the journey, and here the danger, up to now theoretical, would become a reality.

At Fort Chiswell Daniel Morgan, the Colonel's old companion in war, once again became a topic of conversation. Many years before, when he was a young officer, he had been stationed at this very place. Here he had been involved in an altercation with a fellow officer who had insulted him —and who had later apologized for his words. Morgan, defending his "honor" in the manner of the day, struck the other man and rendered him unconscious. He was punished for this fight by being tied to a tree and whipped. The tavern-keeper at the Fort showed the Colonel the white oak tree to which his great fellow soldier at Saratoga had been tied during his ordeal. Few people who heard this story of a respected officer being publically humiliated were as sympathetic as was the Colonel, who had reason to know very well the sting of a similar, if less physical, humiliation.

Passing by the new courthouse in the new town of Abingdon, the travelers were once again swallowed up by the dark forest, though the presence of the river to their left give them comfort and assurance that they were on the right path. Then the road began to leave the river, which gradually moved south while the road stayed its course west. The landscape became more and more hilly and rugged, and somewhere along the way they passed the nebulous border between Virginia and the western territory belonging to the State of North Carolina, known by some as "Tennessee." Only a few months before their arrival this territory had been ceded by the State of North Carolina to the Federal Government, at about the same time it had ratified the new Constitution of the United States of America. The borders (and the Constitution, for that matter) still were fuzzy and subject to different interpretations, as indeed they would continue to be for many years.

But regardless, they would soon be in Tennessee, no matter where the border actually lay. Now it was just a matter of following the North Fork of the Holston River, moving ever westward.

A few more miles and they saw a large island in the river, which the settlers called "Long Island." When they heard the name, the Latimers glanced at one another and smiled, sharing a thought which would have been totally foreign to those who were moving alongside them. It was the now distant memory of another Long Island, with its ships and battles and fine old towns. An already murky memory of a faraway land.

This new Long Island, covered in our day with the machines and towers of heavy industry, was a place where the Native Americans had often met in council. Because of this, they had named it "Tana-see"—"the Meeting Place." And so the settlers had borrowed the word for themselves. They were now in "Tennessee." This was the spot where the road once again forked. Off to the northwest it led through the Cumberland Gap to a land called "Kentucki." And to the west, through the threatening wilderness, it led to the Cumberland—that land "at the back of beyond." There the travelers would, at last, find their new home.

Groups of immigrants who were headed for Kentucky were already meeting on the banks of the Holston at Long Island and forming themselves into parties. Once there were enough gathered together to provide some safety in numbers, they were moving off toward the Cumberland Gap. The Latimers, however, would continue on to the west by what some called "The New Holston Road."

White's Fort

James White, like Jonathan Latimer, was an officer of the Revolution—though from North Carolina rather than New England. Nevertheless, when the Colonel and his party arrived at the Fort White had built alongside the mighty Tennessee River they formed an immediate friendship based on their common experiences. White had built a two-story log house in 1786, and surrounded it with a stockade fence two years later, enclosing several other cabins within as well—one at each corner of the stockade. He was friendly with the Cherokee and they with him. So here, at least, there was nothing to fear from them. Inside the fort, the imposing fence, eight feet high, was used to keep horses, cows, pigs, and sheep safe from the wild animals. And outside, the trees of the forest had been cleared, and there were large gardens for growing vegetables and even some tobacco. White told the Colonel of his plan to build a town at the place, and in fact only one year after the Latimer visit he began his project. He would call it Knoxville.

The Latimers' camped near the stockade, unafraid of being in an exposed place—a welcome respite from the constant threat which usually caused the evenings to bring uneasiness.

As they were settling down for the night, the Colonel called the men in his company a few yards back into the darkness, beyond the campfire, and spoke to them with grim earnestness.

"We must not be lulled into thinking that there will be many nights like tonight. I know that from here on there will be many able-bodied fellows camping near us, and we can hope that most of them are well armed. But at the same time, we must have at least two or three of you awake at all times, with guns loaded and prepared to shoot. I have been talking to men who have come here to this place from Kentucky and the Cumberland, and they bring stories of unspeakable atrocities. But we will not speak of this to the women folk and certainly not to the children. There is nothing they can do in many cases, and there is no reason to make them fearful."

"At least no more than they already are," replied young Joseph Latimer, perhaps a bit too light-heartedly. He was the only one of the Latimer men not bearing the responsibility for the wife and children of his own.

Later that evening, after the women and children were safely asleep, the Latimer men who were standing guard had a visit from James White. He was making the rounds among the various travelers' camps, partly to welcome them and partly to warn them of the dangers.

"As you know, I have enjoyed a good relationship with the Indians. But not everyone has been so fortunate," he said to the Colonel and his sons.

"We are very much aware of that," the Colonel replied.

Meanwhile, Robert had also been circulating among the travelers gathering around the station and came back to camp at supper time with some distressing news. He awakened those adults already asleep for his important report.

"I'm afraid the road ahead is not wide enough for our fine Conestoga Wagons," he announced. "Some men coming back from the Cumberland told me that in places it is hardly more than a footpath, and we'll be fortunate to get our pack horses through; wagons are out of the question."

Robert's wife Lucinda put her fingers to her mouth in surprise. "What will we do? Our wagons are full of the things that meant the most to us in Connecticut. Our furniture. Our kitchen utensils and dishes. Our big iron pots and pans..." The other women joined her in composing the list, which grew longer and longer.

"Well," Robert continued, "there is also some good news; or at least some hopeful news. It is possible to pack up our possessions and send them off by boat down the river here, over to where it meets the Ohio, then down the Cumberland to Nashville. We can pick them up when they arrive."

"But that will be weeks, maybe even months!" Lucinda countered. "What will we do in the meantime?"

Lucretia, who had long ago learned how to handle disappointment, simply smiled and with a tone of assurance answered Lucinda's question.

"Somehow we will manage," she said. "We always do."

The next day or two were full of activity as the Latimers unloaded their wagons and carefully repacked their precious possessions into big wooden boxes. These they wrapped with long strips of leather to keep them from breaking apart, held tight by dozens of hand-made nails they had bought from one of the supply stores along the way. The nails had been meant for the houses they would be building in the Cumberland, but, never mind, more can be purchased later.

Decisions had to be made about what to take along on the Holston Road. Everything would have to go on the backs of the horses, and that meant that every family member able to do so would have to do a lot of walking. The travelers were still more than two hundred miles from their final destination; the most challenging and dangerous part of the trip still lay ahead of them. And they would have to travel at grueling speed in order to cross the Indian lands just ahead of them as quickly as possible. Experienced travelers at the Station told them to expect two weeks of relentless movement, with little time for rest. Everyone pitched in as the packs were prepared. Only the things most necessary could be retained. The rest, if not already sent away on the river, simply had to be given to other travelers or discarded.

The Reunion

Traveling on, they came to Campbell's Station, built by David Campbell, also an officer in the Revolution, and therefore also an instant friend of the Colonel. The road they traveled still exists, cutting through the suburbs of Knoxville, now lined with a host of strip malls, fast food restaurants, parking lots, and various garish franchises to entice modern travelers to spend their money. Somehow, the site of the fort has escaped the machinations of the developers, and a large green lawn marks the spot where the station once stood and the Latimers had their camp.

Once the travelers were settled for the night, Campbell called the Latimer men together and said to them:

"I see you have many children with you, and they appear to me to be a fine lot. And that is all the more reason for me to make you aware of the situation along this road. I must tell you that only a few months ago a man named Joe Johnson, who lived over on the Clinch, not far from Rye Cove...just back up the road from which you have come"—he pointed toward the north and east—"had to watch in horror as the savages captured his family, his wife and nine of his eleven children, and set his house on fire. The poor man found the bones of one of his children among the ashes and the bodies of his wife and another child, murdered and scalped, a quarter mile from the house."

"Mr. Anderson, who built a fort in that area, wrote an urgent letter to our government, begging them to give us better protection, but so far there has only been disappointment. They were quite interested in having us volunteer to fight in the late war, but less in helping us now in our desperate circumstances. I think there are enough of us here at the moment, settlers and you folks, to hold off any attacks. And there will be soldiers to accompany you from here on. But let what is happening to others be a sober warning to you as to travel on. Keep one eye out for Indians, the other on your children, and your guns at the ready."

Here at Campbell's Station, they would wait for the much anticipated military escorts, who would then usher them through the great forest, with its gauntlet of dangers. The escorts were to be available only once every three months. This year, 1790, they would meet the immigrants in the Fall. Fortunately, the Latimers had timed their journey well, and would easily arrive at the station in time to join them.

Now came the waiting. The militia guards who would accompany them through the Cumberland Plateau—which the immigrants all called "the Wilderness"—should arrive any day now. Other travelers would join the Latimers, since the militia protocol called for taking at least fifty settlers on each trip. Sometimes there would be almost as many soldiers as settlers, especially as the Native Americans grew more and more angry about the incursions through their land, and the arguments about the amount of toll payment owed to them grew hotter and hotter.

Finally, early one morning, just as September was coming to an end, the militiamen appeared at the Station. Their leader, Captain William Glass, was the first to arrive and, to the family's great surprise, he rode directly to Colonel Latimer and greeted him by name.

"We are honored to have you travel with us, sir," the Captain said, dismounting and coming forward with his hand extended. "And to have you and your family join us in the Cumberland!"

"How can you possibly have known we would be here?" said the Colonel, still incredulous.

"You will learn the answer to that question soon enough," the Captain said, his eyes twinkling and his mouth turned in a broad smile.

It was the children who saw them first. In the days before spectacles, when the progression of near-sightedness, not to mention the natural growth of cataracts, had no remedies, children usually had the advantage over their elders when it came to discerning objects in the distance. Even old Ben Franklin's spectacles had their limitations, even if someone were actually lucky enough to own a pair.

"Uncle Witherel! Uncle Griswold!"

Both men had served in the militia and were welcome additions to Captain Glass's company. They were dressed like the other soldiers (though no one was wearing a uniform, of course), mounted on fine horses, and looking like mighty heroes to the Latimer grandchildren, tall and invincible. Then it suddenly dawned on Daniel Fitch Latimer (eight years old), and James Luther Latimer (six years old), that their dream had become a reality.

"Papa! Papa!" they cried, running forward as Witherel almost threw himself from his horse and rushed to meet them. They wrapped themselves around his long legs and burst into tears. It had been almost three years since they had seen him. For little Jimmie, who had been only three years old when his father left, he had become only the faintest of memories. Witherel fell to his knees and covered the boys with kisses. His eyes filled with tears. The family watched in delight, moved to see a man they knew as a paragon of self-control, someone who almost never betrayed his inner feelings, as the tears became sobs of joy.

But more than joy. In the faces of these little boys, he could not help but see the lovely face of Abigail, their mother, torn from them, and from him, far too soon.

Lucretia was weeping, too, as she embraced Griswold.

"Mother," he whispered. "What can I say? Nothing is so sweet as seeing you again."

"May God be praised. It is His doing," she whispered back.

"And what news do you bring?" she asked.

"Not all the news is good, Mother. But for the moment let's rejoice and be glad." His eyes dropped to the ground as he was pierced with the realization that they would have to talk about Borodell…and Eusebius…but let it be later. Scriptures learned long ago in New England suddenly flooded into his consciousness. *"Sufficient unto the day is the evil thereof."*

The Colonel lingered in the background as the emotional greetings continued. For over sixty years he had done what men were expected to do—face the good and the bad with resolution and strength, and keep one's feelings to oneself. He would do the same today.

Witherel and Griswold walked to him and shook his hand with manly firmness. He put his hands on their shoulders and allowed himself to squeeze them just a little. It was enough. They understood.

"We must not linger," Captain Green said. "I take it you are ready?"

"We are ready."

The militia men organized the travelers into smaller groups that could be carefully watched and then moved forward. For a while, the trail was relatively level, following the valley created by the Tennessee River. But then, as they turned more directly to the west, the terrain became wilder and wilder. One ridge after another loomed before them, causing the trail to move first this way and then that, searching for the easiest routes. When they reached the Clinch River, the whole party crossed over at a place called Pappa Ford, just north of where this river and the Tennessee River came together to form another formidable barrier to anyone seeking to reach the Cumberland.

Only two years after the Latimers passed through, an impressive structure called Fort Southwest Point was constructed at this place. Here immigrants were met by soldiers who escorted them the rest of the way to the Cumberland. But in 1790 it was necessary for travelers to negotiate with the Cherokee chiefs, in order to get their permission to cross—and to pay a tidy sum for the privilege.

Here the Latimers had their first encounter with the fabled warriors of the Wilderness. They were tall, and rode on fine-looking horses. Some of their clothing seemed familiar, and they spoke in perfectly understandable English, but the cut of their hair and the painted markings on their faces and arms was startling and unsettling to the new-comers. The Indians seemed friendly enough during this transaction, but more than one of the Latimer's noticed, and were disturbed by, the penetrating gaze of these men, who, it seemed to them, were sizing up the group for some pernicious purpose.

"What if the soldiers were not with us?" Lucretia wondered, but kept her thoughts to herself.

They would now go deeper and deeper into Indian lands. The next outpost of civilization, Blackburn's Fort, at a place called Double Springs, would be seventy miles away, seventy miles of rugged mountains, rushing streams, and hostile natives. Once there, the travelers could find food and supplies, a safe place to sleep, and a blacksmith to see to their horses and livestock. But seventy miles is a long, long way.

An Ominous Visit

When they crossed the Clinch, it became clear that they must turn away from the relatively easy terrain along the river valleys and assault the forbidding mass of the Cumberland Mountains. The minuscule trail, hardly wider than their horses, headed directly toward the mountains through a place called Emory Gap. To call this a "road" violated the limits of language. But here at least Mother Nature had thoughtfully provided for them a way to cross the mountains and move toward their Land of Promise. The rocks were torturous for the struggling horses, and the ground was alternately wet and muddy or dry and dusty. Often the inclines were precipitous and posed a serious threat to both man and beast. Yet, despite the difficulties, the travelers had to keep moving. This was Indian country. There would be no rest and no safety until Blackburn's blockhouse was in sight.

As they crossed through the gap, the travelers came to a clearing. Hot and exhausted, they begged the militiamen to stop for a few minutes of rest. They had hardly had time to dismount—those few who were on horseback, or to sit for a sweet moment or two in the shade, when they were startled to see eight or ten men ride into the clearing from the other direction.

Indians!

Something about the surroundings, the deep green of the forest, and the sudden appearance from its seemingly endless darkness made these men and their horses seem larger than life. Their dress seemed less familiar than before, their demeanor more inscrutable. They spoke only to one another, quietly, in strange sounds which seemed to have no meaning to the awestruck travelers.

Captain Glass stepped forward and spoke not to the visitors, but to the travelers—in a loud voice. "Everyone stay where you are! These men do not intend to cause us harm. We will have a pleasant conversation with them. We are, after all, their friends and brothers." This he said, fervently hoping he was correct, more as a suggestion to the visitors than as an attempt to calm the alarm that could be read in the faces of the travelers.

The older Latimer grandchildren looked on in absolute fascination, wonder now overcoming fear.

"They don't look like savages to me," whispered young Daniel Fitch Latimer to his brother Jimmie. Sam Rogers, their somewhat older cousin, agreed. "If it weren't for those turbans, and that feather they have tied to their hair and the dark skin, they would look just like the rest of us," he said. And indeed they would have. They were dressed in shirts and pants and trade coats with not a sign of war paint or naked skin.

And when their leader spoke the amazement only increased.

"You are passing through our land, and the land of our fathers, and the land of their fathers," he said, solemnly—and in perfect English, delivered with an unmistakable Scotch-Irish accent.

"Remember," Captain Glass said, from the side of his mouth, head turned toward the travelers, "most of their leaders are half-breeds. But don't think that because this man sounds like one of us that he is one of us. Everyone keep very still and let me do the talking."

The leader continued, "We have signed papers saying we would allow you to cross our land. But you have promised to pay us for this. We have come to collect."

"And of course we will pay the amount our chief men and yours have decided upon," Captain Glass replied, his tone pointedly respectful.

"You will pay us one shilling for each man, and six-pence for each woman and child," the leader said, a look of grave resolution on his face.

"But that is more than our agreement!" Glass answered.

"It is what you will pay."

The Colonel moved to Captain Glass's side. "What shall we do?" he asked.

"We will pay," the Captain said. "I know this is too much, but there are reasons we must not resist or even try to negotiate. I will explain when we are rid of them."

And so the Colonel paid for his entire family—no small sum. And the other people traveling with them did the same.

The visitors took the money, nodded to each other, turned their horses aside, not into the road, but into the dark forest, and disappeared.

When they were gone Captain Glass called the men among the travelers together under a large tree at the edge of the clearing. "I know this was an unexpected expense, and a significant one. But there is something you must know. These Cherokee raiding parties have been using disputes about tolls as an excuse for some unspeakable violence lately. Perhaps you have not heard about it. I tell you so that you will understand, but I suggest you say nothing to the women and children. Knowing what I am about to say will do them no good and perhaps great harm."

"You must understand that we are in hard times in the Cumberland, regardless of what you may have been told. Griswold and Witherel will confirm what I am saying to you. No one is completely safe. Men and women and children die in their beds or working in their fields, or on the road to the mill or to a neighbor's house. The attacks are sudden and the murders without mercy or any sign of humanity. I could give you names. Alexander Neely and his sons James and Charles. Poor Benjamin Williams, and his wife and children. These were people living very near where you are going—over near Isaac Bledsoe's place. And every indication points to more trouble ahead. Better to pay a few shillings and hope to placate these murderers for a while at least."

The Colonel nodded solemnly. "Rest assured, we are under no illusions," he said. "We have known from the beginning that we are attempting a hard thing. We can only hope for a safe passage and a good future."

"So then," the Captain said, "let's be on our way. Watchful, but hopeful."

For the rest of the journey to Blackburn's Fort, every Latimer man kept a careful eye and a vigilant ear on the surrounding forest. It was plain to them that the visitors from the clearing had not really left them at all, but were watching their progress from the thick cane breaks and forest darkness. They could hear the constant birdcalls and animal sounds which the Indians used to communicate with each other. They were aware that they were being followed and their every move was being observed. They rode with rifles in hand, loaded and ready to fire. This was no superabundance of caution. During the months following their journey, over one hundred of their fellow settlers would die on roads like this one.

The travelers struggled through Crab Orchard Gap, up on the mighty Cumberland Plateau. They wound through the tree-covered mountains, crossing one stream after another, some tiny, and some, like the Obed River, wild and full of treacherous rapids and falls. Some thirty miles along the trail which moved across the Plateau they came to something which pleased the children very much. There, alongside the trail, was a massive stone, standing upright on a sandstone ledge to the height of more than thirteen feet. Little Polly Rogers, the eight-year-old daughter of Jonathan and Lucretia's oldest child Hannah, riding in front of her mother on a fine red horse, saw it first.

"Look, mama! It's a giant gray dog!" she shouted. Her sharp cry of delight could be heard up and down the moving column, and soon all the youngest children were shouting in excitement too. This striking monument, well-known to those who were immigrating to the Cumberland, and a welcome symbol of good progress, was called the "Standing Stone." No one knew how old it was, but only that it had been set up long ago by the Native Americans to mark the boundary between the lands of the Cherokees and the lands of the Shawnees. Despite the need to move through the forest as quickly as possible, Captain Glass could not resist the pleading of the children to stop for at least a few minutes to stare in wonder at this thing.

Bad News at Blackburn's

Another twenty miles. The blockhouse and fortress at Blackburn Springs came into view. A welcome sight indeed. Here a man named Benjamin

Blackburn had only recently completed a lodging place and supply store beside the springs. This would be a safe place to sleep and a source of supplies—whatever was needed to protect the travelers the rest of the way through the Indian lands. Fellow travelers told them of the rumors that there were graves of immigrants almost continuously along the road for the next several miles. The strange sounds in the forest continued until they were almost within the protective fence around the blockhouse.

The travelers arrived at Blackburn's Fort safe but totally exhausted. The darkness was approaching, and the Latimer children were hurried onto cots and quickly fell asleep. Witherel and Griswold gathered the adults together beside a fire built against the cool breezes of the September evening.

"It is time to talk about Eusebius," Witherel began, his chin set a bit firmer than usual, his eyes not quite looking directly at anyone, his words slow and deliberate. Griswold stood by his side. As a younger brother, he could leave this difficult task to Witherel, but he must at least show his support. This was not going to be easy.

"First, let me say in his defense that he meant to do well by his family by coming here. In that, he is no different from the rest of us. And despite what I am going to tell you, you must be assured that he has always loved Borodell and his children. I know that to be true. And we all know that he is a man of great energy and talent. There are several men gathered in Nashville who, like him, are beyond the ordinary. And he was quickly accepted as one of them. This is not a place like New England, where custom and tradition and respect for God and law and order are the rule. Here men are like those in the days of the Old Testament judges when every man did what was right in his own eyes. There are very few shared values among the settlers here—values that would give them the same set of ideals to govern themselves. There is some reward to be had in limitless ambition and even naked aggression. And most often here it is the strongest or the most fortunate who wins, not the most deserving."

"I say these things not to excuse any of it, but only to try to help you understand the world in which Eusebius has been living. Within days after he and Borodell and the children arrived, he had gained the confidence of men like General Robertson, who is by far the most powerful man in the settlements. And Major Hays. And a certain up and coming young fellow—you will meet him soon enough—who has the strengths and the weaknesses of Eusebius but multiplied many times over—Andy Jackson."

"These men took Eusebius in and infused him with a spirit not common in our home country, but very common here: a spirit of risk, of audacity, of the love of winning by any means, of the love of the possibility of becoming very rich."

"And there is something else. No one here—man, woman, or child—can lie down at night and be absolutely sure that they will survive to see the dawn. We have seen horrors. We have lost the dearest of friends. We have wept over dead children."

"In such a place and time men act differently. They risk far more. They push the limits. They take hold of the present moment like those for whom there is no tomorrow."

"Eusebius saw the possibility of becoming rich. Some of the powerful friends he made had already done so, and some others are bound to join them. And with wealth comes the possibility of great power. I would not be surprised to see someone among them ordering great armies to the field someday. And not in the spirit of selfless duty I have always seen in you…" His eyes turned to the Colonel. "But in the interests of self-exaltation and even self-indulgence."

"And though these men come and sit on the rough benches in our primitive meeting houses and sing and pray with what looks like enthusiasm, there is little of the true Spirit of God in them. Our forefathers in New England, who thought they were creating the Kingdom of God on earth, would be struck down in grief if they could see the world in which their descendants live."

"And so Eusebius borrowed great sums of money from families like the Robertsons. They were convinced he would do great things. He found himself a partner, Mr. Dobbins, and they began to buy and sell land though they had no money of their own to buy and should have known that most of their customers had none to pay. So as they became greater and greater debtors, so did those whom they convinced to buy become greater and great debtors as well."

"And as if this were not enough, Eusebius fell into league with those who were courting the King of Spain. It may be hard to believe that men who fought for the independence of the United States of America could seriously consider abandoning this cause and once again swearing allegiance to a European sovereign. And a sovereign worse by far than the one from whom we have liberated ourselves. But this is exactly what happened."

"Some of those who secretly plotted tell us now they were not serious; that they simply wanted to provoke our leaders in Congress and our President Washington to pay more attention to them and give them more protection from the savages around them. And perhaps that is true. I don't know. I was not privy to their machinations nor did I want to be."

"I say all this because I must now tell you that Eusebius has gone away to Louisiana and that from all we hear he has already pledged himself to the Spanish king. And his reason for going is simple. It was the only way left for him, at least in his own mind, to free himself from his impossible obligations."

"But what about the children?" Lucretia's eyes were full of shock and pain.

"He has left them with Griswold and Polly," Witherel replied. Then, quickly, "I believe he has every intention of doing right by them. But taking them along was impossible. The girls are nearly women now and are attractive and talented. I think they will soon marry and find their own path through life. The boys, we must hope, will be reunited with their father when he is established in Louisiana."

"And I must say this about Griswold." His eyes turned with obvious tenderness toward his younger brother. "He has acted as a true man of character in all of this tragedy. He has been patient with Eusebius, loving to poor Borodell, and so faithful to the children that they love him like a father."

Lucretia stepped forward and embraced both her tall and handsome sons. "Bless you," she whispered. "May God bless you."

It was time to weep once more for Borodell, and then to sleep.

The Journey Ends

From Blackburn's the trail turned to the northwest and followed the beautiful stream that ran near Blackburn's place, down into the Cumberland River Valley. It was the buffalo that had first found this way to the west, though they were mostly gone now. The trail moved up the ridge and then followed another stream called Flynn's Creek to the place where that stream flowed into the Cumberland River.

Near here the travelers' escorts guided them to a spot where the presence of sandbars made it possible to wade across the great river. Here they found another place of refuge, called Fort Blount. The children, hot and dusty from the primitive trail, found the cool waters a great relief, as did the animals. Now they would remain on the north side of the river all the way to the settlements in what the government of the United States had, in this very year, given the rather dull sounding name "The Territory South of the Ohio River." The Captain said they could also call their new home "The Mero District"—since General Robertson had named it after Esteban Rodrigues Miro, the governor of Louisiana, at the time when he and his friends were making overtures to the Spanish.

Turning West, with the river to their backs, the travelers breathed a sigh of relief. They were in Sumner County now, safely through the Indian lands, back to a place where here and there the forests had been cleared, crops planted, and modest but inviting cabins dotted the landscape. Civilization!

But perhaps not quite. The cultivated fields were no more than tiny oases encroached upon by the great trees and massive cane breaks. This wild vastness was populated by all sorts of wild creatures—wolves, bears, wildcats, cougars, foxes. And the hardy farmers who had wrenched these fields from the Wilderness still lived in constant fear of Indian attacks. The possibility of sudden and awful death danced before them night and day. Lucretia urged her daughter and daughters-in-law to keep the talk of Indian outrages away from the ears of the children. But not every story could be suppressed. There were often sleepless nights when every sound seemed a harbinger of doom.

The party passed by the large log home of Major Tilmon Dixon, himself a soldier in the Revolution, and stopped for a refreshing drink from the nearby springs. Lucretia and the other women looked with admiration at the house, said to have eight rooms. It was still quite new, built with great skill, and was a source of relief and reassurance to the women. Judging by what they saw, one could apparently live in the Wilderness in at least a modestly civilized way.

The Latimers were now sixty miles from the Standing Stone and half that distance from their destination. Their next stop was yet another fort, built by a man named Isaac Bledsoe to protect the locals and travelers like themselves. No one knew the need more than old Isaac, who had lost his brother at this very place a couple of years before and would himself be struck down before three more winters had passed. The water in the nearby spring was disappointing, tasting as it did of sulfur and salt.

As they rested that evening, Witherel reported to the Colonel on the search he and Griswold had made for lands suitable for a Latimer family settlement. They had located a fine tract of 640 acres (a mile square) just west of Station Camp Creek in the new county of Sumner. It could be purchased for 200 pounds—about $65,000 in today's dollars. It belonged to a man named Daniel James, who had himself only owned the land a few months, and was eager to turn a quick profit. His price was not cheap, but the land was very good. It lay quite near the very road along which the Latimers had been traveling. Nashville was not far away—fifteen miles or so to the southwest.

Settlers had been in the Station Camp Creek area for several years. Strong stations with blockhouses had been constructed, and a well-organized militia was in place. There were already cabins on or near the property where the family could live until they had built for themselves. The nearest neighbors were persons of character from well-established families—among them Elmore Douglass and David Looney. There was enough land for several of the Latimer families to establish themselves as farmers, or, in the local parlance, "plantation owners." More land would be needed, but this was a good start.

"I bow to your judgment," the Colonel told Witherel. "We will buy it!"

"There will be some papers to sign in Nashville," Witherel said. "No need for everyone to go there. But some will want to go, even perhaps Mother, when Griswold and I give you the next bit of news. But that can wait until tomorrow." He smiled in a mysterious sort of way.

This bit of teasing might have been unbearable for some members of the family, but not the Colonel. He was perfectly willing to wait. His aging bones were crying out for a few hours of rest.

The next morning the Latimers gathered their possessions for the last time as immigrants. Tonight, though they might well be sleeping on the ground once more, it would be the soil of their new home. The land around was beautiful. The trees were turning bright red and yellow, and the tall grass in the open spaces looked like grain fields ready to harvest. Out among the tall, undulating waves there were herds of deer and often, along the road, the wild turkeys raised an ear-splitting row as they made their escape into the safety of the forest.

"Now, son, don't you think it is time for that bit of good news you said you would save for today," Lucretia said to her sons as they rode the last few miles toward their destination.

"It's some Bushnell news that will please you, unlike what we had to tell you yesterday," Griswold said. "At least we think you will be pleased."

"Well, hurry up and say it," Lucretia replied, feigning impatience.

"Young Hannah has a beau! And a fine one, too. At least Witherel and I think so. He has made it plain he wants her to be his wife. But we told them they must wait for your blessing."

Hannah Bushnell had been only twelve years old when Lucretia had last seen her, and the announcement made her realize how time rushes by and how quickly children become adults. She would marry young, sixteen years old. But Lucretia had been no older herself as a bride. Her intended was only twenty-five and, according to Griswold, who was for all practical purposes Hannah's foster father, he was an honorable and highly regarded man.

"He is a born leader," Griswold said. "An officer in the militia."

"Oh, I see," Lucretia replied to this—not entirely with enthusiasm. She was well acquainted with the life of a militia wife. But all in all, it seemed a good thing. Poor Hannah was almost an orphan, after all, and her only prospects for a secure future lay in a good marriage.

"And his name?" Lucretia asked.

"Thomas Murray," Griswold answered. "Captain Thomas Murray."

It was about noon when the Latimers reached the banks of a lovely little stream which would become their new address. The locals called it Station Camp Creek, remembering old explorer-hunters called the Longhunters who had first made their headquarters along its banks. Here they found an imposing building built a few years before their arrival by Elmore Douglass, who would be their neighbor soon. The structure served as a house for Mr. Douglass, a fort for the neighbors when needed, and the meeting place for the courts of the new county called Sumner. He and his large family came out to greet the new-comers and offer them a wonderfully delicious meal. The Latimer children and the Douglass children were friends instantaneously.

Life seemed good again.

EIGHT: THE INDIANS

Matters of Right and Wrong

Station Camp Creek
Fall, 1795

One night, after the events we are about to describe had run their course, and the Latimers were securely at home in the Cumberland, and the terror had finally subsided, Jonathan and Lucretia sat in the quietness of the evening, listening to the cadences of the insects and the night birds. There was mostly silence at first. Partners for over half a century, they did not always feel the need to converse, but only to sit together. This could be enough. But often they talked—seriously talked about things they had seen and done together, or feelings or opinions they had which were not to be shared with anyone else.

This particular night it was Lucretia who first broke the silence. Looking out at the tree-shadows and the haystack-shadows in the fields beyond the house, she said, as much to herself as to her partner, "Jonathan, what about the Indians? Have we done right by them?"

"It was not for us to decide the question of right and wrong. Leave that to men of the cloth like your saintly father. We have done what we had to do, Lucretia. Soldiers do what they have to do."

"But at this very moment, we live on land which was theirs for generations."

"When two men seek to stand in the same place, and neither has another place to stand, then someone must give way," the Colonel said. "Is there some place we could have gone where no other human had ever laid a claim? And is it not true that the Indians have from time unknown pushed one another out and moved into other men's dwelling places when it seemed the best thing for them to do? Are they any different from us, really?"

"They are different, Jonathan," Lucretia replied. "They are simple people who do not understand our idea of 'owning' the land. We have the advantage of them because we are civilized and we are educated, and we have learned how to use our wits to break our word and get what we desire from those who are weaker than we are."

"These are words you learned at your father's table, sitting there with Pequots and Mohicans and the Niantics—the pathetic remnants of the peoples who lived in New England before any Englishman. Your father felt the sympathy for them that a sophisticated religious man feels for those who have been brought down by circumstances. I honor that. But here in the Cumberland, it was not a matter of pathos and righteous sympathy. It was a matter of survival. And the people who threatened us were not gentle children of the forest; they were brutal, bloodthirsty savages, who killed our children and burned our houses and ripped the scalps off of our honored grandfathers and grandmothers."

He paused. And then said, "I am truly sorry for the losses—theirs and ours. I am sorry that their days of glory, as they define glory, have come to an end. But all the same, we have done what we had to do."

The Latimers had arrived in the Cumberland at a bad time. They were not naïve, of course. They knew about the dangers. They had already been well and truly tested in the crucibles of violence and fear and insecurity, of course. They had learned to cope with such things. They had had no choice. Nevertheless, the first years after their arrival in the wilderness had thrust them into a maelstrom violent beyond even the sober and clear-eyed pragmatism they had carried with them from New England.

The most enraged of the Indians, particularly among the Creeks and the Cherokees, and particularly the militant branch of the latter that had chosen to call itself the Chickamaugas—"River of Blood", had lost any confidence in the white man's promises and solemn treaties. The white man had no right to be in the Cumberland, and he was a liar besides. The time for talking to him has gone; it is time to drive him out. And if he will not go, it is time to kill him—him and his delicate little women and all his pale children.

Dragging Canoe, the greatest of the Chickamauga chiefs, had given fair warning. "If you do not leave," he had warned, "we will turn the Cumberland into a dark and bloody ground." He was true to his word. The blood did indeed begin to flow—crimson rivulets in the shadowy forest.

Neely's Bend

Neely's Bend, Near Nashville
1788

Witherel had been the first Latimer to experience the terror, before the Colonel and his family had arrived. He had only just purchased his land a short distance up the river from the village of Nashville and was in the first stages of clearing and plowing when one day a group of young neighbors, all on horseback, rode up to where he was working. There was a woman with them, an older lady with that leathery and worn look you saw in such old women on the frontier. But along with that look, she wore an undeniable expression of resolution and tough-mindedness on that wrinkled face.

"Now, young man, I need your help with this bunch of fancies I'm riding with here!" she called to Witherel. "I have a little field of flax down close to the bend that needs to be cut, and these fellows don't seem to want to go with me to do the job. Seems like they are scared of the Indians. What do you think of that?" She grimaced and lowered her face a bit in a gesture of disgust.

One of the young men rode forward and spoke, "Let me introduce you to my hard-headed mother, the Widow Neely," he said. "Why she wants to tempt fate for a few handfuls of flax I'll never know. God knows she has already suffered enough at the hands of the savages."

"And my name is Sam, by the way."

Witherel nodded a greeting.

"And these are my friends Robert Edmondson and Sam Buchanan."

Witherel had already met Edmondson, who lived at Irish Station, three or four miles from the Neelys, and his neighbor, Sam Buchanan, who lived with his family at Buchanan's Station. They were among his first acquaintances—along with the Reverend Craighead, of course, the Presbyterian minister who had come to bring learning and civilization to this wilderness. Witherel had heard how the Widow Neely's husband had been unmercifully slain a few years before, and how her daughter had been taken into slavery by the Indians. He wondered at her courage—or bravado—despite all this.

"And I will tell you what I have told these young fellows," Widow Neely continued, ignoring her son's protestations. "If you do not wish to come along and help me, then at least loan me your rifle, so I can give it to some girl who has the backbone to do the job!"

"Well, men, she's got us. We can't let her go down to the river by herself," Robert Edmondson sighed.

So the four young men, and Widow Neely, each with a gun in hand, mounted up and rode off toward the flax field. Edmondson was in the lead when he saw movement in the bushes ahead. Suddenly thirteen painted warriors rose up as one and fired a volley at him like the blast of a firing squad. Six bullets hit him. Miraculously, none of them were fatal, though one shattered his arm into uselessness—a wound he carried to his dying day. Howling in pain, he turned his horse and rode to the rear.

Sam Neely, the widow's son, tried to return fire, but his gun lock broke in his hand. He rode toward his mother, calling for her to give him her rifle.

But the Widow Neely suddenly seemed another woman. The façade of courage broke; her face wrenched in terror. She hung on to the gun with a powerful grip and froze in panic.

"Mother, please...the gun! The gun!" Sam yelled in desperation. She took the weapon from his outstretched hand and spoke not a word.

Sam Buchanan got off one shot, to little avail. His effort only served to make Witherel's horse, charging forward beside him, rear up in panic and try to run away. With great difficulty he extricated himself from the saddle, jumped to the ground, and lurched toward Widow Neely, trying to fire on the run. He met with another volley of musket balls which whistled by on all sides, but incredibly somehow missed him.

Widow Neely was now completely confused and bewildered, and to the horror of the young men she turned her horse and rode directly at the Indians. Her son tried to go after her, but the other men restrained him. To follow her was suicide. Then they could only watch as the warriors pulled the old woman from her mount and dragged her away to her death. She was found later in the woods, her body broken and her clothing stripped away.

The incident at Neely's Bend was only one of many similar ones. Almost every day word came of another horrible atrocity. Many of the settlers found this all too much. For everyone who arrived in the Cumberland, there was someone else who had had enough and rode away with the militia guards back East where life seemed more possible.

Witherel had now experienced the terror in the most intimate way. "But I will stay," he thought to himself. "I am going to stay."

The Settlement on Station Camp Creek

Station Camp Creek
Fall, 1790

The incident at Neely's Bend had occurred before the rest of Latimers had arrived at their new home in Sumner County. Witherel had thought it best to say nothing of it. They were well aware of the dangers, but distracted at first with the complicated and pressing matters connected with getting several families settled and beginning to organize their farms. For Witherel, of course, the memory of the Widow Neely being pulled down from her horse and mercilessly slaughtered was something still burned in his memory like a stock brand.

The Colonel had already conducted several planning meetings with his family in the last days of their long journey from New England. It would be clear to everyone just what would be done and who would do it. He had purposely waited until after Witherel and Griswold had joined them to make final plans, in order to have the benefit of their considerable experience in this new place. And of course, the family had visited several settlements throughout their journey. They were by now well aware of how such places were built and why they were constructed in the way they were. And besides, the Colonel had presided over the building and strengthening of more than one fort back in New England, during the days of danger there.

"We must approach our task in the same way we would a military campaign," the Colonel said. "We must look for ground which is easy to defend from Indian attacks. We must build our houses so close together that they become a unit—a fort, if you want to call it that. And between the houses, we must build strong fences, topped with sharpened pickets—too high to climb easily and threatening the enemy with impalement if he should try to climb over. There must be no windows or gaps so open that an enemy could fire into our homes, no doors or gates which cannot be securely bolted. These must be strong enough to withstand the pounding of huge forest logs an enemy might use as battering rams. We must have at least one tower or 'blockhouse,' tall enough for us to see into the distance—two of them if possible. The second floor of the block-house must be lined on all sides with narrow loopholes we can fire our rifles through without exposing ourselves."

"Eventually, of course, when there is peace, we will each have our own separate homes on our own separate farms, surrounded by our own fields and gardens. I promise you this."

"For the moment, we must do what must be done now right away, before the winter cold sets in. To hesitate is to invite disaster not only from the marauders but from old Mother Nature. She will try her best to freeze us out."

The last family strategy meeting took place on the grassy field in front of the Douglass home, which was itself strong enough to serve as a fort. The community around had known for many weeks of the Latimers' coming, and their actual arrival had been broadcast from Station Camp Creek in all directions by word of mouth. New neighbors began to appear from all sides, riding in on sturdy horses. There was a wagon or two, full of tools and other needed supplies. Everyone gave an enthusiastic welcome. To these neighbors, the Latimers represented more strong arms, more soldiers for the battles before them, more well-educated minds to help them to build an organized and civilized society. Everyone was full of advice, and not in the least shy to give it: men explained men's work, women explained women's work. The division of labor was well-defined and perfectly understood among the settlers.

Several of the men who would be close neighbors chose a bare and dusty spot in the field before the large log station and began to draw a crude map on the ground with sharp sticks they had cut from nearby saplings.

"We are here at the moment," said David Looney, whose land bordered the tract the Colonel had purchased. He poked his stick at the ground and created a small circle. "Your land is here." He drew a rough square to show the boundaries. "The two strongest stations near where you will live are the Douglass place—right here—and Hendrick's Station, which is not too far away off to the northeast. Here. Over to the west, there is Hamilton's Station. It is a little further away, but a safe place in that direction if such is needed. You will enjoy meeting the Hamiltons, who are fine people indeed."

"And where do you think we should build?" asked the Colonel.

"I think I know just the place," David Looney replied. "The stream here, as you well know, is Station Camp Creek." He made a wiggly line with his pointing stick. "Unfortunately it doesn't run directly through your land, but a nice branch that empties into it crosses the north edge of your place. You've got to have water near your houses. It's not safe not to; you can't risk running off somewhere to get water and get yourself ambushed. You'll need more water than this small stream can provide once you have a lot of livestock, but this will do for now."

"If you take this little road that leads north alongside the creek—it's the very route the Long Hunters used when they first came to this country—you will find that just near where the branch I mentioned runs into the Station Camp Creek, there is a cabin. It's been there a long time. It needs some work. But it's built in the perfect spot—high ground, good vision in all directions, near the water, and there's even a clearing beside it for a garden next spring."

"If I were you, I'd build right there, and use the old cabin in the meantime." Once again, the pointing stick punched a mark in the dusty ground.

Griswold and Witherel looked at each other and smiled. "David, you are a genius!" Griswold said. And everyone had a good laugh and a sigh of relief; such a complicated decision made with so little effort.

"Well, then," the Colonel said in his loudest military voice. "What are we waiting for?"

The women and children spent the night at the Douglass place, while the men rode on up the road along Station Camp Creek and quickly located the cabin David Looney had told them about. The journey from the Douglass place was less than two miles up the road. Sure enough, its location was perfect; that was obvious at first glance. Since the darkness had come, the men made camp until morning, taking turns at guard all night long. They were awakened the next day by the sound of approaching horses. But there was no need for alarm. More than two dozen men from the neighborhood had come to help them get started—a good sign for amiable times ahead.

Leading the group of friendly neighbors was David Looney and his brother Peter—who were old hands in the Wilderness. Everyone seemed to know exactly what to do. A rectangular square was laid out, one side lined up with the existing cabin. There must be room for several cabins so that each Latimer family would have its own lodging place. The cabins would be quite close together, their outer walls forming a part of the stockade wall, with sections of the wall connecting them. The location of each cabin was lined out, as was the location of the block-house at one corner of what would be the enclosure—only one for now.

The neighbors had brought along their own tools: fine sharp broadaxes to cut down and shape logs to be cut from the surrounding forest; wooden mallets and gluts to split them; here and there an adz to shape the logs to fit each other, and froes and drawknives to make shingles for the roofs. The ground was cleared—a fairly easy job since the area around the old cabin had already been cleared by previous inhabitants. Some of the men began to dig a ditch three feet deep where the stockade wall would be erected. Others headed into the forest to select logs a foot or so in diameter to make up the stockade wall. Later in the day the women and children came and began to work hard at clearing and preparing a garden plot where they hoped next spring they could plant the seeds they had brought along with them, or obtained during their journey. If they were successful, it would mean that along with the various varieties of wild game the men would hunt in the forest, by next year there would be cabbage and beans, ears of Indian corn, potatoes, and even cucumbers.

The Latimer men, assisted by their friendly neighbors, worked very hard for the next few weeks. By the time the winter breezes were beginning to sting the cheeks, they were inside their new, simple cabins and able to sit near the warmth of their new fireplaces. The Colonel planned to build a "big house" for Lucretia, not unlike the one she had left in Connecticut. He felt he owed her that. But it would have to wait until spring—maybe even longer. In the meantime, they, too, would live in one of the little log houses.

"Are the women and children content?" he asked her, after a day of particularly hard labor.

"Very content," she answered. "The children see all this as a grand adventure."

He was relieved to hear this. To transport one's beloved family this far, and to such as place as this, still sometimes caused a tinge of guilt to rise in his heart.

Through the good offices of Witherel, and that of his brother Griswold, and the negotiating expertise of the Colonel, the Latimer lands quickly became extensive. There was the original square mile purchased immediately on the Colonel's arrival from Daniel James. In a few months there would be a fifty-acre adjoining tract granted to the Colonel for his military service during the Revolution, a tract with lots of water on it, and another one hundred and fifty-acre purchase from a man named Justin Cartwright. Eventually, there would be more than one thousand additional acres to the west, across the Ridge, near the lands by then belonging to Witherel and Joseph. Altogether, in a few years, the Latimer's would control lands literally numbering into the thousands of acres.

The Wedding of Hannah Bushnell

Next came the wedding.

Eusebius Bushnell had been gone for some time when the Colonel and his brood arrived in the Cumberland. As we have seen, in leaving his creditors behind he had also left his children. It was a particularly awkward time for his daughter Hannah. Still only sixteen years old, she had been left in the grey Purgatory in which orphaned teenagers, particularly girls, lived in those days. Griswold and Witherel had tried to help, of course, but one of them was newly married and the other a widowed man trying to make plans for the arrival of his own children, whom he had not seen for almost three years.

"What shall we do with Hannah?" Griswold had asked his brother. "The poor girl needs a protector and a secure life."

"Maybe the Lord will provide," Witherel had replied, without really having confidence in equal measure to his piety.

At this point, Prince Charming had arrived, in the form of young Thomas Murray. He had come to the Cumberland the same year as the Bushnells and had known young Hannah since she was but a child. He was twenty-six years old. The age difference was not immense and certainly not unusual for the time. And he was absolutely besotted with the beautiful young Hannah. Thomas had a good reputation and was a leader of men. He had a respectable vocation—he was a cabinet-maker—and was highly skilled in this valuable trade. He was an enthusiastic militia man and had fought with honor against the Indians. He would be in the thick of the Indian Wars that were yet to be. Everything seemed right. And so an agreement was reached, in the manner of the time. Hannah was only one party in the affair, but she didn't mind. Tom was handsome, interesting, and had good prospects. So why not? And besides all this, he had recently received a grant of 640 acres near Nashville. As his wife, Hannah would become a woman of substance.

Griswold's wife Polly cautioned her to count the cost. She would have to move quickly from childhood to the responsibility of running a household. And she could not count on Captain Murray always to be there; his responsibilities as a militia officer would take him away, and into the arms of danger, very often.

"We had better wait on this wedding for a while," Griswold said, conscientious in his position as Hannah's foster father. "I think we had better wait until your grandparents get here and give you their blessing."

Hannah, who loved Griswold and Polly, but still felt alone in the world, and admired this handsome man who wanted to marry her, was disappointed. But she would wait for the blessing.

It was not long in coming. Jonathan and Lucretia, forewarned of the situation, had had some time to think the matter over during the last few days of their journey, and as soon as they met the dashing young Captain Thomas Murray they enthusiastically approved of the marriage. On October 12, 1790, Hannah and Thomas became husband and wife. Within a few weeks Thomas was appointed a Captain in the Davidson County Militia by Governor Blount, serving under James and Elijah Robertson. Fortunately, these two men did not let their intense frustration with Hannah's father Eusebius affect their relationship with his new son-in-law. James Robertson even served as a bondsman for the couple. But that did not mean they were finished with the matter of the large debt Eusebius had left in their hands when he rushed off down the Mississippi.

The Gathering Storm

The wedding was a joyous time and briefly took everyone's mind off the disturbing tales which were circulating about the Indian atrocities. But it was not long before the realities were once again unavoidable. Throughout the next year, there was one tragic event after another. In April 1791, a black man, a slave of Captain Caffrey, was killed while working in a field. Great numbers of horses began to disappear from the settlements, and particularly from around Station Camp Creek, where the Latimer's had settled. Then they began disappearing from the neighborhood of Nashville, and then from farms along the Red River.

The year 1792 brought no relief. Quite the contrary. The great Chickamauga chief Dragging Canoe, who had promised to turn the Cumberland into a "dark and bloody ground" had made good on his promise for several years now. He had found eager accomplices in this from the European enemies of the new United States—first the British, and then the Spanish. Both were more than willing to provide him with the guns and horses he needed to carry on a full-scale war against the settlers. When he died, at the beginning of 1792, some thought the situation might improve. It did not. His successor, John Watts, took up the cause with a passion equal to his mentor. His plan was to launch many attacks on many different settlements, using the fine weapons supplied to him by the Spanish. In this way, he would cover himself with triumphant glory and establish himself as the true chief of the Lower Cherokees.

His plan was elaborate. It would be three-pronged. One group would carry out ambushes on the Kentucky Road, another on the road by which the Latimer's had arrived at Station Camp Creek, and Watts himself would lead the main army, made up of several hundred Cherokees, Shawnees, and Muskogees in a bold attack on Nashville itself. We will soon discover how disastrous for the Indians this latter campaign turned out to be, and the part one of the Latimers played in that disaster.

For months before John Watts began to put his plan into effect, the list of terrorist acts against the settlers had been growing.

On the 5th of March, twenty-five warriors attacked Brown's Station, eight miles from Nashville, killing four young boys. On the next day they burned Dunham's Station, and a week later they killed a man named McMurray on his own plantation at the mouth of Stone's River, not far from the land Witherel had bought from Eusebius when he first arrived in the Cumberland. About three weeks later marauders killed a mother and her three children; three days later they killed Benjamin Williams and all eight men in his party, right in the heart of the settlements. Along Station Camp Creek the dangers were mounting by the day. A boy was shot in ambush, hit by three bullets. In the same place two boys, the sons of the Latimers' neighbor Robert Desha, were killed while working in a field near their home—in broad daylight. Day after day news of more casualties came in—and the year was not half gone.

And in the midst of all this mayhem, the Colonel continued to quietly add to his land holdings along Station Camp Creek. He got the fifty-acre grant in January, a reward for his military service, from the State of North Carolina. In August he bought the 150 acres from Justin Cartwright for fifty pounds—land that would later go to his son-in-law Daniel Rogers. He was obviously confident that the troubles with the Native Americans were beginning to fade and that peace was not far away.

Then, in September, John Watts began his march toward Nashville. With him were several hundred men and several famous chiefs such as Tom Turnbridge, Siksika, the older brother of the famous Tecumseh, the Muskogee warrior Tahlonteeskee, Little Owl, brother of Dragging Canoe, and Pumpkin Boy, the brother of Doublehead. In short, the very flower of the native warrior class.

On their way, not far from Nashville, this Native American army encountered what for them was a rather minor inconvenience—a stockade and group of log houses, the home of Witherel's friend Sam, called Buchanan's Station.

The Battle at Buchanan's Station

Madison, Indiana
November 4, 1854

"Grandpa, Grandpa, you have a letter!" Young Johnny rushed into the sitting room, where his grandfather sat in his favorite chair, reading. Getting a letter was not a common thing in 1854, and particularly not one which looked so formidable. It was addressed to "Mr. John Buchanan Todd, Madison, Indiana." And in the upper left corner was the name of the sender: "Lyman C. Draper, Secretary, Wisconsin Historical Society, Madison, Wisconsin."

"Open it and see what it's about!" Johnny said, unable to hold his excitement in check.

John Todd took his time, opening the letter carefully so he wouldn't tear the paper. He read it silently, and slowly as well, and Johnny was beside himself.

"Grandpa...*please!*"

"This fellow says he has heard that I was at Buchanan's Station at Nashville in 1792 when the Indians attacked and that I saw the battle with my own eyes," John Todd said, almost casually. "He wants me to write him back and tell him about it. He's writing a book, he says."

"And did you see it with your own eyes, Grandpa? And are you going to write him back?"

"Well, I guess I will. But first I've got to get my mind working hard to remember everything that happened. Some of it is clear as a bell, and some has sort of drifted away. After all, it happened over fifty years ago —and I was only ten years old at the time."

"Then tell it to me, Grandpa, to help you get it back in your mind."

"That might be a real good idea," said John Buchanan Todd. "Sit up here by me and I'll see what I can do."

Johnny drew himself together on the floor at his grandfather's feet and looked up at the elderly gentleman in great anticipation.

And then John Buchanan Todd began his tale:

"For some reason, I can remember the people there in the station as clear as can be—every single one of them. Of course the station, really a fort, had been built by my Uncle John Buchanan (as you can see, I was named after him), and our family lived close by. It had two strong block-houses and a study stockade fence around it, and several smaller buildings, cabins and such, built right next to Mill Creek, only a couple of

miles from the center of Nashville back in the Cumberland. That's where I grew up, you see. My daddy Jim used to have to take the family to the station quite often to spend the night when it seemed like the Indians might be a danger. At the time they were slaughtering men, women and children right and left. That's why we were there when the battle broke out."

Fig. 11: The site of Buchanan's Station on Mill Creek

"This particular night there were fifteen or twenty families and the handful of militia men who had gathered there to guard them. There was my uncle Jim Mulherrin, and John McCrory, and Jimmy O'Connor, who happened to be drunk at the time (not unusual!), the Kennedy brothers, the Castleman brothers, a couple dozen riflemen from the local militia—maybe even fewer than that."

"And I remember that Mr. Latimer was there—Witherel Latimer. He was a fine, religious man, and knew how to handle a rifle for sure. He lived just north of the river, not far from the station, and had been in the militia since he arrived on the Cumberland a few years before. He had fought in the Revolution up in New England, and so had several members of his family. Most of the Latimers lived over in Sumner County where the old patriarch, Colonel Jonathan Latimer, had led them to a new life in the wilderness only a couple of years before the battle. Everyone knew and respected the Colonel. He had known George Washington personally and fought alongside him in New York, not to mention how he led troops at the Battle of Saratoga and saw the British General Burgoyne give up his sword to General Gates. The Latimers were good people, and leaders, too; even if they did talk with that strange Yankee accent."

"But what about the *battle*?" Johnny said, eager to get his grandpa back on track.

"Well, there had been rumors, so we all knew that something was brewing among the Indians. We even sent two men out during the day to see what they could find out. John Gee and a young man named Clayton. Poor fellows."

"Why is that?" Johnny asked.

"You'll see," Grandpa Todd replied.

"At the time we didn't know how many Indians there were, but later we heard that three or four hundred Creeks had come up from the South, picked up another couple of hundred Cherokees from their towns on the way, then added a few more Shawnees, and that the whole lot were heading for Nashville, ready to scalp some settlers and run the rest of them out once and for all."

"The Indians had several chiefs with them, including two big ones, Tom Tunbridge and John Watts—both of them half-breeds. Siksika, the older brother of the famous Tecumseh, was also there. These fellows usually had big egos and were constantly arguing among themselves, and that turned out to be a big advantage for us."

"They were on their way to Nashville, of course, but when they got to within a mile of our small fort, Tom Tunbridge decided he wanted to take us out first. It was a clear moonlit Sunday night—September 30. The Indians moved in complete silence, something they were very good at. They got so close they could hear our cattle and horses moving around just outside the stockade and see our lanterns as we walked around inside. We had no idea they were there."

"That's when Tunbridge and John Watts got into a big argument. Tunbridge insisted on doing us in then and there. 'Better stick to our original plan,' John Watts said. 'You're a squaw and a coward besides,' Tunbridge replied. "I burned down Zeigler's Station all by myself, and I can do the same here." The argument went on for a long time. Finally, Watts said, 'You go ahead, then, I'll just watch, thank you.' But when the fighting started, Watts and his braves joined in anyway."

"Of course, inside the stockade, we didn't know anything about all this fuss. The adults were sitting around telling or listening to stories, and the children were listening, too. We stayed up pretty late, and then people started going to and fro, carrying their lanterns, looking for comfortable places to lay down under a blanket and get some sleep. It got quieter and quieter and one by one we dropped off to sleep."

"All but one. John McCrory was a young man who had fought in the Revolution same as Witherel Latimer and some of the other militia men. He had learned to be a good shot and calm under fire. When most everyone else fell asleep, he 'kept one eye open,' as people say, in case anyone tried to sneak up on them. It was a good thing that he did."

"Now the thing about Indian warriors is that they sometimes seemed to be overly interested in showing how brave they were and how tough they could be on an enemy. At least that's the way it seemed to me. And that fact saved our skins more than once. If they had ever gotten together and fought like a disciplined army, our goose would have been cooked. In this case, some of them got busy stealing the horses and cattle that were in the pasture around the station, and some others got a big log to use as a battering ram to knock down the gate. And Tom Tunbridge had a plan of his own. He was going to go around to the back with a torch, climb up on the roof of the blockhouse, set it on fire, and then the warriors could just kill us off one at a time as we ran through the gate trying to escape the fire."

"Well, the first thing to go wrong for the Indians was that the ones fooling with the cows upset the beasts and the cattle started moaning and groaning real loud and the horses started stirring around in a state of panic. John McCrory heard the ruckus and peeped through a porthole just in time to see the warriors running toward the gate with their log battering ram. He stuck his rifle through the hole and fired. He fired just one shot, and it went ricocheting here and there among the Indians. Several of them dropped in their tracks, screaming in pain. One of the Kennedy boys was nearby, and he jumped up from his sleep and got a shot off as well, and some more of the attackers fell down. Nobody tried to knock down the gate again after that."

"Of course everybody was wide awake by now, and the men were rushing for the portholes in the blockhouses and the gaps in the stockade fence, and shooting like the dickens, as fast as the guns would allow. We all knew we were in serious trouble."

"And what about the women and the children?" Johnny asked, his imagination racing with the drama he was hearing.

"Now that was something!" John Buchanan Todd said, throwing his head back with a hearty laugh. "They got busy as bees. There was no hanging back or hiding out with that bunch! For one thing, they took all the men's hats they could find, and ran back and forth among the empty portholes, waving the hats to make it look like there were lots more men there than was the case. It was important for the Indians to hear lots of shooting to make them think there were a lot of defenders—that meant that the men had to keep shooting, and had to use lots of bullets. So my two aunts, Sally Buchanan and Maggie Mulherrin, gathered up of the knives and forks and other kitchen stuff, melted them down in a big pot in the fireplace, and poured the metal into bullet molds."

"Aunt Sally was a wonder. She was a big woman, muscles like a man, tough as leather, a fiery talker, and completely fearless. She was the perfect frontiersman's wife. All through the battle she moved around encouraging the other women and us children. And also the riflemen—not only keeping them supplied with brand new still-hot bullets but also offering them a sip of household brandy, if they were so inclined. And the woman was only eighteen years old and nine months pregnant at the time!"

"The Indians were coming up to the station so close you could smell the war paint and hear their voices plainly, muttering insults as us in English. There was one port hole just below the overhang on one of the blockhouses that was low enough for them to stick their rifles through. One by one they would come up, put the barrel of their gun inside, and fire. That meant the folks inside had to put up with bullets whizzing past their heads one after the other. But the braves could only fire at one angle, so the bullets all hit at the same spot near the ceiling on the other side of the room. That made it easy to duck them and everybody inside just laughed and threw a few of the Indian insults back outside!"

"Mercy!" Johnny said. That was all he could think of to say, so he said again, "Mercy!"

"After the battle, we went and looked at the spot where all those bullets had hit. It was no bigger in size than a man's hat. And we counted thirty bullets buried right there. Of course, by the time the thing ended the whole station was peppered with bullet holes. I'm sure you could see them today if you ever went there."

"The fighting went on for hours, and a lot of Indians got hit trying to run up to the Station with torches to set it on fire. Now Tom Tunbridge (we called him his Indian name Running Water), who had had this idea about burning the station, got real upset that no fire was started yet. He grabbed one of the torches and screaming like a panther he ran directly through the line of fire and climbed up on the roof of one of the cabins. That was when a rifleman in one of the blockhouses fired at him point blank. Tom Tunbridge yelled in agony and rolled end over end off the roof. But he didn't stop fighting—and I'll give him credit for his courage. Bleeding to death, he still kept trying to start a fire and yelled to his men to have courage and keep up the fight. Several of the riflemen could see him clearly now, and they fired again and again until he finally lay still. Then the torch he was carrying fell on his chest and caught his clothes and then his body on fire. It was awful to see—and everyone on both sides saw it.

"This had a terrible effect on the Indians. Tom Tunbridge was the main leader of this attack, and he was lying in a pool of blood before their eyes, and on fire besides. John Watts, who hadn't wanted to attack Buchanan's Station, stepped in to lead now, trying to change the course of things. But to the horror of the Indians, he had hardly gotten started when a bullet from inside came flying through a porthole and sank deep into his thigh. Then it went right through and pierced his other leg as well. He fell to the ground in agony. He wasn't dead, but he wasn't much help anymore either."

Jimmy O'Connor and the Blunderbuss

"The shooting went on for four more hours before the Indians decided they had had enough. The last straw for them seemed to come right out of Jimmy O'Connor's blunderbuss. Like I told you at the beginning of my story, Jimmy had been too often to the bottle the night of the battle and the rest of the men felt he was unreliable in his delicate condition. But of course, he was raring to fight. Just to keep him busy and out of the way, my Uncle John gave him his mother's old blunderbuss pistol. It was the one she kept under her pillow, and we all called it "Granny's Pocket Piece." The gun was old and unreliable, and Uncle John figured that Jimmy would never get it to fire. Well, as I say, Jimmy wanted to fight in the worst way. He climbed up clear to the top of one of the block-houses where there was a little bedroom for a lookout guard to stay in during ordinary days. Then he climbed up a ladder to the top porthole. From his vantage point, Jimmy could see lots of Indians scurrying about down below. He put powder in the pan, put some more down the barrel, dropped in a bullet, and fired his first shot.

At least he thought he did. Guns were firing everywhere and the air was full of explosive sounds. So Jimmy thought he heard the old blunderbuss fire. He put some more powder in the pan, dropped some more down the barrel, put in another bullet, and fired again. This happened four times. What Jimmy didn't know was that the gun hadn't fired even once, and all that powder from all four musket balls was jammed down its short barrel."

"But with number five she blew, giving off a roar like a cannon and scattered musket balls in all directions. Jimmy flew off the ladder, hit the floor and slid right under the bed, covered with black stuff and clothes in tatters. None of this fazed him in the least. He crawled out from under the bed, ran down to Uncle John, and exclaimed, "Be jabbers, Johnny, they got one alright, didn't they!"

"And in fact, the Indians thought they had heard a cannon, and they weren't about to stay around and get shot at with a cannon. Anyway, they still thought they were fighting a large force, judging from the bullets that kept buzzing around them like a bunch of killer wasps. Most of their chiefs were either dead or rolling on the ground in terrible pain. A couple of braves rescued John Watts and took him away on a litter. You could see he was hurt bad. Like I say, the bullet that had hit him went clean through and buried itself in his other leg. You could see the braves dragging away the other wounded or dead warriors, slipping away into the forest just before the morning light would have made them even clearer targets for our riflemen."

"So ol' Jimmy, drunk as he was, played a big part in getting us out of a sure 'nuf hard situation."

"We waited a while to be sure it was safe before any of us went outside the fort. No sense in tempting fate. When we did go out the first thing we saw were trails of blood leading into the woods. Somehow the Indians managed to take all the dead and wounded with them—except Tom Tunbridge. He was lying there looking like a charred log you would see in a fireplace. Awful sight. Later we heard they had lost lots of chiefs—big names like Tecumseh's brother, and Little Owl, the brother of Dragging Canoe, and Pumpkin Boy, the brother of Doublehead, and Unacate, called White-Man-Killer, and who knows how many more?"

"They left in such a hurry that some of their prizes were still there, scattered around on the ground. There were tomahawks and rifles, pipes and kettles, and who knows what else. I remember there was a beautiful Spanish sword. I imagine those Spanish rascals had given it to some brave in exchange for a bunch of settlers' scalps!"

"Remember the two men I told you about that went out to scout the situation? Sad to say, among all the stuff the Indians left behind, we found a handkerchief we knew belonged to poor Gee, and one of Clayton's moccasins. There was no doubt they had met a terrible fate, long before the battle started. But of those inside the fort, not a single soul was lost. It was nothing but a miracle."

"What happened after that, Grandpa—Did the Indians attack you again?" Johnny asked.

"Not after the whipping they got there at the station. Some people say it was the biggest thing that ever happened in the battle for the Cumberland. I remember that while we were looking at the stuff the Indians had left behind—it must have been about ten o'clock in the morning—we heard some horses coming, and at first we were worried. But then we saw it was none other than General Robertson himself and with him was ol' Andy Jackson."

"Witherel Latimer and my uncles went out to meet them, and they had quite a discussion about what had happened. Mr. Jackson was all excited. Of course, he didn't like the Indians very well, as you may know. I heard Mr. Latimer say, 'Do you really think that is wise?' and Mr. Jackson seemed not to take kindly to being argued with. But then General Robertson spoke up and ended the arguments. Seems like Andy Jackson wanted those poor fellows who had been fighting all night to jump on their horses and pursue the Indians and finish them off. Mr. Latimer didn't mind standing up to him; after all, he wasn't President of the United States yet; as far as we were concerned, he was still just a country lawyer."

"Word of the battle did eventually go all the way back to President Washington. I don't know if anybody knew to mention the names of the defenders to him. If they did, I bet he recognized the name 'Latimer' and wondered if these were the same Latimers he had known so long ago and what in the world they were doing in the Cumberland."

"Oh, and I almost forgot to tell you, Aunt Sally Buchanan spent the day after the battle having a baby."

"Mercy!" Johnny said again. By now he really had run out of anything else to say.

Witherel and the Colonel Contemplate the Indians

When the morning came, and the Indians had retreated, despite his lack of sleep, and a weariness that lay on him like a pile of oak logs, Witherel had saddled his horse and headed for Sumner County just as soon as the General and Andy Jackson left to go back to town. He knew that the family would soon hear about the battle at Buchanan's Station and they would worry about him—especially his children, who were still living with the Colonel and Lucretia.

When he arrived at Station Camp Creek everyone was out somewhere—the men in the fields, the woman and children doing chores here and there. He slipped quietly into a convenient barn, lay down on a pile of straw, and fell fast asleep. In a couple of hours, the men began coming in from the fields and found him there. Knowing how he must be feeling, they woke him gently, and everyone was willing to wait until the whole family gathered to hear what had happened.

He told the story between bites of this and that—delicious snacks from Lucretia's kitchen. He realized that he had not eaten for a long time. The children were captivated, especial his boys Daniel and James. Not yet twelve years old, but nevertheless on the cusp of manhood, they hung onto every word, and everyone could see how proud they were of their father. Witherel's heart ached for them at times like this. It was not natural to have to visit your own children. They should be with him. Once again, he determined that, before long, they would be.

After all questions were answered, and the various Latimer families began gathering up and departing for their own cabins nearby, Witherel and the Colonel found themselves alone, sitting in a couple of well-worn wicker chairs back behind the Colonel's house. The evening was cool and quiet, but at the same time full of the twilight cacophony that one expected in the verdant Cumberland in the late fall. Frogs. Crickets. Katydids. Night-bird sounds. It was the kind of music that could slow the racing heart and bring the breath back to normal. Only now did the tensions of the battle begin to fade, cooled by the evening breezes.

There was silence for a while. Then Witherel said, "Nobody knows better than you do, Dad, what it's like to shoot at another human being and see him fall to the ground—to see the life's blood leave him, the eyes go pale, the struggling stop. That he was trying to do the same to you makes no difference. It's a terrible thing no matter what."

The Colonel said nothing for a few seconds, then, nodding solemnly and quietly, answered, his voice betraying a host of old memories, "You couldn't be more right about that, son. You couldn't be more right."

"And you just have to wonder, Dad, when the white men and the Indians will get enough of killing each other. It's been going on a long, long time. I looked out of the blockhouse, though that little porthole, and I saw all those young men, trying their best to kill us, along with our women and the children, and to take what we have. And I saw them walking that thin line between courage and foolhardiness, and falling to the ground in pools of their own blood. Doing what they thought it was their place to do. And I thought, what a waste! And I wondered why we can't think of a way for them to have a good life, and for us to have a good life as well, and for us to respect each other as God's children."

"Right again, son. I've always felt the same."

Witherel was the family theologian, and he could sometimes put words and reasons together that explained how they all felt—whether the rest could do the same or not. The Latimers of Connecticut may not have been the most pious family, but they were immersed in the Puritan, Calvinist culture of their time and place. Like us all, they were driven by a way of seeing the world that might not rise to consciousness but furnished a structure to live by nevertheless. One of old John Calvin's doctrines was called "total depravity." That meant that all human beings, every single one of them, start out as bad as bad can be. As the Puritan Ralph Venning had put it, back in England, a hundred years before that cool night in Tennessee, "Sin has degraded man and made him a beast. It is true, he has the shape of a man, but alas!—he is degenerated into a bestial and beastly nature. It would be better to be a beast than to be like a beast, living and dying like one. It would be better to be Balaam's ass than such an ass as Balaam himself was."

So, people like the Latimers concluded that Indians might be beasts and savages, but so were the white men. This made a lot of difference in the way they acted. Yes, the Native Americans need transformation. They needed to change. But so did the white men. In the meantime, you had to protect yourself, it's true, but you also had to do what you could to convince both red men and white men to let their hearts be changed from darkness and violence to light and peace. The family had not heard the word "racist"—but their way of looking at the world made them much less this than most of their frontier friends. Maybe wanting to convert the Indians to Christianity seems paternalistic to people nowadays, but for the Latimers and those like them, it grew out of a sincere respect for the humanity of these "savages"—and a sincere longing to see them live better lives. Less fear. Less blood. Less revenge. More hope.

But in the days of the great revival—a story we have yet to tell—they stood with those who abandoned that other part of John Calvin's ideology. The theologians called it "double predestination." This was the idea that God had, eons ago, already decided the eternal destiny of every person. He had decided some would be saved and some would be punished forever. This way of thinking made it easier to be a racist. The Indians obviously were elected to go to Hell. It was not such a bad thing to help God get them there sooner rather than later.

And there's no use trying to convert them, or anybody else for that matter. Everything was settled long ages ago. Don't go meddling with God's eternal plan. This particular line may have been a terrible distortion of Calvin, but it was a common way to think. The Latimers didn't think that way. They thought it was good to go to the Indians with the Christian message and to try to convince them to live by it. From the earliest days in Connecticut, they had tried to do this very thing. They had sat on pews alongside Mohegan families since the days of their earliest memories. There were meals together, games together, prayers together.

Yes, the Colonel had seen Indian atrocities during the French and Indian War, and the Revolution, for that matter. Atrocities that can make a man's blood run cold, and then heat it to the boiling point—eager for revenge. And goodness knows there had been atrocities here in the Great Forest as well. Awful things had happened. Everyone had seen the mangled bodies of young wives and infant children. There was no way to escape the knowledge of these outrages. All you could control was your own attitude. That's what the Colonel tried to teach his children; not so much with words, as with his example.

And so there was Witherel, Indian blood quite literally still on his hands, committing himself even more than before to bring something better to these people who shared the forest with him. His preacher friend Sam King would eventually go even deeper into the Wilderness to carry the message of peace to them, and Witherel would hold up his hands in every way he could. And in the greatest of ironies, decades later, as an old man, he would once again sit behind an Indian brother on a church pew, this time none other than an equally old and weakened chief of the Cherokees, called The Glass, who had once danced around the war camp of his people in the Cumberland with the heart of a white man between his teeth.

It was late, and the two men moved into the house to go to bed. As they drifted into sleep they had no way of knowing that this high-minded talk about the Indians would, in only about a year, be severely tested.

NINE: TRAGEDY

Fagot Comes to Natchez

Natchez, Spanish Territory
Winter, 1790

Throughout the winter of 1790 Eusebius Bushnell got himself settled in Natchez and began to develop a web of business connections as he prepared for a second career in the field of Spanish real estate development. Or whatever other opportunities might arise. The winters were milder here in the Deep South, and they suited him well. He soon became absorbed in his new environment, alive with grey-bearded Cypress trees and ancient live-oaks. The world of the Cumberland gradually faded from his memory.

And while Eusebius was thus engaged, hundreds of miles away, the Colonel had been completing the complicated arrangements involved in moving several families from one world to another. A few weeks before the journey to the Cumberland began, he had sold the land around the old Latimer Mill in Chesterfield to his son Jonathan III. He and his brother George would stay in Connecticut and operate the sawmill. The younger Jonathan would also serve as his father's agent in disposing of the rest of his property in New England. Now, with the journey to the Cumberland completed, the Colonel was beginning to accumulate hundreds of acres in the new land which he planned to distribute among his children to be their inheritance. From his point of view, Eusebius was long gone and mostly out of mind.

Soon after the Latimers' arrival in their new homeland, the Colonel's son Charles and his wife Mary had a son, the first of the clan to be born in the Wilderness. In honor of one of the brothers who had stayed behind, Charles and Mary named the baby George.

Meanwhile, the months went by and, safely ensconced in Natchez, Eusebius threw himself into his entrepreneurial activities. He had almost forgotten the quagmire he had created for himself in Nashville when a new complication arose for him.

André Fagot showed up in Natchez.

The crafty Frenchman wasted no time. He jumped from the flatboat which had brought him to Natchez and mounted the steep incline to the town center, almost running. Only moments later he was standing before the governor's headquarters on the bluff, earnestly requesting an immediate meeting with Señor Gayoso himself.

"I have wonderful news, Your Excellency," he effused. "The men of the Cumberland are ready to swear their allegiance to the King of Spain!" In point of fact, Fagot had little interest in the "men of the Cumberland." In fact, earlier in his career, he had gone up and down the river spreading the rumor that these same men were about to declare war on Spain. His motive for this was revenge. He had been infuriated with the leadership in Nashville for insisting that he pay taxes he owed there. He was primarily interested now in finding a good position for himself as far from the Cumberlanders as he could. But he would use his knowledge of the leaders there as efficiently as possible. He made a particular point of dropping the name of that promising young lawyer who was making a name for himself in those parts—Andrew Jackson.

"And Mr. Jackson thanks you kindly for His Majesty's generous gift," he announced, pretending by his tone a certain casual disinterest in the matter and an intimacy with Jackson. In fact, Mr. Jackson had not only *not* authorized André to speak for him, but he was also quite put out with the Frenchman for making him appear much more willing to participate in turning the Cumberland over to the King of Spain than he actually was. André had let his opinion of Jackson's loyalties be formed by certain inside information he had obtained: Mr. Jackson had accepted a large and valuable tract of land north of Natchez on the Mississippi from the Spanish absolutely free of charge and was in the process of developing a slave-labor plantation on it. What André did not know was that Jackson thought this matter to be a great joke on the Spanish, since he was sure that all their holdings would before long become a part of the United States.

And then there were the Robertson brothers. One of them, Elijah, had sent along a letter to the governor describing André as "a gentlemen of integrity and in high esteem amongst the Americans." But more to Eusebius' interest and concern, had he known of it, would have been another statement in the letter to the effect that Mr. Fagot had been appointed by the writer as his agent "to recover a certain debt."

This was not good news for Captain Bushnell.

A Quick Change of Residence

Somehow Eusebius got wind of Fagot's real mission. Prudence seemed to call for a speedy retreat from Natchez before André Fagot confronted him. There was no time for reflection or hesitation. He gathered his slaves, sent them to his lodgings to gather a few necessities, and ordered them to meet him in the lower town along the banks of the Mississippi. They hurriedly loaded the flatboat and set off down the river. The currents carried the boat downstream with little effort, and within a couple of days Eusebius and his servants made for the right shore, unloaded the boat, and started inland. By the time André Fagot had come to the conclusion that he had been given the slip, Eusebius was securely settled to the west, in the old town of Opelousas, far from the river.

If anything, *le Poste de Opelousas* was a cacophony of ethnic melodies even more diverse than Natchez. The old families were Frenchmen, with their African slaves. More recent were the Spanish and Germans; many of them had been in Louisiana no longer than Eusebius. There were the Creoles, themselves a complex mixture of French, Spanish, African and Native Americans. And there were *le gens de couleur libres* ("free people of color")—people not unlike some he had known in Connecticut, but rarer than diamonds in the Cumberland.

Most interesting of all, through a remarkable coincidence, the town was also teeming with Acadians—those Frenchmen whom the British had driven out of Canada. Some of them were the very people who had passed through Connecticut on their way into exile at the time when Eusebius had often been there himself—courting his intended, the lovely and now-lamented young Borodell Latimer. He had no doubt looked upon their faces as they wandered in desperation along the docks of New London. How strange are the twists for Fate—that these "Cajuns" and this capricious Yankee should meet once again among the Cypress swamps and Spanish moss of Louisiana!

There was one other ethnic group in Opelousas that was of particular interest to Eusebius: the Scotch-Irish. In fact, though his escape from Natchez might have seemed to be propelled by panic, in fact, it fit rather well with a plan he had already been formulating in his mind. Living in Opelousas, he knew from earlier business in the area, was a fine-looking young widow by the name of Margaret McCarthy.

Not a man to waste time in the face of opportunity, he made for her house almost as soon as he had arrived in town. The courtship was methodical and respectable in every way if a bit rapid. It was also entirely successful. On April 21, 1792, Margaret McCarthy became Mrs. Eusebius Bushnell. Or, as the Spanish parish priest recorded this Protestant nuptial in the records of his church, Mrs. Eusevio Boisnel.

Witherel Also Finds a Mate

Witherel Latimer was not the Colonel's firstborn. But in the Cumberland, it became his lot to play this role since his two older brothers, Jonathan III and George, had stayed in New England. His sister Hannah Rogers was older than him, of course, but in this patriarchal culture, it was the oldest male who held pride of place. And since he had been the first to come to the Wilderness, along with his much younger brother Griswold, he knew that much was expected of him. Paralleling this great sense of responsibility was his rather intense inclination toward the things of the Spirit. The Latimer men were somewhat taciturn when it came to religious expression, and to a certain extent so was Witherel. But he felt the same sense of duty toward his Puritan-inspired religion as he did toward his relatives and so he often served as a sort of surrogate pastor for the family.

Crushed by the death of his young wife Abigail, who lay in the quiet cemetery in far-away Chesterfield, and burdened with guilt in being absent from his two young sons Daniel and Jimmie for so long, he had often felt waves of depression. He longed to have a family again, to have his children around him and a loving companion to share his home and his life.

As a faithful member of Reverend Craighead's church in Nashville, he had become well acquainted with the group of religious folk who formed a small but significant minority within the rough and generally profane community of the Wilderness. Back in Connecticut, the Latimers had been dutiful members of the state-sponsored Congregational Church for many generations. There were no Congregational churches in the Cumberland, of course. But for them, the most compatible group on the frontier was the Presbyterian Church, whose Calvinistic theology was essentially the same as what they had been used to in New England. This denomination had a well-educated clergy, valued education for everyone, and seemed an orderly force and a beacon of civility in an otherwise rather chaotic world. And so the Latimers became Presbyterians. Witherel and Thomas Craighead became friends as well and spent many evenings in the little village of Nashville discussing arcane topics like predestination and substitutionary atonement. Reverend Craighead was delighted to find someone who could discuss such themes intelligently.

Soon after the Colonel's brood had settled along Station Camp Creek Witherel began the habit of visiting his family there as often as possible. It was a relatively easy trip along the Holston Road which stretched from Nashville to Knoxville—the road the Latimers had used on the last leg of their long journey from New England. At first, his visits were mostly about spending time with his two sons, who were still being cared for by Lucretia and the Colonel. He usually arrived at the end of the week, and that meant that on Sundays he gathered with the family and a number of like-minded souls to worship under a great tree next to the well-worn Holston Road not far from the Latimer lands—no more than eight miles away. Sometimes the Reverend Craighead came along to preside at the service, and sometimes one of the local men, or even Witherel himself, served as the leader. Among the books the Colonel had brought to the forest were Bibles, hymnbooks, and books of sermons. These became the basis for a Wilderness liturgy.

It was under that tree that the Latimers met some of the remarkable personalities who would have such a formative impact on their future—people like Sam King and William McGee. These were men who would find their place in books about what the historians came to call "The Great Revival" and who would play a vital role in the establishment of a uniquely American way of doing religion.

And then there was the Anderson family. The Andersons were, like the Latimers, well-educated for the times, good leaders, and pillars of the Church. And among them was a lovely young woman named Margaret. Witherel fell in love precipitously. He had lived alone now for eight years, without his two sons. His youth was rapidly melting away; he was thirty-six years old. And it was time. Margaret was closer to twenty years old, but she had a gravitas beyond her years and reminded Witherel very much of his mother, Lucretia. Would it not be wonderful if Margaret could be for him what his mother had been to the Colonel?

The courtship was brief and highly satisfactory. Though neither of them knew it, he and his rambunctious brother-in-law Eusebius had found their second soul mates at precisely the same time and, though separated by hundreds of miles, and living in two very different worlds, married with weeks of each other. And each to a woman named Margaret.

The wedding took place in Nashville on a lovely Thursday in March, so that the couple could immediately set up housekeeping at Witherel's place there. Thomas Craighead served as the clergyman, and James Mulherin, one of the founders of Nashville and Witherel's good friend and a fellow rifleman at Buchanan's Station, signed the marriage bond.

Not long after the marriage, Witherel decided to move his newly completed family away from Nashville and nearer to the Latimer clan now firmly planted in Sumner County. Sumner had been created about the time Witherel and Griswold had arrived in the Cumberland before the

State of Tennessee had come into existence. Their years in Nashville had been full of adventure, danger, violence, and back-breaking work. They had served with distinction in the militia and Witherel had been involved in two well-known confrontations with the Indians—at Neely's Bend and at Buchanan's station. This kind of life was well and good for a single man, particularly one who wanted to free himself from painful memories. But now there was a wife and two little boys who would soon be in their teens. Perhaps it was time to join his other brothers and his parents and live the life of a farmer and family-man—and to practice his citizenship in the halls of local government rather than as a rifleman.

And as for Griswold, it was his turn to feel the pain so familiar to Witherel, and to Eusebius, too, for that matter. His young wife Polly died trying to have his first child, and he was left alone again. He would move, too. Lucretia and the Colonel invited him to come live with them on Station Camp Creek, where he could find solace in the comforting presence of his loving mother and stalwart father.

And so the brothers bid farewell to the little village of Nashville, with its half-dozen framed and hewn log houses, a dozen or so log cabins, and two hundred hardy citizens. They departed feeling rather satisfied about the way they had lived their lives there, confident of the respect in which they were held by their Cumberland colleagues.

Sumner County was divided by a rugged stretch of hills and valleys cut through with rushing fountains and covered by a wild forest blanketed with a tangle of vines and undergrowth. Locals called it simply "The Ridge." The fertile land south of the Ridge was now all taken—including a large portion which now belonged to the Colonel. But there were still some good, if not great, tracts on the other side, towards the north and west, and Witherel found and purchased one hundred and fifty acres there, on the western slope of The Ridge. His young brother Joseph, ready to establish a family himself, bought a tract next to Witherel. To complete his plan, Joseph needed a spouse. And in fact, he had his eye on a pretty young lady who also lived near The Ridge, and thus he was what real estate people sometimes called a "highly motivated buyer." It must be pointed out, however, that it took Joseph several years to bring his grand marital plan to full fruition. The brothers were only a few miles from the rest of the family now. Visits with the family necessitated a trip of a few miles through the rugged terrain of The Ridge, but this was nothing to these seasoned frontiersmen.

In the same year the praying segment of the population in that area, who had been meeting under the big tree along the Holston Road, organized themselves into a Church. In a proper Presbyterian way, a duly ordained minister, and good friend of the Latimers, William McGee, took the role of founding clergyman. Several in the small group which gathered were well-educated. Margaret's kinsman John Anderson and the minister McGee had been fellow-students in the famous Log School of Dr. David Caldwell in North Carolina. Dr. Caldwell had taught them Latin and Greek and Presbyterian theology. Five of their classmates became governors of states, and many more were to be legendary lawyers and physicians. There they had become friends with men destined to change the face of American religion, men like James McGready and Barton W. Stone. These were men in a new land, with new ideas, and the courage to question what needed to be questioned. They were precisely the kind of people the Latimers liked and quickly befriended.

The new church was called Shilo.

Peter Looney

Station Camp Creek
Fall, 1793

More than two years had now passed since the Latimer clan had arrived in the wilderness. By the time the trees were turning in the fall of 1793, their lives had begun to take on the inevitable patterns of sowing and reaping, hunting and cooking, building and repairing. But alongside these ordinary patterns, the Cumberland settlers still found themselves living in constant fear and danger. If anything, the situation had gotten worse since their arrival.

The Colonel was sitting outside in the cool twilight, looking first toward the warm orange glow of the fireplace inside, then toward the darkening tree line across the pastureland which he and his sons had diligently carved from the forest. Sitting with him were his two youngest sons, Joseph and Nathaniel. They were not talking, simply sitting in the crisp air with their own thoughts. The Colonel's mind moved quickly from old New London, down along the Shenandoah, into the green fields before him. He tried to push the scenes of murder and devastation—there and here—away, though they kept crowding back into consciousness, seemingly determined to dominate his reminiscences.

His thoughts were interrupted by the noise of a wagon driven with some speed through the gathering darkness, coming up the road toward the Latimer Station. It was Peter, the brother of his neighbor David Looney, younger than the Colonel by twenty years or so, but so long on the Cumberland Frontier that he was already something of an institution.

Despite their very different characters and ages, Peter and the Colonel had become good friends. Peter's young son Michael and one of the Colonel's granddaughters, still a toddler, would eventually become man and wife.

Peter lived to be a very old man and the stories about him were legendary. One of the most famous occurred many years after this twilight chat with the Colonel. Peter had the misfortune to lose two wives in his lifetime—something not unusual in those days. His second wife had some financial assets of her own and even before he left this earth their blended families, which together were very large, fell out with one another over the considerable estate—this despite the fact that three of his second wife's sons had married three of Peter's daughters. Peter, by this time almost 90 years old, and even at this age "hotheaded and fiery," according to his associates, had little patience with the legal wrangling or indeed with the court itself.

One day in court a lawyer, a fellow named Smithson, particularly irritated him. At one point Smithson said something especially distasteful to old Peter, who proceeded step across the courtroom and give the barrister a good swat with his walking stick, knocking him off his feet.

"Mr. Looney," said the judge, "that kind of behavior is going to cost you. You are in contempt of court. You are hereby fined the sum of fifty dollars."

"Fifty dollars!" exclaimed old Peter. "I did not know it was so cheap. Why, at that rate I'll give you another fifty dollars if you will let me hit him again!"

Peter had the kind of toughness it took to survive in the earliest days in the great forest—those days when the Colonel had been leading his men against the Redcoats in places so far away from the Cumberland. Peter had done his part in the War of Independence, even here in the deep forest—and he had received hundreds of acres on Station Camp Creek for his service. So he had been among the first of the neighbors to welcome the Colonel and his family when they arrived and settled along the creek as well. And neighbor in those days meant friend as well—it had to mean that, even if the two men could have hardly been more different.

Peter leaped spryly from the wagon, his precautionary rifle still in his hand, and was already talking as he approached the Colonel. "Jon, we've got to do something about these savages. I don't care who did what to who, or who is to blame for what, we can't let them just keep massacring our wives and children. And to tell the truth, I blame it on those blasted Spaniards and Englishmen. They keep the young braves so stirred up and well-armed that it's no wonder they come up here to rob and kill. We are easy prey to be sure."

"I could give you a list as long as your arm. How many horses have disappeared right here along Station Camp Creek? How many people have died? George Wilson. Ben Kirkendall, over near Winchester's place —in his own house. And they took everything he had they could use. Thieves and robbers! And poor John Dixon, right there nearby. Valentine Sevier—three fine sons gone. And right here along the creek we lost three little boys, two of them sons of Robert Desha, killed the broad daylight out in the field working—innocent as little songbirds. The savages burned down Zeigler's Station, with people inside. They tomahawk young girls. They don't just kill, they scalp and they mangle. There's blood on the ground all around Bledsoe's Lick. They put twelve balls through John Haggard and killed his wife. There are five little Haggard children left in wretched condition without a penny. And in just the last few weeks the list of the dead is too long and too horrible to even mention. And where is our so-called 'government'? Nowhere to be seen! We sink or we swim on our own—that's the plain truth."

"So what do you think we should do?" the Colonel asked. It was not the first time he had heard this liturgy of grievances.

"We've got to get our militia into some bold action and go after those rascals. Anytime they come up here and begin stealing our livestock and hurting our families, we've got to go after them and strike like lightning!" Peter Looney had worked himself into something of a frenzy, and his enthusiasm was not lost on Joseph and Nathaniel Latimer—who were among the most likely to do the going, should someone be called on to go.

There was a kind of cold and foreboding spirit in the air which the Colonel had felt more than once in his lifetime. He was no prophet, but it required no special gift of insight to see what lay ahead.

Tragedy at Rock Island

Cherry Grove Seminary
Knox County, Illinois
Summer, 1865

"Students, you have received a fine education, and you must now go out and take your place among those enlightened, pious, and patriotic citizens of our Republic who are the salt and light of our society. This day is particularly significant, and your class as well, since this is the last convocation which shall ever be held for this fine academy which has served our community so well for almost thirty years. I am proud to call it my *alma mater*. I am proud to be its Principal, though, sadly, its last one. I am proud of the foundational part my family, the Latimers, have had in the establishment and support of this institution: my father Jonathan Latimer, his brother Alexander, and their father Joseph Latimer, son of the illustrious patriot, Colonel Jonathan Latimer of Connecticut and Tennessee."

The speaker was Joseph F. Latimer, fluent and college educated, only recently returned from his service in the Union Army during the last days of the Civil War. He would move on from Cherry Grove to a career as a college professor and Republican politician.

"I thought it particularly fitting to ask my uncle Alexander, who happened to be visiting from his home in the State of Minnesota, to be our speaker on this occasion. You have heard him before, telling you stories about his friendship with our lamented President, Abraham Lincoln—a friendship which began in their youth in Sangamon County, and continued by the exchange of letters until our beloved leader's tragic murder only a few weeks ago."

"This horrible war has made us all acquainted with grief, and no one hearing my voice today has escaped the loss of husbands, fathers, sons and dear friends. These events of our wretched times may cause you students to think that only our generation has suffered such perils and calamities. But in fact, these disasters are the common lot of mankind. I have asked my uncle Alexander to tell you a story of such a loss in our family as passed along to him by his father, the grandfather who gave me my name, Joseph Latimer. This man, who is still revered in our community as one of its foundation stones and pillars, lived through the terrible days in the Cumberland when the settlers and the native tribes were engaged in a bloody battle over who would dominate the land. It was a time of terror when violence inhabited not only the battlefields, as it has for us, but the very hearth and home of our ancestors. But I must let my uncle tell his story. I present Mister Alexander Latimer."

Alexander Latimer rose from his chair and stepped behind the podium. He was tall and straight, his hair only slightly sprinkled with white, with a vigorous demeanor which would have belied his sixty years had it not been for a fulsome snowy beard. He did not indulge in the common practice of beginning his speech with flowery preliminaries. He would give his audience no time to settle into their own revelries.

"My father Joseph was born in Connecticut and remembered well the days of the Revolution. He remembered the Tea Party at Boston and how his family showed their solidarity with the people of Boston by drinking only 'Yankee Tea.' He saw the smoke rising up when Benedict Arnold burned New London and retained for all his life the sad picture of people driven from their homes by the ravages of war, and families weeping for the loss of their young sons in battle."

"And then, after a long and dangerous journey to the great forests of the Cumberland, my father's family found themselves once again in a maelstrom of violence. True, the Latimers had arrived in what was called 'The Territory of the United States South of the River Ohio' at the end of the killing years. For decades before their arrival, the settlers lived in constant fear of horrible death at the hands of the Cherokees, Creeks, and other tribes who were desperately trying to keep control over their ancestral hunting lands. Dozens of children had been carried away or cut to pieces before the eyes of their parents. Women were taken and never seen again. Bodies had been mutilated and scalps ripped from victims of all ages and genders."

"Things were better now. But that did not mean that matters were settled, contrary to what my uncle Eusebius Bushnell the land speculator might have said in his attempt to attract potential customers for tracts of uncleared forest and cane breaks. Bands of brash young braves still marauded here and there among the settlements, seeking to prove their bravery, exact vengeance, and carry away the remaining spoils of a war with the white men already lost. All through the summer of 1793, there were troubling incidents. As fall approached a band of Indians killed the entire large family of a poor widow named Baker, save only two. Then a settler named Robert Willis came home from a necessary journey to find his wife and two little children slaughtered in their own home. Something had to be done."

"This is the story my father Joseph told me: 'One day, not long after these atrocities, my brother Nathaniel and I were working in a field not far from our father Colonel Latimer's house. Mr. Snoddy, a lieutenant in the local militia, and our neighbor on Station Camp Creek, rode up to us and shouted from his mount,

'Listen to me boys! A band of marauding Indians has been seen near Croft's Mill, not twelve miles from this very field. And several horses are already missing from your neighbors' barns. Colonel Winchester, who owns the mill, has called on me to muster some men to handle the situation. Duty calls us to retrieve what is lost, and to make those scoundrels pay. Are you willing to help us?'"

Alexander Latimer continued his story: "My father and Nathaniel were more than willing to come along with him—to do their part in eliminating the constant state of terror by those cruel savages skulking about in the nearby forests. This was the way most people thought about the Indians, be it right or wrong. Both young men had grown up hearing stories of battles from their father and older brothers, and they were willing, even eager, to experience such excitement themselves. My father was still a single man, and eager for adventure, but Nathaniel, who was younger, had already married and had a beautiful little boy named William. And his sweet wife Mary was once again with child. My father was worried for Nathaniel's safety and tried to persuade him to stay at home for his family's sake. But he would not."

"'It is not right to leave the hard tasks to others,' he had said. Nathaniel was a tall, handsome man with a demeanor so pleasing that he was universally loved and admired, not only by our family but by everyone who met him."

Alexander paused for a brief moment, and his nephew, sitting near him on the podium, could see that his eyes were glistening, even though the events he was describing had happened years before his birth. Then he continued his story, his audience of young scholars waiting in rapt anticipation.

"There was no time to lose. Joseph and Nathaniel rushed to get their horses, saddled them in haste, and rode away. Nathaniel took time to give his apprehensive companion Mary a quick goodbye kiss, and to assure her that he would come to no harm. She replied with a hesitant wave of her hand, her face pale with anxiety."

"The young men rushed away to the east, leaving behind them a swirl of dust. Others soon joined them. By the time they arrived at the mill below the house of Colonel Winchester the party of volunteers numbered thirty-two men. The Colonel distributed food and other supplies, along with plenty of ammunition for their rifles, and Lieutenant Snoddy ordered the men forward. The Latimer brothers rode alongside their neighbor, young David Scoby, and the Reverend James Gwin, who was both a Methodist preacher and a fervent Indian fighter. He was a great friend of Andrew Jackson and later served as his chaplain in the Battle of New Orleans. He and my father's brother Witherel served as county court judges together. An interesting man…"

Alexander Latimer paused for a moment, trying to regain his focus. There were so many good stories to tell!

"But I digress…"

"There was time left in the day to ride eighteen miles before dark and to camp for the first night at Dixon's Spring. Joseph and Nathaniel remembered the place well, since they had camped there only three years earlier on the last leg of their journey from New England to the Wilderness. The November night was chilly, and the younger volunteers, many serving for the first time as soldiers, sat near the campfires and talked late into the night, too excited to sleep.

"The next day they headed south, toward the Caney Fork River. On the third day out, they crossed the Collins River at Flat Shoals and shortly arrived along the banks of the Caney Fork. Lieutenant Snoddy ordered them cross the river, then to spread out and look for the Indians, hoping to find their main camp. Joseph, Nathaniel, and their friend David Scoby were within sight of each other, moving systematically through the woods, looking for signs of the Indians. Their commander, Lieutenant Snoddy, was not far away. Suddenly there was a great commotion in the bushes ahead of them. The men put their rifles at the ready, and shouted out a warning to the others, in case they had come upon the enemy."

"From his position, Lieutenant Snoddy could see what the three friends could not. The movement in the bushes was caused, not by the enemy, but by a huge black bear, awakened from his siesta and in a very foul mood."

'Chase him down if you can; he is too dangerous to be skulking about as we try to do our search,' the Lieutenant ordered; 'And try to take him with your tomahawks. A gunshot might alert the enemy and we'll lose our advantage of surprise.'

"This order was perfectly reasonable, but not very practical. As they were chasing the bear through the forest, the great beast turned to face the Latimer brothers and charged Nathaniel at full speed. He had no choice but to fire his rifle and hope for a perfect shot at his target. A miss would prove disastrous. As an expert rifleman and a brave one at that, Nathaniel stood his ground calmly and pulled the trigger. The bullet smashed through the forehead of the bear with a loud 'pop' and the beast, still propelled by his great bulk and speed, ran almost to Nathaniel's feet before dropping his head and rolling forward, crying out in the agony of death."

"Only then, looking up, did Nathaniel and the others notice what was lying before them, just behind the still-shuttering body of the great bear. They had stumbled directly into the Indian camp. Laid out on the ground in a perfectly orderly fashion were twenty-eight Spanish blankets, two match-coats, eight new brass kettles, one firelock, three new swords— fine Spanish blades, a bag of vermilion (which the warriors used to paint their faces and bodies), powder, lead, several bayonets, spears, war hatchets, bridles, and halters. An absolute treasure trove!"

"And standing at the edge of the camp were two young braves, looking at the intruders with a mixture of surprise and panic. The rest of the Indian raiding party, numbering more than sixty men, were a few yards away, just returning from a hunting-and-fishing expedition along the shores of the river. The two Indian guards shouted a frantic warning to their colleagues and then ran for their lives toward the river. There was a great splashing and general clamor as the Indians plunged into the water and swam over to an island across the river, called Rock Island. There they watched in helpless fury as the white men loaded their treasures onto their own horses, laughing at the irony of the situation and shouting insults across the water.

"'Look how much of this stuff they got from the Spaniards,' Reverend Gwin growled. 'When will we finally rid ourselves of those duplicitous Europeans?'"

"Lieutenant Snoddy ordered the men to gather up all the booty and carry it to the high ground nearby, where they could best protect both themselves and their prize. As darkness enveloped their camp, the river, and the island on the other side, they could hear the chief of the Indian raiders addressing his men with great eloquence, fueling their rage and urging them to defend their honor and revenge their humiliation.

"This kind of talk was deeply disturbing to Lieutenant Snoddy and his men, many of whom were inexperienced in this sort of confrontation. He told them that perhaps they should attempt to steal away in the darkness before the Indians made their counterattack. But one of his men, Captain William Reid, who had fought the Indians many times, urged him instead to stay put, bed down for the night—but with plenty of guards watching on all sides, and every man sleeping—or trying to sleep—with his loaded rifle by his side.

'They will not attack in the dark,' Reid said. 'But they are certain to make their move when the dawn comes, and we want to show them our fronts and not our backs when they attack! I say we hold this high ground and make them fight us here.'

"'Of course you are right, Captain,'" Snoddy replied. "Men, let's do as he suggests."

"Learn this lesson, young people," Alexander said, setting aside his narrative to import a bit of wise counsel, as was the custom of the day. "Great leaders are confident enough of themselves that they are willing to take the advice of others and not always insist on their own way. This is not a sign of weakness, but of strength and wisdom."

And after a pause for this counsel to register with his audience, he continued.

"The Lieutenant ordered his men to form a sort of square, with the horses inside where they could not be taken without a fight. And inside the circle of horses, he put the plunder. He picked the poorest horse they had, hobbled her and put a bell around her neck. Then he put the horse out in open ground, several yards from the camp, hoping to use her as bait to draw the braves close enough to fire at them.

"Dusk turned into deep darkness, a darkness one only finds in the forests of the wilderness. There were no more speeches over on Rock Island. Instead, there were the screams of mountain lions, the barking of foxes, and the twittering of the night birds. Those who had experienced Indian warfare knew well what they were hearing—signals sent from brave to brave as they prepared their attack. Unfortunately, one of the white men's horses neighed and gave away their position among the trees on the ridge. They listened tensely to the warriors' signals, the hooting of owls, the howling of wolves, as the Indians crossed the river and slowly closed in on the camp. But then all fell silent. The men dozed, half-awake and half-asleep, fitful in the presence of danger.

"The first rays of sunrise appeared, piercing the still, semi-darkness. The animal sounds had stopped. The forest was silent. Lieutenant Snoddy began to think that the braves had stolen away in the night. He started to give the order to move out. Once again, William Reid spoke up.

'They are still here, sir, I assure you. There will be a fight. We best prepare for it and stand our ground.'

"And once again his sound advice prevailed."

"As the morning light intensified it was clear that the Indians were not only still there, but that they had formed battle lines before the settlers' camp and were preparing to mount an attack. The white men, outnumbered two to one, quickly formed their own lines and prepared to fight. Nathaniel and Joseph, along with their friend David Scoby, took their places to the right of William Reid, emboldened by his calm and assured demeanor. Everyone selected a tree and stood behind it for protection. Scoby was on the right, Nathaniel on the left, and Joseph between them. Reid moved a few yards ahead, no longer protected in this way, in order to see what the enemy warriors were doing. A single shot rang out, and Reid yelled out in pain."

'I'm hit!' he cried. The blood was streaming from his right arm, where the bullet had traveled for several inches before exiting. The arm now dangled to his side, useless.

"The Indians got into position and began to shoot. Then everyone began to fire. The air was suddenly full of the smell of smoke and powder.

The bullets flew from one line to the other. Snoddy turned in time to see four of his men in panic, running away from the battle as fast as their legs would carry them. He shouted curses at them—to no avail. But all the rest stood firm. Men on both sides began to cry out in pain and some to fall to the ground.

"Snoddy later reported that 'the whites were as brave a body of men as could have been collected anywhere.' They made their bullets count. The Indians wanted hand to hand combat, but they were afraid to run directly into the gunfire, so the battle continued from tree to tree.

"As I have said, Nathaniel Latimer, his brother Joseph, and their friend David Scoby had each found a massive old oak tree to protect them from the incoming fire, allowing them time to load and reload and step into the open for only three or four seconds each time they fired. All their attention was straight ahead, where the braves were running forward, from tree to tree, hoping to overrun and massacre the whites. Gazing intently into the forest ahead, not one of the three noticed the two fig-ures creeping toward their left flank—bent so low they seemed almost on all fours. Both had rifles at the ready, and in the din of the battle seemed to make no sound at all. Now they were crouched in the underbrush, parallel to Scoby and the Latimers, who without knowing it, were now totally exposed. One of the braves nodded a signal to the other, and both suddenly rose to their feet, screaming like angry panthers, and the first of them fired.

"There would be only two bullets. The first one struck poor Scoby in the side of his head, just above his ear. His body was blown by the force of the shot to his left, and sprawled headlong into the grass of the forest floor. He gasped only once and was dead. Nathaniel had time only to turn slightly toward the right and to see the flash of fire from the end of the second brave's rifle barrel. The bullet found his heart as accurately as if it were the center circle of a practice target. Fired at such short range, it passed entirely through his body and struck Joseph as well, though its lethal power and speed had already been spent. Joseph did not fall, but he could not yet rush to his brother's aid because the bullets were still flying.

"The battle lasted several minutes longer until the sun was fully in view. There was time for three rounds of firing on either side. Finally, the Indi-ans retreated and the firing stopped. Now there was little left to do but for the Indians to gather up their dead and wounded and for the white men to do the same. Joseph, shaking with grief and the strains of the battle, could finally kneel by his brother's side, hoping against hope. But the bullet had found its mark. Nathaniel lay silently in a pool of blood. There was no hope.

"Only then did Joseph notice that his own coat had a bullet hole in it and realized that it was the same bullet that had killed his brother. Such are the vagaries of fortune. For some, an inch to the right or left means life; for others, it means the end. Joseph and his friends gathered up the bodies of Nathaniel and Scoby, along with the body of one Indian left on the ground by his fellow-braves. They crossed the river and buried all three on a point there, facing the battle site."

Alexander Latimer's voice broke and, unwilling to be seen weeping in public, he bowed and turned from the podium, unable to gather the events of the story into a series of further moral lessons, as he had planned. There was a moment of respectful silence, and then the students and faculty politely applauded and murmured their approval—sincerely touched by what they had heard.

Joseph's Terrible Task

Station Camp Creek
November 11, 1793

The Cherry Hill scholars may not have heard the rest of the story, but the Latimers all knew it well. It goes without saying that in the best of worlds no parent should lose a child. It is an event against the very nature of things. It shakes one's confidence in the basic rhythms of life. But it was nevertheless a reality in the lives of almost everyone Lucretia and Jonathan knew or had ever known. The dark angel had already visited them four times—once for a baby, once for a small boy, once for a strapping young man just ready to be on his own, all in New England, and once for their beloved daughter Borodell, here in the forest.

But no death in this close-knit family pierced to their hearts like Nathaniel's. He was only twenty-five years old, the youngest surviving child of Jonathan and Lucretia—tall and handsome, full of life and promise. He and Mary had spoken their vows back in Connecticut when the idea of a journey into the wilderness was already taking form. The young wife had known what lay ahead. At least she thought she knew. She was pregnant on the thousand mile journey. Little William had been born within weeks after the Latimers had arrived in the Cumberland. The journey was hard but full of hope and promise.

Now it was November. Fall in the Cumberland was being transformed into winter. It would be their third winter in the wilderness. It had been more than a year since the big battle with the Indians at Buchanan's Station. Mary was pregnant again.

From inside the house, she could see the horse and rider bursting into the Latimer compound on Station Camp Creek. The horse was glistening with sweat and panting in exhaustion. The rider waved his arms, calling the men from their nearby tasks—including the old Colonel. The rider was Joseph, next to Nathaniel as the youngest of the Colonel's surviving children, and not yet married.

He was alone.

Mary's blood ran cold. Even inside the house, she could hear him shouting to his father and his brothers:

"Nat is dead."

Joseph Latimer dismounted and walked slowly and reluctantly to the house. When he started to speak Mary put a finger to her lips and quietly shushed him. "I heard you," she said. Her eyes were full of tears. The other women had already gathered around her and were sobbing with the kind of open grief that woman allowed themselves on the frontier.

The horrors were not finished, though the Latimer women and the old Colonel himself thankfully never learned the rest of the story. Joseph's task as the bearer of ill tidings seemed horrible enough to him, and so he tried to say as little as possible beyond what would have been obvious in any case. Sometime later some settlers in the area came to see the place where the fight had taken place. They found that the Indians had returned after the battle. They had dug up Nathaniel's body...and scalped it.

The Colonel coped with Nathaniel's death in his own way. He was acquainted with grief, and he was acquainted with war. He had seen the sons of many mothers and fathers fall in battle. He had learned to steel himself in such cases and divert his grief into what he felt were more constructive paths. He would see to it that Nathaniel's children, born and unborn, were well cared for. He would give Mary the assurance of that. That was really all he could do. What had happened had happened. It could not be changed.

He sat down and wrote a letter back to New London—a letter which would, of course, take weeks or even months to journey to the family home in the woods at Chesterfield. It arrived in mid-January of 1794. It was addressed to his sons George and Jonathan, Jr. who had been left behind to operate the mills on Latimer Brook. The letter was written in a matter-of-fact sort of way—like the report of a field officer to his commander. It recounted the details of the battle and reported on the casualties. The sons passed it along to the local newspaper, *The Connecticut Gazette*, and from there it was reprinted in all the cities of the east—the

Columbian Gazetteer in New York, the *Hartford Gazette*, the *Boston Gazette*, Philadelphia…

After all, the Colonel was well-known in all those places. Many men who had served under him during the Revolution, and remembered him fondly, would want to know what had happened. They would want to say a prayer for the Colonel and his family, far away in the wilderness.

Two days after the article appeared in *The Connecticut Gazette*, Mary Latimer was delivered of a baby boy.

She named him Nathaniel.

Peter Looney was called on for the somber duty of administering the estate of young David Scoby and of seeing to the needs of that young man's grief-stricken young widow Ester. Though not a man of subtle ideas or emotions, he could not help but think of his twilight discussion with Colonel Jonathan about the Indians—and what should be done about them. It is one thing to speak with boldness about war and retribution in the abstract. It is quite another to settle the estate of a young soldier and to try to dry the eyes of his teenage widow.

Captain Murray

The next several months after the tragedy brought no relief from the anxiety. Grief piled upon grief for the inhabitants of the Cumberland. In the larger scheme of things the action at Caney Fork was something of a victory for the settlers, but it was hard for the Latimers to regard it that way. And the kind of pain that had fallen upon them continued to strike their neighbors as well; almost daily there was more bad news.

The only distraction from the gloom was the rapidly spreading rumor that the young lawyer who had made such a name for himself in Nashville, Andrew Jackson, had been seen at the courthouse in that town, getting a marriage license for himself and his sweetheart Rachel Donelson Robards. Robert Hays, Rachel's brother-in-law, whose barn had been the place Eusebius had stored the things he sold to Griswold during his hurried departure from Nashville, signed as security for the license. The town was a-twitter, and the whole affair was the object of excited whispers all the way from Nashville to Sumner County. Some people said the couple had already secretly married during a clandestine trip down to Natchez. Some said that Rachel was still legally married to her first husband, who was a wife-beater, and that she was committing bigamy. But an angry Andrew Jackson was not someone to be trifled with, and it seemed best to ask no questions, let the matter lie, smile, congratulate, and move on.

Anyway, given the course of events, there was little time for gossip.

The new year (1794) had hardly begun before word began to spread that once again small parties of Indians were spreading out systematically throughout the area, intent on taking scalps and plunder and lighting the fires of terror among the people there. In such small groups, they could move swiftly and with almost no danger of being discovered until it was far too late to put up a defense. The action began in February, on the plantation of General Robertson himself, where a young fellow employed by the General's son, and working near his house, was chased down, murdered, and scalped. It was as if the marauders were saying, "even your mighty men cannot stop us." During the next few weeks, the small bands moved from path to path, plantation to plantation, carrying with them death and destruction; murdering, burning, and stealing horses in such numbers that almost all these creatures in the area simply had disappeared. Not content to kill their victims, they often dismembered them as well, piling horror upon horror.

James Robertson was consumed by his rage. "You know well enough that I have many friends among the Indians. These are respectable men; I treat them with respect, and they do the same toward me. But the savages who are doing these things must be made to pay," he told his family and friends. "They must learn that they cannot come up here to the Cumberland, steal and pillage, and then return to their safe havens in the south and enjoy the fruits of their thievery and murder. And I know just the man to teach them that lesson—Tom Murray."

Hannah Bushnell Murray's husband had made an excellent reputation for himself, even before their marriage, as a scout and Indian fighter of great courage and craftiness. Recently he had been appointed a captain of the local militia, charged with protecting the settlers from Indian attacks. His company received its pay directly on the orders of the Governor, Willie Blount. He and Hannah had been married almost three years now, and he had become a respected member the Latimer clan. Just as Griswold had treated Hannah as his own daughter when she was left in his charge, so had Tom come to be regarded as a valued son-in-law. When Thomas secured the title to the 640-acre plot on the north side of the Cumberland River left to him by his father, it was Griswold and Joseph Latimer who signed the deed as his witnesses.

Thomas had been appointed a Captain in the militia for Davidson County soon after his marriage to Hannah and quickly enhanced his good reputation as an Indian scout and leader of men. At the same time he had been honing his skills as a cabinet-maker and joiner. This profession became much needed in the Cumberland as some of the early settlers were now ready to have something better than the rude furniture they had built themselves. As was the custom, Tom would find apprentices to work with him, boys without family or prospects who would live with their employer and his family almost like adopted sons.

In doing this, he also solved a family problem—what to do with Hannah's younger brother Ezra. Barely fifteen years old, Ezra would soon be on his own, despite the kindnesses his uncle Griswold had shown him. Although his father was still living, Ezra was legally considered to be an orphan, and something must be done for him. Thomas stepped in and agreed to make him an apprentice. In this way, Ezra could work for Thomas, learn a trade, receive food, clothing, and lodging, and prepare to fend for himself in the larger world.

And so it was that Ezra was working beside his mentor one day, holding a walnut board tight against a workbench as Tom skillfully smoothed it with his hand plane. It was a cold January morning, early enough that the crystalline frost still blanketed the ground outside. There was no fireplace inside the workshop, so it was cold there, too. A single horseman rode up close to the large double doors and shouted,

"Anybody inside?"

"We are here," Tom replied, "Ezra and I are here."

The horseman was a young man about Ezra's age, a slave of James Robertson. He was well known and well-liked by both Thomas and Ezra. As he tied his horse to a nearby tree, Ezra opened the doors for him.

"What brings you out on such a cold morning?" Thomas Murray said, though in fact he already knew the answer to this question.

"Massa Gen'l Jim says to tell you he has orders for you, and to come quick, and to be ready for some time away from home."

Tom already knew what the orders would be.

"You boys get yourselves some hot coffee while I get ready," he said, gathering up his tools and putting them in their places on the wall. He would leave some work for Ezra, but he was well aware that he might not be back to his own work for days or even weeks.

Hannah had seen the boy ride up to the workshop, and she also knew what was about to happen. When Tom entered their cabin, she smiled, then put a finger to her lips and made a shushing sound. "No need to explain," she said. "Go—and please be safe."

Capt. Thomas Murray kissed his young wife, gathered together his gear, his rifle, his heavy coat, his hat, some coffee and a pocket full of hard biscuits. He saddled his favorite horse, which has somehow been overlooked by the marauding Indian raiders and headed for General Robertson's place.

Hannah was left alone, the smile on her face frozen into place. She was too distracted to bring it into line with the sadness and apprehension in her heart. Thomas was setting out in the same way, and for the same purpose, as had her beloved cousin Nathaniel. She said a quiet prayer that, unlike Nathaniel, Thomas would return.

Signs in the Heavens

When they heard that Tom Murray had been sent off after the marauders, the Latimers became concerned about Hannah's welfare. Despite the dangers, they decided that some of them should travel the few miles from their Sumner County compounds over to Nashville to be sure she and her young family were safe and sound. It would not do for anyone in the family to travel alone. To be alone on even the most traveled roads these days was to invite disaster and maybe even violent death. Griswold and Charles, along with some neighbors who had business in the town, set out for Witherel's place across the Ridge as rapidly as possible, rifles at their sides. They would stop there and ask him to join them on their mission.

They arrived at Witherel and Margaret's place at dusk. After Margaret had fed them and they had fed their mounts, they bedded down for a night's rest. Before they slept, Witherel's sons Daniel and Jimmie began to beg their father to take them along to Nashville. With only a moment's hesitation, he agreed to let them do so.

Margaret, who had come to love the two as though they were her own, was worried but resigned to the situation. Though only ten and twelve years old, they were after all already approaching the age when boys were expected to become men in the Cumberland.

"There is no way to protect them from danger," Witherel told her. "There is no more danger on the road, provided you have comrades with you, than there is in our home every day. This, for the moment, is our life. They will learn from us by seeing how we travel under such circumstances. And they can be of more help to us on our way than you might think."

"You are right, of course," she had said with a sigh.

Early the next morning, the men in the group gathered for coffee and breakfast, checked their rifles and ammunition once again, and rode away.

The journey was uneventful. Even if Indian raiders had been lurking along the road (and they probably were), the sight of several well-armed men, who looked as if they were men of experience and knew what to do if attacked, would discourage any attempts on them. They were making good time and were no more than eight miles or so from the village of Nashville when Witherel, who was leading the group, signaled for everyone to stop.

When the sound of the galloping horses was silenced, another sound could be heard, over toward the west. At first, it seemed to be the sound of other horses, hundreds of them, far in the distance. Then it began to sound more like distant thunder, gradually becoming a constant roar.

Witherel gestured off to his right and said, "Look there."

And then, at the distant horizon, still miles away, a dark, moving cloud appeared, stretching from north to south in an unbroken line—as thick as storm clouds, moving up and down in swirling patterns. There was a rushing sound like wind, accompanied by a noise like a million wood-frogs croaking in concert.

The swirling mass moved closer and closer; the sound became louder and louder. Now what had seemed to be one massive cloud, reaching across the whole sky, became millions and millions of pairs of bluish grey wings and dark red breasts the color of homemade wine. The front of the cloud moved up and down, like waves on some mighty sea, some-times almost touching the ground. It was approaching at a speed far faster than any horse could run.

Daniel and Jimmie, who had braced themselves against the threat of Indians, and started the journey with no fear at all, were suddenly terri-fied.

"Only pigeons," Witherel reassured them. "We had them in huge num-bers, even back in Connecticut, though we certainly never saw anything like this. When they land in the forest the trees break down under their weight. But don't worry, boys. They won't hurt us. If they fly directly over us, as it appears they will, we'll shoot a few and roast them for our lunch. The younger ones are very tasty!"

By now the great cloud was very near. The growing shadow beneath it gave warning that when it passed by it was going to block out the sun, and cast a blanket of darkness over the land at the middle of what had been a bright and cloudless day.

"They are coming from over toward White's Creek," said Griswold. "I have heard they nest there by the millions. And now they appear to be on the move."

As the birds flew directly overhead, the land became dark and the sky made a sound like the roar of a massive waterfall.

"Time to gather in our lunch," Charles Latimer said, cheerfully, shout-ing above the din. "And why don't we let the boys shoot?" he added. "They can hardly miss!"

Daniel and Jimmie knew something about guns and how to use them; it was a necessary part of a frontier child's education. But being allowed to fire a rifle was something rather special and was in its own way a sign of growing up. Everyone dismounted, and each of the boys was handed a rifle, loaded and ready to fire.

"Remember," Witherel warned, "the rifle is going to kick you when it fires. Be ready and don't let it knock you off your feet."

"And fire only once, boys," said Griswold. "We don't waste bullets. And, anyway, you will see why only one shot is necessary."

"Where do we aim?" asked Jimmie.

"Anywhere!"

The boys fired at the same time, straight upward, and suddenly passenger pigeons began to fall from the sky as the leaden projectiles made their way up through the seething heavenly host. Almost twenty birds came plummeting down from the sky, all hit by one or the other of the two shots. The travelers gathered them up and put them into their saddlebags.

"We'll take them to Nashville and have Hannah roast them for lunch," Charles said. The cloud of birds was heading east, and the travelers were heading south, but it was still more than two hours before they were finally out of sight. In the meantime, dozens of people from the countryside had gathered along the road and were shooting their rifles into the air. The pigeons were falling like rain. Some of the birds were pushed by others above them so close to the ground that they could simply be knocked out of the air by long poles.

Not everyone enjoyed the spectacle. People could be seen hiding among the trees in abject terror at the sight. There was a self-appointed preacher shouting that people should remember that the Good Book said that on the day of Christ's crucifixion the Sun had disappeared and darkness reigned. "And now we see the same sign once again!" he shouted. There were even some people kneeling and praying in a loud voice; surely this was the end of the world, or at least some kind of sign from Heaven.

The Latimers arrived at Hannah Bushnell Murray's cabin and found her well, if a bit shaken by stories of the avian visitation. Jimmie had been thinking about the prayers he had heard from the frightened citizens along the road.

"Do you think it is a sign, Papa?" he asked Witherel.

Now Witherel was a good Presbyterian and believed strongly in Providence. But he wasn't much on "signs."

"I doubt it, Jimmie," he replied. "The pigeons do this sort of thing from time to time, and they've been doing it for hundreds of years. And besides, the Lord said, 'A wicked and adulterous generation seeketh after a sign…'"

"Maybe it is a sign to the Indians, that they should stay down in Alabama and leave us alone," Jimmie said, apparently unconvinced by his father's appeal to Scripture.

"Let's hope you are right, Jimmie," Hannah said. "And let's hope they get the message."

*

Colonel Latimer decided it was time to begin to put his long-range plans in place. From the very beginning of this exodus into the wilderness, it had been his goal to give each of his children the means to live a good and prosperous life. He knew that meant more than material wealth, but this was an age when the basis for security was Mother Earth Herself. He fully intended to see that all those who were his responsibility would have enough good land to feed themselves and their families and to live with a modicum of comfort in an age when comfort was hard to come by.

The first step would involve his oldest child, Hannah, wife of Daniel Rogers. Daniel was the only male in the party that had come to the wilderness from Connecticut who was not named Latimer. But he was dearly loved and was in his own mind and the minds of all his brothers-in-law a Latimer at heart. He would be treated as a son. The Colonel would transfer to him one hundred and fifty acres of prime land, one of the tracts he had acquired soon after the family's arrival in the Cumberland for a very favorable price. As soon as it was safe, Daniel could build his family their own home on this land, plant crops and run livestock, and hopefully live a prosperous and happy life.

A few days after the new year (1794) began, Jonathan and his son Griswold, who was living with him and Lucretia, along with Daniel and Joseph, set out for the house of Ezekiel Douglass, which was serving as the seat of county government. It was time for the years' first meeting of the County Court of Pleas and Quarter Sessions, where transactions like the one the Colonel was intent upon took place on the frontier. These meetings occurred four times a year, following an ancient custom going back to England itself. These meetings of the Court were not only called to handle all sorts of government matters but also served as a great social occasion for the scattered settlers. Friends and neighbors would be seen there who had not been seen for a long time. News (and both true and groundless gossip) would be eagerly exchanged.

Government was a simple thing on the frontier. Volunteer militia units served as the police force and the army, guarding their own families and property and insuring that criminals (who were scarce) and Native American marauders (who were plentiful) were either prevented from doing mischief or punished for doing it. There were few laws, and they were the province of the far away state legislature, and the even farther away federal government. Not much to do on that count. After all, wasn't that what the Revolution was mostly about? There was a more pressing need for a way to settle disputes, construct and maintain roads, license ferries, mills, and taverns, apportion taxes (the sheriff would collect them), take care of orphans and widows, and settle estates.

These tasks would be undertaken by men called Justices of the Peace. They were selected by the legislature and were the most important and powerful government officials in the settlers' daily experiences. They could decide if someone had done something illegal (like having a child out of wedlock, cheating a neighbor, being a n'er-do-well, or some other thing of the sort), and punish them if necessary. They could also perform weddings. Their four-times-a-year meetings were called the "County Court of Pleas and Quarter Sessions," and it was one of these meetings that the Latimers and Daniel Rogers set out to attend. There one of the three judges, or Justices of the Peace, would sign the necessary documents to transfer ownership of the land from the Colonel to his son-in-law.

The men enjoyed conversations with neighbors while the clerk drew up the necessary document and the Colonel took it immediately to the roughhewn desk where one of the judges, Captain George Winchester, was holding court. The Captain was a favorite of Colonel Latimer, though he was a considerably younger man—the age of the Colonel's own sons. He had been an officer during the Revolution, and the Colonel enjoyed talking about the war with him. Major George was General James Winchester's brother, and a lesser man might have chaffed some about being forced to live in the shadow of such a great sibling. But everyone in the Cumberland knew that Major George had nothing to fear in being compared to the General. Some thought he was actually the better man. Who wouldn't admire such a man—courageous, honest, smart as a fox, kind as a dove?

Despite the line of men waiting outside for the services of the court, the Major insisted on chatting with the Colonel a bit. He admired the Colonel's experience and wisdom and always enjoyed what he had to say.

"What will we do about the Indian marauders?" he asked the Colonel.

"You ask a difficult question," he replied. "I believe the old chiefs are of one mind and the young warriors of another, and I wish there were some way that wise heads would prevail. I think our major problem lies down along the Tennessee River at the Lower Towns, and I suspect there will be trouble as long as there is a safe haven for the trouble-makers there."

"And I agree entirely," Major Winchester said. "In the meantime, I guess we simply keep sleeping with our rifles and hoping for the best. I myself feel no particular danger, but I grieve for those who have suffered great loss and those who sleep in constant fear."

"As do I," replied the Colonel.

"We never know who will be next," the Major said.

"Indeed," replied the Colonel, handing Winchester the paper for the land transfer. The Colonel signed in his usual way at the bottom of the document and Griswold and Joseph signed as witnesses. Major Winchester would add his signature some months later after all the proper protocols had been completed. The Colonel often looked at his copy of this document and more than once commented to Lucretia about the signature, which began with a large "G" and "W" attached to one another like a monogram.

"Reminds me of the way George Washington signed his name," the Colonel would always say.

TEN: PEACE

Do you want to have no fear of authority? Do what is good and you will have praise from the same; for it is a minister of God to you for good. But if you do what is evil, be afraid; for it does not bear the sword for nothing; for it is a minister of God, an avenger who brings wrath on the one who practices evil.

—New Testament, Romans 13:3-4.

He Does Not Bear the Sword in Vain

Sumner County
February, 1794

Several days passed before word came to Sumner County about the results of Tom Murray's expedition, first from a militiaman who lived near Witherel's place, a member of Tom's company, and then from Tom himself, who told Witherel in a chance meeting on the Nashville Road what had happened. He asked him to report to the Colonel and Lucretia.

"I don't think I want to look them in the face and tell them myself," he said, "especially not Mother Lucretia."

"The word is that you had great success," Witherel said. "Why don't you want to talk to mother and father about it?"

"When you hear the story, you will see," Tom said, his eyes fixed on the ground.

"When General Robertson called me in for my orders he was almost beside himself, enraged by the horrible death of John Helen, his young employee. The boy had been chased down and slashed without mercy, 'butchered' is a better word, and then scalped. He didn't die right away. He was carried by his friends into Jonathan Robertson's cabin. He clung to life far into the night, crying out in agony until finally, it was over. The marauders had ridden away with a herd of stolen horses and other plunder, shouting insults and yelping like wolves. As they faded into the forest one of the warriors put young John's bloody scalp on a pole, waved it back and forth, yelling like a coyote that has just killed a rabbit."

"You know as well as any man, and the Colonel will certainly know as well, that an officer takes his orders and carries them out. He uses his own judgment only as far as he is ordered to use it. In this case, the General was very explicit, and the orders were different from any I had ever received before."

"How so?" Witherel asked.

"'Enough is enough,' the General told me. His face was red and his lips were drawn tight. 'You will not go off after this band to merely fight with them and fire a few shots back and forth before they disappear again into the forest. We must teach those other sons of Satan, who lurk around the edges of our fields, waiting to rob and kill us, what the penalty for their behavior will be. Your task is not simply to reclaim our horses and goods or even to defend our fields. Your task is to kill them.'"

"'All of them?' I asked, not quite able to absorb what I had been told. 'Even the women?'"

"'All of them,' he replied. His face grotesquely distorted and his teeth were clenched."

"The General was a different man from the one we have always known. He and the Indians have always gotten along pretty well and seemed to respect each other. But when this particular murder was committed so near the home of his son Jonathan, it must have raised the terrible memory of the death of his two sons Randall and Peyton, only five or six years ago. You know the story well. Their poor mother was forced to watch the two boys die in agony and see them mercilessly scalped, within sight of their home, almost at their doorstep. It is not something easy to forget, let alone forgive."

"This band of terrorists was relatively small, only eleven warriors and five women. Despite their ferocity, they were relative amateurs in the murderous profession they had chosen. I say this because they seemed to have been so pleased with themselves that they forgot even the most rudimentary rules of escape into the forests. They left a trail which our scouts could read like a book—smoldering campfires, signs of herds of stolen horses, remains of meals scattered on the ground. And they spent most of their evenings in noisy singing and dancing around the fire, raising up the scalp of John Helen and mocking it."

"Of course they had several days' head start on us, but once we determined their trail, it would be just a matter of time before we caught up with them. They seemed to be headed for the safety of the big Cherokee towns along the Tennessee River down at Muscles Shoals. Knowing their destination made our pursuit even easier. About twenty men had volunteered to go with me. They were riflemen with experience and cool heads. But when I passed along the orders, their reaction startled me. I thought they would balk at such orders. They did not seem troubled at all, most of them. Maybe a little eager, if anything. Almost all of them had some personal reason to hate the people they were pursuing, and this was worrisome to me from the beginning. Hate sometimes muddles an otherwise cool head."

"We crossed the Duck River and headed south, gradually gaining on our prey, though we had to ride almost a hundred and twenty miles before we caught up with them. We had given ourselves almost no time for rest, riding day and night as fast as we could, determined not to let the marauders get away from us. I kept a group of four or five of our best scouts out in front of the company to determine the exact trail of the Indians. As I said, this was not difficult. As the scouts approached the mouth of the Elk River, where it empties into the Tennessee, they saw the campfire of the raiders and were able to come close enough to hear them shouting toward the villages on the other side of the river, shooting their rifles, and howling like wild beasts to attract the villagers' attention. What folly!"

"Thinking they had made a clean escape, the Indians had made one mistake after another. Their trail obvious, their presence betrayed by much-undisciplined noise, they had camped at a place where a slope extended out into the river in a sort of half circle. It was obvious to me that we could easily surround this spot from the high ground above in such a way that they would have no choice but to jump into the river to try to escape. There would be no other way. Once in the water, they would be no more difficult to deal with than a flock of floating ducks."

"Jonathan Robertson, the General's son, was with us, and he and I rode up as close as we could to survey the situation, and then finalized our plan. Jonathan, like his father, was a man driven by anger and a desire for vengeance. John Helen was not simply his employee, but also a friend. And then there had been the appalling death of his own brothers. But I tried to keep thinking of this as a military action like any other. By now it was getting dark; we would have to wait for the morning to attack."

"When the sun began to rise I ordered our scouts, who were also our best riflemen, to take up positions on all sides of the camp. The Indians were beginning to stir in the morning light. They were totally unaware that we were there. 'Let's get this over with,' I said to myself, and ordered the scouts to fire at the figures moving to and fro in gathering light of the sunrise."

"Bullets poured down on the camp from above, but despite their usual skill, the riflemen brought down only one warrior, who gave out a choking half-cry and fell dead. At least they thought they had made only one kill. Later we discovered that the first volley had also killed three of the women, still asleep. As a soldier and a human being, I tell you this with shame. Then the scouts rushed forward, brandishing tomahawks and knives, ready to finish their deadly work. I ordered the rest of the men to rush in from either side. The Indians saw that there was only one way of escape and, just as I had intended, they ran toward the water."

"Now came the chaos that always comes with hand-to-hand fighting. One of my men shot another brave as he was rushing toward the water. Two of them gone. Then four of them tried to take the offensive. They began to chase another of my men, determined to cut him down. One of my best scouts, Will Pillow, jumped off his horse, grasped one of the warriors by the shoulder, turned him around, and buried a long knife into his chest. Number three. Another warrior managed to mount Pillow's horse and five of us, all still on horseback, went after him. I will say this: He was a brave man. One of my men shot him in the shoulder, but he did not stop. His mount still at a gallop, we were finally able to surround him. Bleeding profusely, his strength failed him and he fell from the horse, but he kept trying to shoot his rifle from the ground. It snapped again and again without actually firing. My man Cox rode up, pointed his rifle downward, and killed him with a single shot. Number four."

"By this time all the remaining marauders had reached the water and were attempting the hide under the rock ledges along the banks. They knew that swimming out into the river itself meant sure death. They also realized they were trapped, but there was always the hope that the white men would show mercy."

"Not this time."

"The militiamen were now fully under the influence of the bloodlust that sometimes captures men in battle. It is something I'm sure both you and the Colonel have seen more than once. They (I will mention no names) simply walked along the bank, watching for a head to appear above water whenever a warrior could hold his breath no longer, and fired point blank. Long streams of blood began to color the river like ribbons. No one was left alive."

"At this point one of my men walked up to me, pushing before him two terrified squaws, young women who were apparently wives of some of the warriors—mere girls, really. They had remained hidden in their blankets throughout the fight."

"'Shall we shoot them?' he asked, almost without any emotion."

"'We will not,' I replied, almost shouting."

"'But those are our orders,' the young militiaman protested."

"'As far as I am concerned, we have not been ordered to become savages ourselves! Have we reached the point where the outrages of others have caused us to lose all sense of humanity? These are innocent, un-armed, terrified young women. How can we shoot them down in cold blood and then claim that we represent human progress and civilization? No! We will not do it!"

"The two young women began to whisper to one another, and I was surprised that the language I heard was not Cherokee, which I can speak and understand in a rudimentary fashion. And when I asked them, in Cherokee, what they were saying, they obviously didn't understand me. It was several days before we got them to admit they were actually Creeks, and that their party had decided to try to masquerade as Cherokees, so that the Cherokees would get the blame for their atrocities."

"I wish this were the end of the story, but it is not. My men began gathering up the plunder which these marauders had stolen from us. One of them opened an abandoned saddlebag. What he pulled out made everyone around him grimace in revulsion."

"It was the bloody scalp of John Helen. Someone reminded his col-leagues how they had had to watch as the scalp had been raised on a pole and paraded around and around the Indians' campfire on more than one night during the chase. Then this young fellow, eyes flashing in raw ha-tred, dragged one of the corpses up from the river bank, unsheathed his own knife, and cut off the dead warrior's scalp."

"Several other militiamen began to do the same with other corpses. Eventually, every dead Indian had been scalped, including the three women, except for the braves whose bodies had already been carried away by the river. These trophies they put all together in a saddle bag to carry with them back to Nashville. I suppose I could have stopped it, but somehow I felt that this was the least destructive way for them to work out their anger. And at least I knew that Indians of every tribe would un-derstand and accept as reasonable what looked to me like pure barbarism."

"When we arrived back in Nashville, the men took the scalps out of the bag where they had been kept, fixed them to poles they had cut from the forest along the way and marched into town with shouts of triumph. And the villagers began to shout as well. And all of this at the very time of day when the children were on their way to school, and could not help but see the bloody spectacle."

"Now do you see why I don't want to tell Mother Lucretia the story?"

"Indeed I do," Witherel replied.

One Too Many

When Witherel had returned from his visit with Hannah Bushnell Murray in Nashville and his encounter with Tom on the road, he had given his parents a greatly censored account of the expedition. But in fact, they had gotten the whole story from others by that time.

Hoping to lighten the situation, he also told them about the great cloud of pigeons.

"Dan and Jimmie thought it might be a divine sign to the Indians to stop the murderous rampages," he said with a sad sort of smile.

Lucretia returned the smile, now even a sadder one. "If that is the case," she sighed, "they have failed to pick up the message."

"If anything," the Colonel added, "matters have gotten worse. The awful vengeance meted out by Tom Murray, and his men may have satisfied our sense of justice, but has done very little to solve the problem, maybe even made it worse. While he was gone, we lost Benjamin Lindsey, Daniel Read, Ezekiel Caruthers, Jacob Evans, Frederick Stull, Jacob Morris, and James Davis, and others, too, I am quite sure. And every day names are being added to the list."

The Colonel was not exaggerating. Throughout the Spring of 1794, the list of atrocities grew. In April the Bledsoes, the Latimers' neighbors who had been so helpful to them when they had first arrived in Sumner County, were the victims of another terrible visitation. The sons of both Anthony Bledsoe and his brother, on their way home from school for a visit, were ambushed, killed and scalped. In July, five miles from Nashville, Isaac Mayfield was standing guard over his son-in-law as he tried to hoe their cornfield. More than a dozen warriors suddenly appeared, and though he tried desperately to fend them off, they left him with eight bullets in his body, an English bayonet through his face, and a body covered with the wounds of two bloody tomahawks, which the warriors left lying nearby. He was the sixth member of his family to die at the hands of the Indians.

*

Eventually, there comes the straw that breaks the camel's back.

Major George Winchester saddled his horse and rode off down the main road from Nashville to Station Camp Creek. It was a fine summer day, hot as nearly every Cumberland Summer day was, but the air was bright and clear as crystal. It was time for the third quarterly meeting of the County Court of Pleas and Quarter Sessions. The Major enjoyed these occasions and his mood was ebullient. The journey was on the main road leading toward Nashville; only seven miles or so on a fine mount. The birds sang, and a slight breeze moved the great trees along the way. The Major was content.

He was quite near the Latimer compound when he began to sense that something was wrong. He had lived in the wilderness long enough to know such things, without any specific evidence yet to back up his rising feeling of unfocused alarm. Was the rustling of the underbrush caused by the soft breezes—or by something else? Was the barely audible sound of snapping twigs no more than evidence of a passing herd of deer, hiding from the dangers of the open road?

Everything happened so quickly. A tall, sturdy figure stepped into the roadway, his rifle fixed on the forehead of Major George Winchester, Justice of the Peace of Sumner County, a pillar of the community. The Major instinctively put his hand up; he was a skilled rifleman himself and knew very well what the trajectory of the bullet would be. The marauder fired. There were no words. The Major did not even groan. His body was flung backward by the force of the blast and fell from the fine horse he was riding onto the roadway. Two more warriors appeared from the brush. As his life was still ebbing away, one began going through all the Major's pockets, at the same time tearing off any articles of clothing that seemed of value. The other, with the skill of a surgeon, made a circular slice around his head and tore off his hair. Then, still without a word, the three men disappeared into the dark woodland, taking with them the Major's fine horse. His corpse lay in a kind of diagonal across the road, mired in blood.

It did not take long for the body to be discovered. After all, this was court day, and there were many people on the road, taking their business to the meeting at Ezekiel Douglass' house, which served as the county seat. The first men to come upon the scene wrapped the Major's body in a blanket to hide the humiliating mutilation from the eyes of the crowd that would be gathering at the Douglass place. They respectfully lay the bundle over a horse's broad back and moved on toward their destination.

Some settlers came upon this scene, learned the details, and rode on ahead. Among them was Witherel Latimer, who was on his way to register his stock brand in the county records: "a crop off of each ear, and a crop off the upper side of each." He had written this description on a scrap of paper to hand to the judges. The crowd that usually gathered on court day was now much larger than usual as the word of what had happened began to spread throughout the neighborhood.

The atmosphere of rage was palpable. This, seemed the murmuring consensus, was one too many. Some other Latimers were now among the multitude, and so was Peter Looney, who was fit to be tied.

"Where are the federal soldiers?" he shouted to anyone who could hear. "Where is this 'United States' that we all risked our lives and fortunes to create? George Winchester fought for his country; is his country fighting for him?" The crowd shouted their approval and began to slam anything they could find against the trees and fences and wagons, creating a sound very much like the beating of Indian war drums.

"But President Washington says we must honor our treaties with the Indians and pacify them to kind words and gentle actions!" someone said, their tone tinged with more than a little sarcasm. "'Defense only!' is what our government is telling us."

Peter Looney lowered his voice, but spoke with his teeth and chin as tight as a well-made whiskey barrel: "No one admires General Washington more than I do," he said. "If he wants to coddle these murderers he is free to do as he likes. But it seems to me it is time for us to solve our own problems in our own way."

The crowd once again shouted their approval. Major George Blackmore then rose and asked for fifty volunteers to leave immediately to hunt for the killers. Witherel and his brothers did not volunteer, but they told the Major that if and when a calm and reasoned decision was made to settle this matter once and for all, they would do what needed to be done. Somehow the mob spirit they were seeing did not seem right to them. When their business was completed, they all went back to the Colonel's place to report to him and ask his advice.

"You were wise not to ride off with that group of angry avengers," he said. "What we need now is careful planning and a clear objective."

"But you agree that something must be done," Griswold said.

The Colonel gave an almost imperceptible nod.

Nickajack and Running Water

Over the next few weeks, community leaders met several times to plan a course of action. The Colonel and his oldest children had a sense of *déjà vu*. The atmosphere reminded them very much of what they had seen in far-away New England, in the days following the events at Lexington and Concord, now almost twenty years ago. Public meetings, shouting, anger, calls for revenge, and finally, calls for volunteers. Over the next several weeks, military units were organized in Sumner and all the surrounding counties, and even northward across the border in Kentucky. General

Robertson, a usually mild-mannered man and a friend of the Indian chiefs, acted on his own, despite orders not to do so. He had finally had his fill. There had been one too many. Almost all the officers had lost friends or family members to the marauders, and they were ready to shed blood. Major George Blackmore, a friend of the Colonel's, would officially organize the volunteers from Sumner.

Most of the Latimers again declined to volunteer. Lucretia was full of anxiety about it, and even the Colonel had his doubts; the whole enterprise seemed likely to become an organized massacre. Nevertheless, it was possible that this expedition would be more than mere vengeance, and would bring an end to the terror. It was that possibility which brought a certain tolerance, even tacit support, from the Colonel and his spouse. Their son-in-law Captain Tom Murray agreed to go once again, and they did not try to dissuade him. As an officer in the militia, charged with protecting the citizens, he had to perform his duty as he felt he was bound to do, however unpleasant the prospect.

All the units came together at Brown's Block House, just two miles to the east of Buchanan's Station, where Witherel had been part of a small group of riflemen who held off hundreds of Indians. The expedition moved out on the morning of September 7, 1794. There were more than five hundred men—almost certainly a force able to crush the enemy. But their mission was not simply to win a battle. It was to cut off what the settlers could only see as an evil vine, one which had so often wrapped its deadly branches around them and their families, strangling the settlements at their very roots.

It was by now common knowledge that the murderous raiding parties were coming from two remote villages along the Tennessee River just at the border between what would become the states of Tennessee and Alabama, not far from what is now called Lookout Mountain and the city of Chattanooga. The renegade Indians were quite sure that these villages, more than a hundred miles from Nashville and deep in the wilderness, were beyond the white man's reach. For more than a decade these towns had been the staging area for the raids into the Cumberland. Here they kept the stockpiles of arms and supplies provided by the Spanish and the French. The towns were populated by the most radical elements of the Creek and Cherokee tribes, mostly young men who were impatient with their chiefs and elders, who unlike them saw the wisdom in the pursuit of peace, and were instead eager for blood, booty, and scalps. Some were motivated by the age-old codes of manhood; some by a sense of injustice. Others were no more than thieves and murderers. Together they formed the self-styled Chickamaugas—the "River of Blood."

Their chief was called "The Breath." "Cut off their Breath," some wag had suggested, "and the whole lot will suffocate." The pun was clever, but this old chief was, in fact, something of a lover of peace, though he had lost control of his young men, who loved violence instead.

The march to the "Lower Towns," as they were often called, took five hard days. On the 12th the expedition reached the river. Rafts were built to carry across supplies. The soldiers mostly swam across the wide river, some on their horses. The units were organized and rode swiftly toward the first town, called Nickajack. The force was divided into two and caught the hapless villagers completely by surprise, along with those in the neighboring town, which the Indians called Running Water. The villagers had no way to escape except to jump into the water. Tom Murray thought of the killing at Elk River and of how history sometimes seems to repeat itself. Hundreds of bullets rained down upon the Chickamauga warriors and their families as they tried to get into canoes and escape down the river. Some succeeded; many did not. The warriors from Running Water rushed in, trying to fight from rock to rock and tree to tree, but were soon crushed. Those who survived scattered into the forested mountains.

The American troops now began a systematic annihilation of the two villages. The homes of the Indians were very much like those of the white men, and the towns themselves looked very much the same as well. Skill would be required to burn the heavy timbers, tightly caulked with mud. The orders were to destroy them completely, so that the two towns would essentially disappear from the earth. First, there was a systematic search of the contents and furnishings. Time and again the militiamen recognized items that had been stolen from friends and relatives, some of whom had been brutally killed. Anger escalated to rage when two fresh scalps were found, along with several older, dried ones. Each time a cabin was engulfed in flames a shout of exaltation went up among the soldiers. The rage was suddenly redirected at the Spanish when one of the buildings was discovered to be full of powder and lead, a newly arrived gift from the Spanish Governor of New Orleans. There were also letters there, making it clear that the recent outrages had been strongly encouraged by both the Spanish and the British governments.

Tom Murray could not help but think about Eusebius Bushnell, his father-in-law, more than likely living in comfort in Spanish territory, maybe even in New Orleans itself. Of course, he said nothing to anyone about these thoughts.

Meanwhile, his men, along with others, began counting the corpses, scattered over a large area along the river. There were seventy, maybe more.

Among them was the old chief called The Breath.

There were many captives as well, who begged piteously for their lives. The Americans, to their credit, Tom thought, spared them all. Had the situation been reversed, he suspected, there would have been no mercy.

By September 17 the men were back home. It had been a bloody business, and it was difficult to be proud of such slaughter. Nevertheless, except for a few isolated incidents, the terrible years of the Indian Wars were over. The application of an iron fist at Nickajack, along with the big victory of the northern tribes by General Wayne at almost the same time, had finally broken the spirit of those Native Americans who still wanted to resist the inevitable. James Robertson lost his rank of General as punishment for ordering the expedition. But, he said, it was a small price to pay—peace had finally come to the Cumberland.

There were still a few acts of violence, but there were also treaties, agreements signed by the older chiefs who had long ago put practical necessity into the place where idealism and pride had earlier found a home. Life would be different now, both for the Indians and for the settlers of the Cumberland.

Peace at Last

Jonathan and Lucretia urged their family not be unrealistic about the benefits of peace. They remembered all too well that six years of war with the British during the Revolution had been followed, not with the glorious fruits of victory, but with the *Anni Horribiles*. True, one no longer went to bed at night uncertain about ever seeing another sunrise. The terror had ended. But their experience had taught them that as hostilities die, terror can be replaced with deprivation, hunger, and the breakdown of order and civility. They remembered the grass in the streets of New London. They remembered the shuttered shops, the bankruptcies, the wagons rolling off to the west to the "Fire Lands" of Ohio, where families ravaged by war would seek to start over.

Yes, they were free; they were at peace. They were also hungry.

Here in the wilderness, the Latimers had once again known the terror. They had been in the Cumberland five years. There had never been a day without peril. They had survived. They had suffered sad loses, but they knew many whose losses were far greater than their own. To have been ungrateful would have been unthinkable.

Now, they knew, would come another time of testing.

"Sometimes we are overtaken by the subtle melodies of peace and security,' Lucretia told her family at a big after-church feast, just before the saying of grace. "These melodies must not be mistaken for childish lullabies. They call us once again to battle—a battle of a very different kind."

"What a remarkable woman!" the Colonel thought to himself, "She can speak like the most eloquent preachers of New England."

There was still a need to stand ready for more violence. Treaties had been made before and broken by both sides. Tom Murray was made the commanding officer of the militia in Davidson County. Witherel joined the militia unit led by his neighbor Zechariah Greene immediately after the destruction of the Lower Towns. The other Latimer men of military age did the same in their own neighborhoods. It still seemed prudent to sleep with one eye open, and a loaded rifle nearby.

And the wilderness was not yet tamed—not by a long shot. It was still blanketed with dense forests of great trees and huge stretches of cane growing so thick that a man, even a man on a horse, could not penetrate them. And the sounds heard in those dark places could be herds of buffalo or deer, or a solitary bear or panther, or, worse, a renegade Indian warrior—perhaps with comrades—filled with hate and a lust for revenge, too proud and too stubborn to accept defeat as had his aging chiefs. The days were filled with back-breaking toil, and a lingering anxiety, and the darkness still came mixed with an undefined sense of foreboding. It would take a while for this unease to finally disappear.

And if the Indians were not the menace they had been before, the forest still formed a formidable barrier to civilized life as the settlers understood it. The mighty trees must be felled, large portions of the dark forest must be cleared; the virgin soil must be plowed for the first time in the history of the earth; crops must be planted and cultivated and harvested. There was no time to rest on one's laurels.

Both Witherel and Griswold were now settled in Sumner County, having left the relative bustle of the town of Nashville behind. Witherel, as we have noted, was now on the "other side" of the Ridge, and next to him the youngest surviving Latimer brother Joseph. Griswold and Polly lived in a cabin quite near the home of the Colonel and Lucretia. This was partly because the two patriarchs were beginning to show the earliest signs of aging and it was time for their children to keep a watchful eye on them. Though it must be said, they were both still vigorous and active, and still adept in all the skills necessary for frontier life.

Besides this new responsibility, Griswold was still conscientiously trying to play the role of father for the children of the absent Eusebius

Bushnell. Eusebius was, for all the Latimers knew, somewhere deep in the territory of the King of Spain. Hannah, his oldest daughter, had married well and now had a family of her own. Clarissa, the other daughter, was near her twenties now and had a beau. Marriage seemed the most practical next step for her. Ezra, the oldest son, had been bound to his sister and brother-in-law as an apprentice and had learned to be a competent carpenter and joiner. He was old enough now to think about going out to seek his own fortune, and he thought about this possibility almost constantly. Matthew, now thirteen, had moved into to the Murray household as well and had come to idolize his older brother.

There were problems with this arrangement. As the actual events of the past began to fade in the minds of the two young men, their father became more and more an almost super-human, heroic character. They remembered the exciting trip up the great Mississippi River to Kaskaskia that they had made with him. They relived that great adventure over and over. They reflected on how handsome and impressive he had been in his fine clothes and his three-cornered hat. How easily he had moved among the diverse citizens of that magical town. How he had greeted passersby in what seemed to be an endless string of foreign tongues, which he always seemed perfectly to understand.

"Don't you wish we could be with him again, down the river in Natchez or…" Ezra would say, stopping when he realized that he didn't know where his father really was, and that they had heard nothing from him in a very long time.

The boys respected Tom Murray, and of course were intrigued by his exploits in the Indian wars. But he was a rather firm taskmaster, and demanded hard work and good behavior—as most fathers did in those days. This was in stark contrast with the misty memory of their real father, who, they thought they remembered, let them do as they pleased, and counted them as equal participants in his heady adventures.

"Someday we will go and find him, won't we Ezra?" Matthew would say.

"Someday we will indeed."

The girls, whose memories of the trials of their poor mother were still unadulterated by the passage of time, felt differently. For them, the past was best forgotten, except for the fleeting memories of a mother who loved and cared for them as they faced the dark wilderness. Their father had been little more than a phantom when he had been present, and now he was gone altogether.

And yet, as many observers have noted, daughters have no other real fathers than their own, and however incompetent or even defective these fathers may be, they sometimes inexplicably become the standard by which all other men are measured. The application of such a standard more often than not results in poor choices as these unfortunate girls simply trade a bad father for a bad husband. Hannah had escaped this fate, but Clarissa would not.

Clarissy Finds a Man

Isham Baird was a good-looking young Irishman who showed up in the Cumberland full of ideas about how to get rich. He had been born in the old country in poverty, but that was something belonging to a very different time and place. Here, in this new land, everything was possible. He was no further behind than Andrew Jackson had been when he started out to find his fortune—and look at him now! Jackson had recently formed a partnership with John Overton, and they were buying and selling huge tracts of land that had once been promised by treaty to the Creeks and Cherokees and making themselves wealthy in the process. He could do something like that, too. He was sure of it.

Isham's similarities to Eusebius Bushnell were obvious to everyone. Lucretia's intuition filled her with alarm from the first day she met the young man. This time Jonathan saw it, too, as did Clarissa's guardian, Griswold.

"You must be very careful, Clarissy," Lucretia had said. (Final "a's" almost always were pronounced "ee" in the increasingly distinctive dialect of the Cumberland.) "I know that Isham is handsome, and his words are music to your ears. But perhaps you should get to know him better, and see what he does, and put that alongside what he says before you make any big decisions."

This was not what Clarissa wanted to hear. In fact, Isham had already asked her to marry him, and she had already accepted, though nobody else knew this yet. Yes, he was very much like her father. And that was fine with her. The Latimers are too careful, too tentative, too righteous—or think they are. It will be good to get away from them—to live a life of excitement and risk.

But she was not quite ready openly to question the words of her almost legendary grandmother; and so she simply replied, "Thank you for your thoughts, Grandma. You know I value them and will take them very seriously."

But in fact, she had already made up her mind and nothing would change it. Isham would be her husband.

Despite his apprehensions, Griswold agreed to the match. "What real choice do we have?" he had asked his mother. He not only co-signed the marriage bond but actually performed the ceremony for the couple. The wedding took place in the Colonel and Lucretia's house and was followed by a great feast, not only for the Latimers, but for a host of neighbors.

The couple left as soon as decorum would allow, riding two on one mount. They waved goodbye without turning around, leaving a trail of autumn dust behind them. They would live near Nashville. Other than a scribbled note to her brothers Ezra and Matthew, delivered from time to time by some traveler, the Latimers would hear little from Clarissy for the next several years. And from her father Eusebius, who was in fact still seeking his fortune with great energy among the Spaniards—they heard nothing at all.

Justice Witherel

Society in the Cumberland was adapting itself to peace, and the Colonel's family, more inclined to peaceful pursuits than some, and better educated than most, was rising to some prominence, particularly Witherel and Griswold. Those two had been the first in the wilderness and had had longer to develop a reputation for leadership. Griswold now served as an officer in the militia, which was now to become less a fighting force and more a guardian of law and order.

As for Witherel, he was coming into the prime of life—physically strong, wise and intelligent, possessed of a demeanor that radiated *gravitas*, religious without being overly judgmental, quiet to the point of reticence, but for those who knew him well, a pillar of stability and right-thinking. His marriage was going very well. Margaret Anderson was a woman of substance. She reminded Witherel and many other people as well, of his mother Lucretia. Her two step-sons Daniel and James, now entering their teens, adored her. And the family would grow. There would soon be two more sons, the fruit of her own body—Charles and Sylvanus.

Colonel Jonathan Latimer was happy to see his sons taking the same sturdy place in their world that he had taken in his when he had been their age. Now moving into his seventies, he was more and more conscious of the natural order of things. It was more pleasing now to sit than to stand, and to stand than to walk. And riding twenty miles on a horse, no matter how fine that horse might be, was more often an ordeal than a pleasure. He was happy to hear rumors at market days, court sessions, and church that the Cumberland would soon be a part of a new state, to be called Tennessee. That would make sixteen states (Vermont and Kentucky had already been added to the original thirteen). On this matter, his was a minority point of view. When it came to the Federal Government, there was still a certain sense of betrayal among the settlers—a lingering opinion that the United States had left them in the lurch when they were being terrorized and murdered by the dozens. And that not so long ago. Davidson County had voted overwhelming against the idea of statehood, and Sumner hadn't even thought the idea worth voting on at all.

Throughout the first year of the peace, Witherel served on juries for numerous trials in the Superior Court and gained a considerable reputation for perception, fairness, and common sense. It was no surprise then that the governor, the famous John Sevier, in anticipation of statehood, which was bound to come whether the locals liked it or not, named Witherel a Justice of the Peace for Sumner County.

"JP's"—as they were called—had considerable power in the emerging frontier. Almost all other expressions of government, except the militia, were distant and for the most part out of sight and mind. It was the JP's who married couples, dealt with the estates of the dead, punished those who violated the standards of the community and cared for the unfortunate. These were the issues of real life—far more relevant than complicated debates about naval matters, treaties, and such like, back in the U.S. capitol at Philadelphia. Leave those matters to President George Washington and Senator John Adams—and to young Andrew Jackson, who was the Cumberland's man in the House of Representatives. "He loves that sort of thing," said the local wags. "And he can have it." And have it he did, energetically building a foundation for his own rise to ultimate power.

Witherel took his place among the JP's of Sumner County, most of whom had been the founders of Cumberland government and society, holders of the crucial offices of leadership in the wilderness. Some of his colleagues, like James Winchester, were already famous. The Colonel had been a long-time JP himself back in New England, and was often able to give Witherel advice. Witherel was so successful in his role that he was asked to serve again and again over the next several years as Tennessee became more and more a part of the United States. When the Court of Pleas and Quarter Sessions, on which he often served as a judge, heard cases, Witherel often found himself making judgments on defendants who were represented by Andy Jackson. It was well known that Andy didn't like to be challenged, but Witherel was not intimidated, and the two men never showed any personal animosity toward each other.

At the same time he was appointed a JP, Witherel was also made a First Lieutenant in the militia of the new state of Tennessee, along with family friend Peter Looney. His younger brother Joseph, who now had his own tract of land next to Witherel on the western slope of the Ridge, became an ensign in the militia as well. Joseph was almost thirty years old now, and had recently finally managed to marry his pretty young neighbor Ann Dobbins. He was a young man of uncommon abilities, and everyone predicted a bright future for him.

Frontier Theology

The religiosity of the Latimers and their circle of associates was something of an exception in the Cumberland, and even something of a curiosity. Structured religious institutions were hardly in evidence, clergy were mostly missing, and hard living, hard drinking, rowdiness and plain orneriness seemed to be the order of the day. The sentiment in this new society, where the past could be forgotten without penalty, tended to take freedom *of* religion to mean mostly freedom *from* religion. As in the days of the biblical book of Judges, every man "did what was right in his own eyes." Of course it has often been noted that though there may be no atheists in the terrors of the field of battle, there are no theologians, either. There had been no more time for theologizing during the Indian troubles than there was for producing great art, or great music. It was difficult to lift one's thoughts much above mere survival.

Such were the circumstances when a visiting preacher arrived among the settlers of Station Camp Creek. One bright day in 1796 the Reverend Barton W. Stone rode his horse up the road from Bledsoe's Creek to the Latimers' neighborhood. For some, this was a joyous reunion. Stone, who would one day become a famous frontier religious reformer, had some beloved former school mates nearby. He, William McGee, and Margaret Anderson Latimer's kinsman John, had studied together in the famous school of Dr. David Caldwell in North Carolina. In this rustic log schoolhouse many theologians, scholars, and mighty preachers had been trained; but also many powerful politicians—governors and senators.

Barton Stone had come to put some of the fear of the Lord into the Cumberland and he needed an associate. John Anderson immediately agreed to travel with him around to the settlements, where they would preach the Word of the Lord behind rough wooden stands under the canopy of majestic trees deep in the great wilderness forest. The little group of local Presbyterians, including the Latimers, who met whenever they could at the place they called Shilo, were delighted with all this.

It was time the Cumberland "got religion."

The preaching tour started at Mansker's Creek, twelve miles from Nashville, and included a stop at the Ridge Church, which met in a log cabin near the homes of Witherel and Joseph. The crowds were large for the most part. But not everyone was thrilled with the situation, and Reverend Stone spared no words in scolding the nay-sayers.

At Mansker's Creek the problem was a dancing teacher, who, Stone felt, was "drawing the attention of the youth away from religion." And so he gave the fellow a verbal thrashing from the pulpit. The next day, when Stone began to preach, the dancing instructor showed up with a group of supporters (Stone called them a "band of ruffians") who stood in a half-circle directly in front of him, brandishing clubs. Stone's response to this intimidation, he later told his friends, was to "drub them without mercy." The crowd decided in favor of the preacher, and the dancers skulked away in defeat.

He had hardly dispensed with this annoyance when another appeared. This time it was an old gentleman named Burns who confronted the preacher after his sermon, introducing himself as "the celebrated Deist of this neighborhood." Deism dismissed what it regarded as the superstitions of Christian theology and the literal interpretation of the Bible, and was much in vogue with such respected Americans as Thomas Jefferson and other leaders of the Revolution.

Now frontiersmen loved to see a good brawl, and it was almost as enjoyable to watch a debate about religion as to watch a fist fight. The crowd gathered round in great anticipation.

Stone: "Sir, what is the character of your God?"

Burns: "I believe that He is infinitely good, just and merciful."

Stone: "And, Mr. Burns, whence did you gain this information?"

Burns: "From the book of Nature. We see traces of goodness everywhere; hence I conclude that God, the great governor of the universe, is infinitely good."

Stone: "Mr. Burns, please turn your eye to the opposite page of your book and see the miseries, and attend to the groans of the millions who are suffering and dying every minute. And look here, at this page in your book. Here is a good citizen, a good father, and yet his life is full of suffering, pain and want. Here is a bad citizen, a bad husband, a bad father, and yet he is free from pain, and wallows in wealth!"

Mr. Burns lips quivered and he wished he had not started this discussion. The crowd waited eagerly for his response. Finally he said, "Oh, just rewards will be given in another world."

Stone: "But, Mr. Burns, your book nowhere teaches this doctrine. You have stolen it from our Bible!"

The crowd applauded, feeling that they had watched a veritable *coup de grâce*.

Mr. Burns dismissed himself, and Barton Stone and John Anderson went on their way to Nashville. In that village they preached at Thomas Craighead's church, confident that it would be their religion that would win the Frontier, and not that of Mr. Burns, Mr. Thomas Jefferson, and men of their ilk. In this judgment they were ultimately correct, of course, but the harvest was not yet quite ripe.

Certains jeunes Français intéressantes

One crisp Tuesday evening in early spring of the year 1797 the Colonel and Lucretia saw a wagon coming up the path which ran alongside Station Camp Creek from the South—the route the family took always to get from their settlement to the main road to Nashville. The driver was a slave, whom the Latimers recognized as belonging to the Douglass family. Members of that family still lived in the big structure that stood where the Nashville Road and the creek intersected, though the house had recently been transformed into an inn to serve travelers along the now-busy road. Such inns had become quite profitable now that there was peace with the Indians and a good wagon road had finally been completed all the way across the new state of Tennessee from Knoxville to Nashville.

The wagon pulled up before the house with its young driver, whom the Latimers knew well and liked very much. He had some education and, had it not been for his color, would have had good prospects in life. He greeted them enthusiastically. His master wanted them to come down to the inn right away, he said. He would take them in the wagon and bring them back again. He urged them to hurry.

"Is something the matter?" the Colonel asked.

"No, sir, but Mr. Douglass needs your help. He was some unusual visitors and he thinks you and Missus Latimer will know how to talk to them. I think they are some sort of Frenchmen. They claim they are the sons of some French duke."

Not usually inclined to act so precipitously, the aging couple was too curious to resist. It was only a little more than a mile from the Latimer settlement to the Douglass place; even old bones can endure a few jolts for such an adventure. The French had intrigued Jonathan and Lucretia from the time of their youth. Jonathan had fought against them in the

French and Indian War, and alongside them during the Revolution. When the unfortunate Acadians had been unloaded at the Port of New London, to eventually find their way to Louisiana, he had served to help with the details of the transfer. Then, of course, there were still plenty of French merchants and adventurers who passed through the Cumberland. These contacts had caused the Colonel to learn a few French phrases, enough to carry on a simple conversation. And Lucretia, of course, had studied French at the feet of her scholarly father, who wanted her to read French classics (though not all of them, by any means—as he made pointedly clear—"wicked as some of them were"!)

"Mr. Douglass thinks you can say something to them in French, and tell them you know George Washington, and make them feel that this neighborhood is something special," the young man shouted above the rattle of the wagon as they made their way to the inn. "I heard them tell him that they found Americans in these parts to be lazy and ignorant—and he thinks you will furnish proof that isn't true."

"Sounds like a big responsibility," Lucretia shouted back, laughing.

A few minutes later the wagon stopped before the big house and Mr. Douglass emerged from the entrance to greet them.

"Before you go in, let me tell you the situation. There are four men in this party. Three of them are definitely French—you can tell by the accent, though they all seem to speak good English. The fourth is sort of a guide for them, a half-breed named Major George Colbert. He's a Chickasaw, so no worries there. The leader calls himself 'Mr. Orleans.' He's no more than twenty-three or four, and the other two are just boys. He told me to keep it quiet, but that I should know he and his brothers claim to be the sons of the Duke of Orleans. He showed me a map with notes on it he says were written for him by President Washington himself. See what you think."

Fig. 12: The Douglass House on Station Camp Creek

The Latimers stepped into the big room at the front of the house, which served as the dining room for the inn's guests. The large fireplace was filled with pots and skillets, as another slave prepared the evening meal. "Mr. Orleans" and his young brothers were seated at the other end of the room, sipping hot coffee. He stood and walked toward the Latimers, bowing graciously to Lucretia and extending his hand to the

Colonel. He was a tall and handsome fellow, physically fit and obviously full of self-confidence.

"Vous parlez français, je crois," he said.

"Seulement un peu," replied the Colonel.

He turned to Lucretia, "Et vous, madame?"

"Le meme," she replied, summoning up the style of feminine modesty such an occasion demanded in those days.

"We will converse in English," he said, with a certain tone of authority and finality, "though I thank you for providing me with a least a taste of my native tongue!"

For the next hour, the young Frenchmen and the elderly Yankee Frontier couple enjoyed a spirited conversation. They discussed the long road from Philadelphia to the Cumberland and listed the stops they had experienced in common along the way: Winchester, the Natural Bridge, Ingle's Ferry, Fort Chiswell, Knoxville, Fort Blount, Major Dickson's fine home. The young Frenchmen described the new towns which had sprung up along the way since the Latimers' journey and the much-improved road.

"I think you will soon find yourselves inundated with hordes of new immigrants," he said.

They discussed slavery. "If you do not find a way to remove it, it will someday destroy you," he warned, turning his head to the side and almost whispering, so that the slaves at the fireplace could not hear him.

"I do not disagree with you," replied the Colonel. "Though my grandfather owned a slave in Connecticut, and though I have lived with the arrangement all my life, I have never been entirely comfortable with it. Something is not right; I know that to be true."

"And I feel the same, perhaps with an even greater sense of sadness and even guilt," Lucretia added. "And yet our own family is divided on the question. Some of our children already own slaves, and some say they will never do so."

"The situation is ominous, then," said Mr. Orleans.

"I hear you think Americans are lazy and ignorant," Lucretia said, smiling to indicate that she was not hostile. She sensed the need to change the subject.

The visitor was nevertheless taken aback. "Madam," he stuttered, "please forgive my inelegant language. Certainly, my present company is an exception to such a statement! I have simply observed that many of your countrymen, particularly on the frontier, seem to work only when they wish to work, and only enough to provide the bare essentials of life. And they seem to be quite disrespectful to those who lead them."

"You mean to their 'betters'?" Lucretia asked, still smiling.

"Madam, you must understand that I supported the revolution in France, even after they guillotined my poor father, and I believe in democracy and human rights."

"And I applaud you, sir," Lucretia replied. "Perhaps what you interpret as laziness is no more than the behavior of human beings, believing themselves to be free and equal to anyone else, simply living out that freedom. And perhaps the simplicity that you interpret as ignorance is simply the choice to value family, friends, and the beautiful world the Creator has given us, without the passion to accumulate trinkets."

"You are married to a woman of wisdom," the visitor said, turning to the Colonel, "and of strong opinions."

There was more genial conversation and exchange of views and then the Latimer's bid the visitor and his young brothers goodbye and safe journey and returned to their simple home.

On the way, the Colonel remarked to his wife, "By the way, I had a chance to look at the map the fellow had with him. There is no doubt about it, the notes written on the map are in the handwriting of George Washington. I would recognize his handwriting anywhere."

"Very interesting," Lucretia replied. "Makes you wonder who he really is."

Thirty-three years after the fireside conversation beside Station Camp Creek, the traveler known as "Mr. Orleans"—aka Louis Philippe, Duke of Orleans, became the King of France.

The Colonel Divides the Land

Change had come to the Cumberland. The terror was, for the most part, a thing of the past. Better roads were being built—so reliable that there was actually an organized United States' postal service which brought news from the outside world at regular sixty-day intervals.

It was time for the next step in the Colonel's carefully crafted strategic plan. He had never faced as complex a logistical problem as the one which faced him now, even on the battlefield. He had always intended, even before he and Lucretia had any children at all, to provide whatever offspring a smiling Providence might give them a good start in life. From time immemorial that meant land—land to live on, land to cultivate, land to establish one's standing in the community. Just as the family—a man, his wife, and as large a brood as possible—was the fabric of society, so was the ownership of land the basis of the economy. Then add to this the strong moral obligation a man felt to give his children, particularly his sons, a solid foundation to build upon.

Jonathan and Lucretia had brought ten sons into the world—a number not particularly unusual for the times in which they lived. He took stock: Two had died before the family had left for the Wilderness. Another had died fighting the Indians in that Wilderness, leaving two young sons to be cared for. Witherel had been given a farm by his father when he married Abigail. This farm he had sold when he came to Nashville along with Griswold. He had plenty of money from this sale to buy property for himself in the Cumberland. By now he was, if not prosperous, at least comfortable. The Colonel felt no more responsibility where Witherel was concerned.

According to the customs of the day, the oldest sons, George and Jonathan Junior, had received the home place in Connecticut, along with the Latimer Mills. They should be able to live out their lives there, also in relative comfort.

Now he must take stock to see if he could provide land enough for the rest of his family. He still must try to secure the future of his younger sons: Charles, Robert, Griswold, and Joseph. And he must add to his list his two young grandsons, left bereft of a father in the Battle of Rock Island. They must be taken care of as well.

He took a small scrap of paper and drew a rough map of the lands he had now accumulated in the rich rolling landscape of Middle Tennessee. He had bought 640 acres from Daniel James when he first arrived in the Cumberland, and received another fifty acres as a grant. He had bought another 150 acres nearby and sold them at a bargain price to his son-in-law Daniel Rogers. One hundred and fifty acres was more than sufficient to support a Cumberland family, now that the land had been cleared and cultivated; the Rogers would be all right. The land he had bought had been mostly forest and cane break when he and his family had arrived, but now there were literally hundreds of acres of pasture and cultivated fields. It was as fine and as verdant and productive as Eusebius Bushnell could ever have described it during his days as a would-be real estate mogul. There was still not enough of it, however, to provide for his numerous offspring.

Add to this the fact that the new roads were sure to cause the price of land to skyrocket—there were already signs of this. If his plan was to succeed, he must find more land, and soon.

At this point, something very fortunate happened. The Colonel was by chance at the courthouse just two or three days after the new year of 1797 had begun and was enjoying some coffee with his old friend William Cage. Cage was just ending his term as the sheriff and was eager to finish a few uncompleted tasks. A fair portion of Sumner County on the west had been removed from its jurisdiction to become part of a new county named Robertson, after Eusebius' old nemesis the Robertson family.

"I have a bit of business over there beyond the Ridge, along the Red River, that is still mine to settle within the next day or two. Otherwise, it falls to my successor. It is something that might be of interest to you," Sheriff Cage said to Colonel Jonathan.

"And what might that be?" the Colonel asked.

"Well, I've heard you say you need to find more land to pass along to your boys, and I'm sympathetic. We all hope to do right by our children," said the Sheriff. "I add to that the fact that you have made great contributions to your country without sufficient rewards, in my opinion. I know some men who own thousands of acres in military grants who were never more than marginal soldiers."

"And as it happens, there's a couple of big tracts over on the Red that are caught up in some litigation and tax issues, and I've been ordered, as the sheriff, to sell them at auction to the highest bidder."

"How big?" asked the Colonel.

"Each one a mile square," was the reply.

"Twelve hundred and eighty acres!" the Colonel thought. "That would certainly solve my problem."

"I've advertised the land as the law demands, and today is the day I can auction them off. So far, no one has shown any interest—which is a big surprise to me. So we'll wait 'til noon, and if no one else shows up to bid by that time, you're welcome to give me a figure. And that will be the price."

Noon came, and no other buyers appeared. Sheriff Cage stood at the door of the courthouse and made his usual formal statements about the property to be sold by the state and asked for bidders. The Colonel was silent for a moment, sure that someone among the few on-lookers would shout some huge insurmountable bid from a distance.

But no one did.

"Do you wish to bid, Colonel Latimer?" the Sheriff asked, still speaking very formally, in his best governmental voice.

"Ten pounds and ten shillings!" the Colonel shouted, just as one would do at an auction with a large crowd and many bidders.

"Sold!" said the Sheriff.

The Sheriff rustled through the stack of papers on the stand in front of him. "Oh!" he said, with surprise. "I see there is another tract of 640 acres in the same judgment. Are you willing to give me the same price for that?"

"Yes, indeed!" said the delighted Colonel.

When he got home, the Colonel tore a scrap of paper off an old letter and added up the Latimer holdings in the Cumberland. They now totaled considerably over 2,000 acres. "This could hardly have happened back in Connecticut," he thought to himself.

In April, when he was certain of firm legal ownership to all this land, he began to sharpen his plan to divide it among his children. Finding a quiet spot in the woods, he sat down on a convenient log. He took the scrap of paper he had used to tabulate his holdings, turned it over, and wrote the following:

1. Charles, Robert, Griswold one fourth each of the original 640 acres.

2. Nathaniel's orphaned children and Hannah a fourth as well.

3. Joseph 300 acres from the land in Robertson County.

The Colonel knew that the land he was giving Joseph was mostly unimproved and not as valuable as that on Station Camp Creek. But of course, Joseph already had land next to Witherel at the edge of the Ridge and had plenty of time to develop this new parcel.

With peace had come so many conveniences that could only have been dreams in the early days of settlement. Merchants were beginning to appear and set up dry goods stores not far from Station Camp Creek where Lucretia and her daughters-in-law could buy things that only a short time before were out of the question. There were not only cups and saucers, knives and forks, plates and tumblers, but even sugar dishes and sauce boats and cream pots, jars for pickling, pudding pans and frying pans. There was brown sugar, and loaf sugar, coffee and tea—and pots for serving them. And wonderful seasonings from faraway places—cinnamon and ginger root, nutmeg, pepper, and peppermint. And a dazzling array of fabrics for making clothing, and exotic trim to enliven the austere wardrobe of the great forest: calico and flannel, linen and muslin—even velvet and cassimere and fine Kerseymere. There were spangles and satins, ribbons and lace. And thimbles and scissors and knitting pins.

Some ready-made clothing was already beginning to appear: silk stockings and handkerchiefs, suspenders and gloves, combs and hats and gloves. And for the men, there were all the hard-to-get items they needed to keep their weapons and their wagons and their houses and barns in good repair: flint and wire and gunpowder and turpentine; hinges and hammers and scythes, files and nails.

There was writing paper and there were pencils and spectacles and even a few medicines like Gauber Salt for stomach problems and Bateman's Drops which, according to the claims on the box, could cure rheumatism, gout, jaundice, gallstones, fevers, and who knows what else. And if Bateman's Drops didn't work, then there was always British Oil— a gooey cure-all made from petroleum. Civilization was making more and more inroads into the Cumberland.

News from New England

A few weeks later the newly instituted mail service brought a letter from Chesterfield that forced an unexpected adjustment to the Colonel's plan. The letter was from Jonathan Junior. It started with two or three pages of news about people the Latimers had known in New London, and a recounting of recent events there. And then, at the last, these lines:

"My dear Elizabeth has passed from this life on August 3, 1797. She was buried near the grave of Witherel's Abigail in the family cemetery. The children and I are brought very low with grief. I cannot stay here. I understand now very well how Witherel felt and what he did. I will do the same. I will bring the children, except for my daughter Clarissa, who will marry a young man who is courting her, and we will come to the Wilderness. We will leave when I can sell the farm and my interest in the mills. It is family, and not geography, which comforts the broken heart. Your faithful son, Jonathan Junior."

The Latimers gathered to grieve and to remember Elizabeth and their life in far-away New England. The Colonel grieved as well but was also preoccupied with performing the task before him. He excused himself and retreated once again to a quiet spot in the woods. There he quietly remembered Elizabeth, conjured up imaginary visions of the grandchildren he had not seen for almost a decade, and revised his plan. Jonathan Junior would get some of the undeveloped land the Colonel had so fortuitously come to own in Robertson County. It would take his son several years to complete the complicated untangling of his own business affairs in New London, so there would be time to work out the details. In the meantime, he would begin to draw up deeds for the sons who were with him now in the Cumberland.

"It is good," he mused, "at this time of life…to begin to tie up the loose ends."

ELEVEN: REVIVAL

Opelousas

La Louisiane
1797

Eusebius Bushnell thought it would be best to settle in Opelousas, at least for a while. It was a place far enough from the traffic up and down the Mississippi, and deep enough into the interior of the Spanish king's domain, to provide a modicum of security. He was well aware that there were still people from the Cumberland looking for him—people who were prepared to make his life very uncomfortable. True, Andre Fagot, in the employ of the Robertsons, after searching for him for a while, gave up the project as a lost cause. But that did not mean that the matter was settled or that he could let down his guard.

Opelousas was growing, thanks to the land grant policies of the Spanish, who would grant forty acres to anyone who owned livestock and at least two slaves. Former French soldiers were pouring in from Alabama and the old country, and French was the language of the streets. There were also lots of white Americans from the United States. Not a few of them, like Eusebius, were there because they felt the need to stay out of reach of the authorities in the States for one reason or another. Business was good. Plantations based on slave labor were rising in the countryside, forming the foundation of a southern culture very different from that of the Cumberland. Seeds were being sown which would one day bear a terrible harvest for the fledgling nation spilling over toward the South onto the Eastern side of the mighty Mississippi.

Life in Opelousas was more than tolerable for Eusebius. He felt relatively safe there. He was very pleased with his new wife, Margaret. She was skillful in womanly tasks, and pretty besides. He had quickly made friends among the Spanish officials. Once things cooled off a bit, he felt confident enough to begin spending much of his time in Natchez again, where significant business connections were more likely to develop. The great Mississippi River was, after all, the major thoroughfare for the vibrant new frontier in the middle of the continent. In Natchez, he resumed his place as a relatively minor government functionary, dealing with estate settlements, property disputes, and other such matters—all the while on constant alert for promising opportunities.

One way or another he was always able to find out what was happening back in the Cumberland. He knew, for example, that his daughters were married and his sons were living with Thomas Murray. Once in a very great while he even got a message through to the boys, who continued to admire him from afar as an intrepid adventurer. He suggested that they not let the Colonel know about his correspondence. He always let them know that when they were ready, and opportunity knocked, he would welcome them back into his world.

In the year 1797, while the Colonel was beginning to distribute his lands to his sons—"tying up the loose ends" as he called it, Ezra, Eusebius' son, finally worked off his indenture obligation to his brother-in-law Thomas Murray. He was twenty years old now, had learned a trade, and was ready to be his own man. More accurately, he was ready to go back to his father. Not long after this a very well-timed letter arrived for him from Eusebius. It had been mailed from Charleston in the State of South Carolina. There was no explanation as to what Eusebius was doing in South Carolina, or whether in fact he was even there at all. But there was a suggestion that Ezra would soon be getting another letter; a letter that would secure his place as a man in his own right. His father, far from abandoning him, the letter hinted, had great plans for his future.

One day, before Ezra had yet had the time to assimilate all this, Thomas Murray came out to the shed where they built furniture together and called him away from his work.

"Ezra, I've heard from several sources that the Nashville lawyers have hit upon a way to get hold of the land your father has kept tied up all these years since he left. Apparently, he had put his holdings in the names of various friends and made it impossible for his creditors like the Robertsons to get hold of it. But somehow old Judge John McNairy, with or without the help of his good friend Andy Jackson, has worked his way through all this and has gotten everything back into your father's name. That might sound good, but from your father's point of view, it isn't. Since it is clear now that it belongs to your father, the sheriff can sell it all to pay off the debt your father owes the Robertsons. And, of course, you know that Judge McNairy's wife is the widow of one of the Robertsons. It's all very convenient. Elijah Robertson, who tried to find your father in Natchez, is no longer among the living, but that doesn't change matters all that much. There will be an auction, but everybody already knows who the buyer will be and the amount of the winning bid. That's the way things work here. I even heard the number. One thousand nine hundred and thirty dollars."

Ezra felt a combination of anger and panic. His father had told him more than once that he had a plan in mind to bring back his family fortune and that he, Ezra, would one day be a wealthy man. This land was apparently the backbone of that dream—and by all appearances, it was slipping out of Bushnell hands. A few days later another letter arrived from his father, directing the young man to take up the cause and represent the family interests. "You can understand why I cannot take up the cause in person," the letter had said.

On February 10, 1797, the Sheriff sold John McNairy and his wife Mary the massive holdings on which Eusebius and his partner Dobbins had gambled everything. Total land in question: almost 10,000 acres, mostly along Stone's River. The price: One thousand, nine hundred and thirty dollars. The money was immediately applied to Eusebius' debts.

Soon afterward another letter arrived, addressed to Ezra. It was from a lawyer's office in Charleston, signed by his father, giving him Eusebius' full power of attorney. There were instructions: "Should events turn against us, as I am afraid they will, you must go before the County Court and plead our case for whatever you can get."

When Ezra showed Thomas Murray the letter his foster father slammed it on the table and pronounced a string of oaths not often heard among the Latimer clan.

"Is there no end to the flood of humiliation your father is willing to pour upon us all?" His voice was at high volume. "And to call on you to tie your own future here to his affairs in this way? Preposterous!"

But Ezra did not see all this as did Thomas Murray, or Griswold, or Witherel. "Blood counts for more than anything else," he told himself. "I will stand with my father. And I'm sure my brother Matthew will do the same."

A few days after John McNairy acquired all that was left of Eusebius' holdings in the Cumberland, he was appointed by George Washington to be the first judge of the United States District Court for the District of Tennessee. Ezra was not intimidated. Even this appointment did not cool his ardor in fighting his father's battles with his powerful adversaries. Several months passed and he petitioned the Sumner County Court to hear his plea on Eusebius' behalf. The meeting was scheduled for April 4, 1798. He was not surprised that his uncle Witherel, who was a member of the Court, did not appear for duty that day. Though he understood why his uncle would not want to be there, he still felt resentment toward him—and all the other Latimers, for that matter. He was surprised, however, to see Thomas Murray at court. Apparently, he had some business to deal with that day and despite the discomfort, had to be there. But there was no conversation between Thomas and Ezra. They only greeted one another—with eyes quickly averted.

Nothing came of the hearing. Ezra felt insulted by the judges, who seemed to want to put the matter aside as quickly as possible and be done with it. By the time the hearing was concluded he was sure that it was time for him to leave the Cumberland behind and go to his father. Matthew, who was now almost sixteen years old, adamantly demanded that he be allowed to go as well. Thomas and Hannah were very uneasy about all this, but there was really little they could do.

Reunion

The two Bushnell boys made their way to Natchez in the same way their father had a few years before—mostly by catching a series of rides on flatboats full of goods being transported from Kentucky toward New Orleans. Their father had somehow gotten word of their journey and was waiting in the lower town along the river when they arrived. There were outwardly only manly handshakes, but deep internal joy at the re-union. As they made their way up the steep incline to the upper town young Matthew asked,

"Will we be living in Natchez?" The place looked pleasingly exotic and much more interesting than monotonous Nashville.

"Actually, I haven't been spending all of my time here for several months," Eusebius replied. "I've been a hundred miles inland, on the other side of the river, at a town called Opelousas. It is the capitol of the province. But you must know that both it and the Natchez District are in the process of transfer from the jurisdiction of Spain to the jurisdiction of the United States. Natchez goes first, and Louisiana won't be far be-hind."

He would wait to tell them about St. Augustine. Let them absorb this much first.

"We will make a quick trip back to Opelousas now," he said, once again assuming that smooth way of speaking for which he was so well known. "Then we will decide what to do next. Decisions must be made quickly; Louisiana will soon be in Thomas Jefferson's pocket. And you boys will have to understand that this changes my own situation more than a little. For reasons you well understand—I am not proud of them, by the way—I am no longer able to stay in either Opelousas or Natchez because of these changes."

Eusebius' words made Ezra's heart sink. Somehow the bravado of his father—the image of a fearless adventurer—which had grown so significantly in the imagination, quickly dissolved in the bright daylight of reality. In its place Ezra—but not so much the younger Matthew—saw a rather desperate and defeated man whose future was now entirely in the hands of others and who was only safe in the lands of the King of Spain. And it now appeared that staying with their father would condemn Ezra and Matthew to a fugitive life as well.

Actually, decisions had already been made—important decisions, which the boys knew nothing of. First, something momentous about which their father had never yet said not a word. As they approached the broad plaza at the top of the incline Eusebius let the shoe drop gently, looking away as he told them.

"You have a new mother," he said, almost under his breath.

And then, quickly, before they could respond, the second shoe: "And we will all move to St. Augustine in East Florida."

And quickly once again, "Now, before we talk any more, you must give me the money from the sale of my lands in Tennessee. Surely there was plenty left over after you paid off the debt to the Robertsons."

"There is no money, Father," Ezra said, stunned that his father thought such a thing was possible. "The land is gone. It was seized and sold. There is nothing to show for it."

Eusebius was deeply disappointed, of course, but not at all surprised. It would have been better had he not already used the promise of this money in St. Augustine as surety for yet another scheme to be based on someone else's cash. But never mind, he would work it out.

Ezra and Matthew found themselves in a strange new world, and their long-held dreams were quickly being swallowed up like a swamp deer in the jaws of a Louisiana alligator. Ezra, especially, was devastated. Nothing was like he had imagined it during all those years in Tom Murray's workshop. When the three arrived in Opelousas and the boys met their new step-mother, Ezra admitted to himself that she was nice enough; in fact, he rather liked her. But after so long wishing to be with his father he now was very angry with him, without being entirely able to say why. There were sharp exchanges and then an awful argument, complete with name-calling and cursing.

"I will not follow you like some guilty felon from one place to another," Ezra finally shouted. "I'll stay right here. I am a grown man, and I will, from now on, take care of myself. Go on to St. Augustine. Matthew. You go with him if you wish. I will not."

Only gradually had Eusebius revealed the real truth. He had left Margaret with her family in Opelousas more than a year ago and had hardly been in Natchez at all. He had instead made his way to St. Augustine, already an old, old city, and had been laying the foundation for yet another new life there, once again protected by the King of Spain. He quickly became a friend of the governor; a displaced Irishman named Enrique White. White was something of a wanderer as well, having left Dublin at the age of twenty-two and made a life for himself in Spain. He had risen quickly in the Spanish bureaucracy and was especially useful to his king when it came to dealing with the British and Americans.

Enrique White had been governor of East Florida for only a few months when Eusebius had arrived one hot day at the doorstep of the rather grand mansion on the west end of the city plaza. In this "palace" the Governor both lived and ruled. The two men hit if off immediately and Eusebius regaled the Governor with his various ideas and schemes. Enrique liked what he heard and saw in the enthusiastic American fugitive. He had many plans of his own. He dreamed of a St. Augustine filled with impressive townhouses, and the district around teeming with fine plantations and lovely haciendas. And on the plaza, facing the sea, next to his mansion, he would finish the imposing cathedral begun before his arrival. This symbol of Catholic Spain would be the sparkling centerpiece of the circle of fine buildings around the plaza—the house of the Bishop, the treasury, the hospital, the guardhouse, and the slave market. This bustling market was integral to the city's very identity. There were as many slaves in St. Augustine as there were citizens—a thousand of each.

It was not easy to get land from Governor White, particularly if you were a gringo—even though he was as much a gringo himself as anyone in Florida. But Eusebius broke through the barrier almost immediately.

"Look here, your excellency," he said. "I saw as soon as I arrived in this place that you are a man who wishes to leave a legacy—a fine city with fine buildings to decorate its fine port—people trading and building and making lots of money. That's the sort of thing you'd like to leave in your wake. I can see it plainly."

"And I'm quite sure you have an idea or two to help me on my way to success," the Governor said, his smile a mixture of friendliness and cynicism.

"I do, indeed," replied Eusebius. "When I first walked into the plaza I saw two very interesting things—one there." He pointed to the docks. "And the other there." He pointed to the little creek that ran behind the Governor's House, which the people called Maria Sanchez Creek. Near the water's edge, next to the slave market, cattle were being slaughtered, stripped of their hides, and their caucuses cut into manageable pieces for waiting customers.

"Look there, behind your house and along the creek. What do you see?"

"I see sandy swampland—a useless waste," said the Governor.

"Ah, your Excellency. That is what *you* see. What I see is a fine tannery—erected out there where the people on the plaza won't be offended by the bad smell, and where all those wasted hides can be soaked in Maria Sanchez' plentiful water and turned to a hundred useful purposes!"

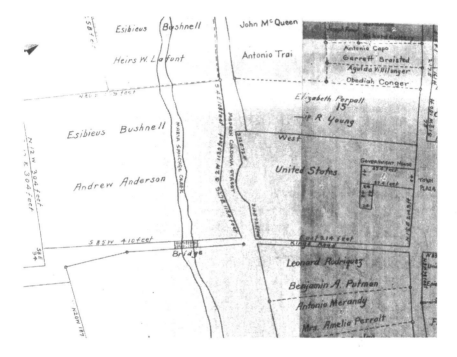

Fig. 13 - An Old Map of St, Augustine shows the site of "Esibieus" Bushnell's Tannery.

"And I suppose you want me to give you the land to build this tannery?" said the Governor.

"It is this sort of instant perception which has made you the mighty man that you are!" Eusebius replied, smiling.

"Oh, and one more thing," Eusebius continued, as though the idea had just occurred to him. "I'm sure the government has a slave or two not otherwise occupied who could well be set to taking off the hair off the hides before the washing and rubbing in the oil afterward. Naturally, I'll buy my own workers—a little later."

The Englishman and the Irishman had a good laugh, and Eusebius became a landowner and businessman in St. Augustine. Within days he had contracted with local builders to construct the tannery—with solemn promises to pay them soon out of funds he expected to arrive from his interests in the Cumberland.

The tannery was all but completed when young Matthew Bushnell and his new step-mother arrived in St. Augustine to begin their new life there. Eusebius had known for some time that the money from the Cumberland was a fantasy, but he kept quiet and work on the tannery continued. He knew he could not pay the workmen and their supervisors, but he would deal with this inconvenience when the time came to do so.

In the meantime, he moved to the next step in his plan. He approached Enrique White once more. This time he asked for six hundred acres of timber in the Twelve Mile Swamp—north of the city.

"And what possible use can you make of this wild terrain?" the Governor asked.

"I need the bark from the trees there to use in my tannery," he replied. "I can hardly be expected to run a proper tannery without a good supply of bark. And, besides, I'll provide the wood from those trees for the townsmen who are building those fine houses you will be so proud of!"

"And I suppose you will need a timber-mill as well?" the Governor said.

"Indeed," Eusebius answered. "But you needn't worry about it. I'll handle that myself."

Governor White, outwardly protesting Eusebius' pestering him, but inwardly delighted with these ambitious plans, signed over the six hundred acres.

As the new century dawned, Eusebius was very pleased with himself. He had a pretty wife, his strong and handsome young son Matthew, and great prospects for a thriving and profitable business. True, there were still financial issues. But had he not always overcome such obstacles before? He would do so again.

Meanwhile, back in the Cumberland, at precisely this same time, the Latimers were once again finding themselves eyewitnesses and participants in a remarkable series of events which were to leave an indelible mark on the culture of the country they had helped to bring to life. Who would have imagined that events of such momentous consequences would come to pass in this great forest which was, after all, "the back of beyond"?

Thomas Hamilton Writes a Letter

McKenzie, Carroll County, Tennessee
April 10, 1869

To Mr. Wellington P. Latimer
Red River County, Texas

Dear Great Nephew:
I am told you are now fourteen years old, and that you are curious about the old days, and that you would like to hear about the great revivals, and how people use to shout and dance at church and fall over like they were dead and lie there for hours—and that sort of thing. Well, I was younger than you when it happened, but believe me, it's as clear in my memory as yesterday. It's not the kind of thing you forget.

I guess you know that I am your great uncle. Your grandmother, may she rest in peace, was my sister Jane. The Hamilton's and the Latimer's had all sorts of connections and do you know why? Because we lived very close to each other on the west side of the Ridge in Sumner County, Tennessee, and because we went to the same church, called the Ridge Church. In those days the chances were you would either marry somebody who lived close or else someone who went to church with you. That was the way things worked.

My father came to Sumner County, Tennessee when the Indians were killing and burning and scalping, so he and a man named Carr built a strong house out of stone out on Drake's Creek near the road to Nashville at a place called Cummings Gap. Then they put a big rock fence around it. It was more like a fort than a house, really, and people called it Hamilton's Station. It's the place where I was born. Neighbors could come there for a safe place when the Indians threatened. Of course, we got to know old Colonel Latimer and the folks that came with him from Connecticut as soon as they arrived. But the two families began to intertwine for certain when the Colonel's son Witherel, who was my father's age and a man highly respected in the neighborhood, moved from Nashville to a place just to the north of us.

Before it was over my sister Polly was married to Mr. Witherel's nephew Lynde, and my other sister Jane, your grandma, was married to his son James Luther, your grandpa, who was called "Jimmie" by most people. And then his niece Aunt Fanny Latimer married my cousin William Henry Hamilton—and so it goes. I don't blame you if you are confused by now!

Now the Latimer's and the Hamilton's were strong Presbyterians, and wherever they went they started a church—even if it was only by gathering up some people and standing out under a big oak to sing and pray. Before too long there were three Presbyterian churches in the neighborhood: one over near what is now the town of Gallatin, called Shilo; one not far from the Latimer farms, called Beech, and one between our place and Mr. Witherel's, called Ridge. And each of these soon had its own log meeting house, built the same way people built their houses at that time.

Now to tell the truth church was not a place most people wanted to be in those days. The sermons, if we had a preacher, were two or three hours long and the preachers were inclined to drone on about strange ideas such as that God had already decided who would go to Heaven and who would go to Hell before any of us was even born. So it was no wonder most people just thought, "Well, then, what's the use?" Then there were still lots of Frenchmen around, and most of them were infidels and proud of it. Some local folks took up with them, like old Mr. Burns who had debated with Reverend Barton Stone. But there wasn't much preaching, actually, and the preachers that did come through were mostly scoundrels, truth be told. "Drunkards, womanizers and heretics"—that's what my father called them. He and Mr. Witherel use to talk about this all the time. But they were both men who felt it was their duty to keep flying the Lord's flag, so to speak, though good times and bad. So the Hamilton's and the Latimer's went on to church, come what may.

About that time the Reverend James McGready showed up. He had come to live in Kentucky, a few miles north of us, just across the line. He was somebody different, as far as preachers were concerned. He was a great big fellow, on the heavy side, with small eyes in his big round face, and a very serious look.

When he got wound up preaching, his voice sounded like the thunder in a summer storm and his eyes got even smaller, and the skin on his face moved around like it was unattached and it was scary, believe you me. He didn't yell, mind you. He was solemn and sometimes he broke down into torrents of tears. And he hated sin, I can tell you that. He gave no quarter to the drinkers and the womanizers and the ne're-do-wells, whether they were preachers or just farmers. He could make a strong man shake in his boots.

Reverend McGready had some good friends in Sumner County. His brother went to church at Shilo where some members of the Anderson family were big leaders; some of them were preachers, too. You are sort of an Anderson yourself, as you probably know. Your father's step-grandmother, Mr. Witherel's wife, was one of that tribe. Then there were the preachers at Shilo and Beech, William Hodge and William McGee. These fellows had all gone to school together, along with the likes of Barton Stone and many others, over at Dr. Caldwell's school in North Carolina. They were pretty well educated; Dr. Caldwell made them learn Latin and Greek, and Theology. But none of them were satisfied with the way religion was working out in the Wilderness. It just didn't seem to take. They started looking for a different way; and, believe me, for better or worse, they found it.

Logan County

Reverend McGready started holding what they called "Sacraments" up in Kentucky. They would start on a Friday night and go all day Saturday—one sermon after another—all out in the forest, with only a temporary shed for the preachers to stand under. Then on Sunday the people would gather around tables and take the communion (wine and bread, I'm sure you know). Then there would be another service on Monday morning and people were supposed to go back home. But when things got going a lot of them stayed on, camping in the woods, for days and days.

Down in Sumner County we soon heard that something was happening up in Logan County; that folks up there were being blessed with the fire of the Holy Spirit. And that lots and lots of sinners were seeing the error of their ways. And that people were being seized by some strange power and falling to the ground like they'd been shot, and lying there sometimes for hours. This was something a man just naturally wanted to look into—see for himself, you know.

The Hamilton's and the Latimer's, and a lot of other Sumner people, thought they ought to go up there to see what was going on. It was only a day's journey from our place, so we all got our wagons together early on a Friday morning and headed for the next Sacrament. Several from the Shilo church came as well— some of them very skeptical of the whole thing. When we arrived we were surprised to see dozens of wagons already there, some from as far as a hundred miles away. It was July and it was hot and steamy. But everybody began to set up camps just like the ones we made when we were taking long journeys in those days. I can't tell you how exciting it was. All the young people talking and circulating. People praying and singing Psalms. Somebody called it a "Camp Meeting" and I guess the phrase stuck because they've called 'em this ever since. We were used to camping, of course, but camping as *church*—well, that was something new.

We finally went to sleep on Friday night and when we woke up on Saturday we could already hear the singing and praying. But it was different from anything I had ever seen before. It was loud and it was coming from first one place and then another. Several preachers were trying to speak at once, all of them having to shout to be heard above the sounds from the crowd. This went on all day Saturday and on Sunday we had the communion. There was something in the air that you could feel, as if a mighty wind was beginning to blow; as if lightning were about to strike.

On Monday we went to the main meeting place, where simple benches had been made out of stumps and rough-cut timber. Reverend McGee, from the Beech Church, was standing at the end of our row and I could see his was getting agitated. His face was glowing red and he was bouncing up and down—hopping, you might say, first on one foot and then the other. I was beginning to feel a little frightened, to tell the truth. Then Mr. McGee started running up and down among the benches crying in a loud voice, "Let the Lord God Omnipotent reign in your hearts!" That was when the meeting broke out into clamor and tumult.

And that was the first time I saw someone get "slain in the spirit." It was a big man from the Shilo Church, strong as an ox and usually as quiet as a mouse. He was standing right in front of me. All of a sudden his body stiffened and he let out a mighty shout. Then he dropped to his knees and fell forward onto the ground. At first he tossed and turned like a person wracked with terrible pain; then he got so quiet you couldn't see him breathing and laid as still as death. In fact, I thought he was dead. But then he would begin to shake and jerk again and cry out for the Lord to save him.

Then other people began to fall down, too. Lots of them. There was howling and screaming. My own mother started to shout and cry "Lord have mercy—I am lost!" at the top of her lungs and that really upset me. All over the forest floor people were shouting that they knew they were lost and going to Hell and pleading for the Lord to speak peace to their souls.

Mr. Witherel and one of the King brothers from Shilo went over to Reverend McGee and asked him to try to calm things down, and wondered whether things hadn't gotten out of hand and if all this didn't look a lot more like something Methodists might do—but not Presbyterians. But he just told them that the hand of the Lord was upon him and he couldn't resist the Spirit and went on shouting and preaching.

Every so often one of the people lying on the ground would rise up, laughing and praising God, and begin to shout that the Lord had delivered them and given them heavenly bliss such as they never could have imagined. Then Mr. King from Shilo—his name was Richard, the very one who had tried to get Reverend McGee to stop what he was doing, fell to his knees and began to cry for the Lord's mercy as well. And I began to feel something creeping up my back running back and forth along my arms and legs and I was sure I was going down as well—but I didn't, at least that time. But several other people from Shilo and our church at Ridge did. Mr. Witherel was known as a very religious man, but I didn't see him go down. He looked solemn enough, and his lips were moving like he was whispering a prayer, but that was all.

Fire on the Ridge

The folks from Sumner County came back home from Kentucky like they were about to explode. They were, like someone said, "as fire in dry stubble." You never saw such praying and weeping and shouting in your life. Not just at church, mind you, but out under the trees, and inside in front of people's fireplaces.

Mr. Witherel was torn in two by all this. One of his best friends, from his first days in the Cumberland, was the Reverend Craighead, over in Nashville. And Reverend Craighead didn't take to the revival at all. He called it "experimental religion" and said he wouldn't give his used-up handkerchief for the whole thing. It had no sense to it, he said. It was just a lot of mindless emotion and near hysteria. But then since he had come to Sumner County one of Mr. Witherel's best friends, there had come to be Sam King, the brother of Rich King, and Sam was for the revival one hundred percent. He was not an educated man himself, but, as he said, the Lord didn't need people who could read Latin and Greek. What the Lord needed were men who had been set on fire by the Holy Spirit. Something in Mr. Witherel wanted to agree with both of his friends, so he tried his best to just sit on the fence between them.

In September the elders of the Ridge Church decided they would have their own Sacramental Camp Meeting and see if the hand of the Lord might fall on some of the lying, thieving, drunken rascals in their own community. They knew the log meeting house would not hold the crowds, so they decided to use a clearing in the woods on the property of Robert Shaw, my Aunt Elizabeth's husband. The Shaws lived just west of Mr. Witherel and his brother Joseph, on the headwaters of the Red River.

Before the meeting even started the people were stirred up in a big way. Everyone was talking about what had happened in Kentucky and wondering if it would happen here, too. There were prayer meetings almost every night in the cabins, and several people experienced the mercy of the Lord every day. The elders decided that the Sacrament would be held the second weekend in September, while the fervor was still at a high pitch. They invited Reverend McGready to come down and preach, along with the local ministers from the area—not just the Presbyterians, but the Methodists, too, and even some Baptists.

All day long on Friday wagons full of people arrived on the Shaw place with food and supplies and began to set up camp around the open space where the long benches and the speakers' shed had been constructed. They hobbled their horses in the lush patches of pea vines where the beasts could eat to their hearts' content while their owners called upon the Lord. Of course, we lived so close we didn't have to camp; we just rode our horses over to the meeting.

Still a hundred yards away, the fires of revival were already surrounding us. Dozens of people had already been stricken down and were lying like corpses everywhere. You had to walk carefully to not step on them. Many others were on their knees, crying for mercy. And there were other "exercises" as well. Some, especially among the women, were standing, their bodies perfectly still at first, their heads jerking back and forth and side to side, their long hair, released from the usual braids, snapping like a horsewhip. Then they would bend forward, almost touching the ground with their forehead, the back almost as far. What they were doing seemed to contradict the laws of nature. Some people were rolling on the ground, some of them screaming and mindless of the mud and rocks. Others were doing a sort of dance, stepping forward and then back, first very fast, then very slowly, until they finally collapsed in exhaustion. I saw many people simply laughing uncontrollably, or singing in a strange new kind of tone that made me think of the angelic host.

It was more than I could bear. I begin to have the same feelings I had experienced in Kentucky and the same mixture of dread and yearning. I fought the growing sense that I was going to fall. But at the same time, I *wanted* to fall. I wanted to rise up like I saw others doing—faces glowing like the very stars above, shouting "hallelujah!" My body began to shake from head to toe.

From the corner of my eye, I saw William McGee and Samuel King circulating among those caught up in the "exercises"—urging them to accept the powerful grace of God. Then, suddenly, the world turned blinding white, and I felt myself going down.

But when the world returned to me, I did not feel God's powerful grace at all. Instead, I felt myself the very vilest of sinners, worthy of the deepest pit of Hell. This horrible burden kept its hold on me all day Saturday and even at the communion table on Sunday. I was like a drunkard in his stupor, conscious of nothing but my own wretchedness. Then, sometime on Sunday night, I suddenly found myself able to make a full surrender of my heart to my blessed Savior and at that moment a mighty light burst into my heart. My guilt melted away. I was happy beyond any description of happiness.

I looked around me in the darkness. People had attached hundreds of candles to the trees. It was the most wonderful sight I had ever seen. Everything seemed to glow with a holy light, at one time purest white and yet all the colors of the rainbow—the trees, the forest meadows, the night sky, even the very stones beneath my feet. O how beautiful! I have forgotten many things in my eighty years on this earth, but I will never forget that!

We returned home to a transformed community. Almost every family in every cabin would retire in the evening for prayer, often along with neighbors; and sometimes we would pray far into the night. The Devil found himself pushed way back. The heavy drinking stopped, and the cursing, and men that had beat their wives stopped it, and men that had lain around while their children were hungry started working and providing for them again. It was something wondrous, I can tell you that.

Hope this answers all your questions.

Your loving Great Uncle,
Thomas Hamilton

Good Tree, Good Fruit

Station Camp Creek
Wednesday, September 17, 1800

One week after the remarkable meeting where Thomas Hamilton's found his soul ignited by the great fire which was sweeping across the Cumberland, an even larger gathering occurred. This time the site was a few miles to the east of the Ridge on a branch called Desha's Creek, not far from the farms of the Colonel and his family. The preachers knew that the Spirit's fire must be stoked and fueled and cannot be allowed to subside, lest the ardor cool. The sponsor this time would be the Beech Church, where the Station Camp Creek Latimers were members. The Colonel and Lucretia had not attended the meeting at the Ridge, but Witherel had given them all the details. He was eager to hear what they thought about what was happening, once they had seen it for themselves, though he was pretty sure he knew what their reactions would be.

The crowd that gathered for this event was even larger than the earlier ones, numbering in the thousands. The wagons were in their hundreds, the woods alight with campfires. The scene quickly surpassed all that had happened elsewhere. Even the preachers were awed to the limits of language. John McGee, brother of the Latimers' friend William McGee, spoke of people falling "like corn before a storm of wind." "Many rose from the dust with a divine glory shining in their countenances, and gave glory to God in such strains as made the hearts of stubborn sinners to tremble." They would, he said, "break forth in volleys of exhortation." The Reverend William Hodge said that the meeting on Sunday evening "exhibited the most awful scene I ever beheld. About the center of the camp, they were lying in heaps and scattered all around. The sighs, groans, and prayers seemed to pierce the heavens, while the power of God fell upon almost all present."

But not Witherel, or his wife Margaret, or the seventy-six-year-old Colonel or his pious partner Lucretia. They stood in solemn reverence in the very center of the wild scene, awed into silence—who would not be? —but on their feet to the last.

By the time they returned to the Colonel and Lucretia's home to spend the night it was very, very late. But there could be no sleep until there had been some serious conversation. Joseph and his wife Anne were there, having accompanied Witherel and Margaret across the Ridge for the Sacrament on Desha's Creek. Griswold was there, too, of course, as were Robert and Charles, their wives, and Hannah and Charles Rogers—the whole clan. A roaring fire burned in the great fireplace in the front room of the big house, casting shadows on the walls made of giant hewn logs and dancing around the simple, but nevertheless almost elegant furniture. Those who sat beyond the light of this fire sat in darkness and when they spoke seemed to be voices coming from another world. Not a one of them had been caught up in the "exercises." But it would be incorrect to assume that anyone in the room had been unaffected by what they had witnessed and experienced.

In our time it is hard to imagine a religious movement so persistent and powerful that it can form or transform a whole society. But this was another time, and a new world was rising up in the wilderness, unlike any world before it. At first, there was silence except for the flickering fire. Then the eyes began to turn toward Lucretia.

"Mother?" Witherel said.

Lucretia was one of the very few people who ever lived to have been present at the center of both of the "Great Awakenings" which determined the form which the life of the spirit would take in the new nation. Everyone waited for her answer. She was also quiet at first, summoning up from the mists of memory those astonishing days in old Connecticut Colony, a ten-year-old child without a mother. Watching. Listening. Remembering the mighty preachers named George Whitefield and Gilbert Tennant—and their coming to her father's little parish and lighting a fire so much like the one she had seen burning this very night in the Wilderness.

She remembered watching in curious wonder as her father, usually reserved and cerebral, began to preach like a man possessed by an otherworldly power. She recalled his mighty sermon in Lyme, speaking like a man possessed. Strong young men shouting, their knees buckling like willow limbs, falling to the ground, young women crying hysterically as if carried away in a swirling, black anguish—not so different from what she had seen this very night. She remembered how her father, certain all this was a visitation from God, had exploded into action—lectures, classes, sermons, prayer meetings. All of these, he later reported, were filled with "outcries, faintings, and fits." And, floating like a storm cloud over all this, an unimaginable sense of sin, divine wrath, and coming doom.

She shuddered as the memories flooded back—not just the faces and the events, but the very feelings she had felt, rising again in the Cumberland darkness. But like the flickering firelight, she remembered how the strangling darkness was overcome by the radiant peace of God, at least for those who persevered in their mourning until grace had done its work. The ardor of most such people eventually cooled, and daily life becalmed the howling whirlwind. But even so it left behind a kinder, less combative, more pleasant community than the one before.

Some people later said that once religion had become a matter of individual experience and not something controlled by clergy and the state, it was a very short journey to the conclusion that as with the soul, so with the body. And somehow, before long, not only would the red-coated hosts of the British Monarchy be driven from the land, but the ideas they represented as well. And somehow the diverse peoples of the Colonies would become one Body, one Spirit, driven by one Hope. But these achievements had risen out of a sea of blood, terror, and loss—and Lucretia had seen that maelstrom from its center as well. The Latimers, and many thousands like them, had lived with war and violence now with little interruption for over twenty-five years. Their grandchildren had known no other world. Every new day was a wager with mighty forces totally beyond their control. No one ever left home with full assurance of returning. No one built without a grim realization of lurking fire and pillage.

The revival fires swept through the settlements in the manner of the great physical fires that roared among the ancient trees of the Cumberland from time to time. They were fires of purging, burning away what was old, and rotten, and full of bloody memories. The aching sense of loss was burned away and in its place there came an absolute torrent of grace and an overpowering surge of glorious salvation from the dark past with its once impenetrable overgrowth of horrors. And though they might seem distant and unresponsive to some, the Latimers felt themselves purged of the past as well, in their own, more quiet way.

Lucretia expressed all this in her gentle, articulate manner, giving her family words for the feelings they all shared, focusing the swirling tumble of events. The family listened to her with rapt attention. The Colonel, in contrast, sat quietly on an old three-legged stool, just out of the fire's light, and said nothing. He seemed a little distant, his eyes looking into the dark corners of the room as though searching for something far away. He was still a handsome man, tall and straight, and a full head of almond hair, parted fastidiously in the middle. His mind was sharp, though it was more and more the easier thing to remember the names of young men in his regiment a quarter of a century ago than of his nearest neighbors here in the forest. Especially he remembered those young men who had fallen on the battlefields doing what he had ordered them to do. He thought of how he had lived three lifetimes compared to what had been allotted to most men—in fact, almost four. He thought once again of the arbitrary way in which Death confronts its prey—taking some almost immediately, in the blush of youth, and toying with others for decades. He was well aware of this macabre game. His victory was in fact not so substantial as it might seem to those who observed it from afar. They could not yet see that one by one the Enemy, though failing yet to kill him, was instead depriving him of clarity—clarity of sight, clarity of sound, clarity of thought. And of energy—energy to plow, energy to ride, even energy to worship. He listened to Lucretia and the children for a little while longer, then quietly pushing the three-legged stool back into the total darkness, rose, and quietly slipped away to his bedroom.

The revival fires continued to spread and reached their zenith at a place called Cane Ridge in Kentucky, over two hundred miles to the east and north, a year after the events at Desha's Creek. Prominent among the leaders of this huge gathering of more than fifteen thousand souls was Barton Stone, the old friend and schoolmate of Margaret Latimer's kinsmen at Shilo. But all this seemed far away, and not everything left in the wake of the great camp-meetings was sweetness and light. Everyone agreed that setting drunkards and reprobates on the right track was a good thing, of course. But there was something about the revivals that didn't seem to rest well alongside the old Calvinistic ideas of predestination and total depravity. Some, especially the better educated, and of course the theologians, didn't see how evil people could be brought to goodness by persuasion, and besides, it was better to leave it to God to decide who was lost and who was saved, instead of trying to force matters by getting people all upset, engineering some sort of emotional thunderclap, and then calling it a "visitation of grace".

So, after the fires subsided, there began to be trouble in the churches around the Latimer lands, and pro-revival and anti-revival factions emerged. One day Robert Latimer had the misfortune of being a witness to an altercation between John Whitford and a woman named Francis Catherine that occurred right in the meeting house of the Beech Church. Apparently, they disagreed on the question of the activities of the Holy Ghost. The woman brought Whitford before a judge in Nashville, who happened to be Andrew Jackson, and a very reluctant Robert was called to court as a witness. Margaret Latimer's kinsman John Anderson was a member of the jury. Jackson threw the case out of court (though he did convict Whitford of disturbing the peace). Such theological niceties seemed of little moment to old Andy, but this kind of thing created bad feelings among former friends in the community. The Latimers tried, with increasing difficulty, to take a moderate course and get along with everyone. Witherel, who as his father progressively weakened with age more and more took on the role of patriarch, was particularly torn. His old friend in Nashville, the Reverend Craighead, was staunchly anti-revival; but his close friends in Sumner County like Sam King and William McGee, not to mention his wife Margaret's relatives, were all for it. Ultimately the Latimers came down on the side of the revival—though admittedly leaning toward a rather tamer, rational, and thoughtful form of it.

"It is the better way for the people here," Witherel would say. "We are no longer in old Connecticut, and we should not ever forget that fact."

An Ever-Rolling Stream

It was no longer easy for the Colonel to get to church, especially when the breezes turned cold and the rough paths turned to strips of mud. Riding a horse became an ordeal; it was hard to mount, hard to dismount, every joint seemed to cry out for relief from the jolting gate along the way, and the next day was most often a day of stiffened muscles and labored breath. Finally only when he could ride in a wagon was the trip worth the effort to him. One grey Sabbath, a few weeks after the great camp meeting at Desha's Creek, he gathered himself together, gaining resolve by remembering how many times he had suffered worse discomfort in the wartime camps as a much younger and stronger man.

"Surely I should give the Lord at least what I gave to the Third Connecticut Militia," he thought to himself.

He was happy that the congregation chose to sing an old hymn he had known since childhood on that particular Sunday because it fit his state of mind near perfectly. And the voices of his neighbors sounded particularly beautiful to him. The words were not happy ones, but they were, he thought, profoundly true.

Thy word commands our flesh to dust,
"Return ye sons of men"
All nations rose from earth at first,
And turn to earth again.

Time like an ever-rolling stream,
Bears all its sons away;
They fly, forgotten, as a dream
Dies at the op'ing day.

He did not sing himself, he had never been exactly the singing type, but rather turned his eyes toward the forest and tried to hide his tears by closing them. Why had he never really listened before to what old Isaac Watts was saying? "He must have been an old man himself," he thought.

A few days later the Colonel's son-in-law Daniel Rogers came down with a bad fever. There was nothing to be done for such things but to take to one's bed, be washed in cool water, and hope for the best. The

Colonel and Lucretia's firstborn, Hannah Latimer Rogers, now in her fifties, sat dutifully by her husband's bedside and wiped his hot forehead with cool towels for hours at a time. The fever seemed to break after a few days, and Daniel went back to work in the fields. It was, after all, harvest time. But soon the fiery ordeal returned. This cycle repeated itself every few weeks and each time was worse than the time before. Sometimes Daniel fell into a sort of trance and babbled incoherently. Between these torments, his strength would return and his mind would clear.

"I feel a cold hand upon me," he told the Colonel one day. "I think it is wise to make a will."

A local lawyer wrote out the document, copying most of it from an old book of legal forms he had brought with him into the wilderness.

> In the name of God, Amen. I Daniel Rogers, being of sound
> and perfect mind and memory, blessed be God, do publish this
> last will and testament...

The will followed the custom of the day. Hannah would have one-third of the estate, the rest divided among the children—sons and daughters alike. When the time came to complete the document, Daniel was once again racked with a burning fever—a stark contrast to the cold January air outside the Rogers' cabin. He signed with an "X"—too weak to write his full name. Peter Looney and the Colonel's son Jonathan Junior were the witnesses. Griswold, whom he called his "brother" in the document, would be his executor.

This time the fever persisted. A few days after the will was signed Daniel Rogers fell into a dark and tangled world where he imagined the green Connecticut fields and the lovely river which ran alongside the docks of New London. And then he was gone.

Hannah had a few weeks to mourn and then, one day when Spring seemed ready to return to the Cumberland; she felt the heat begin to pulsate on her own brow. Unlike her husband, Death did not make her wait for very long.

Two sons, fourteen and eleven years old, were left orphans. The oldest, who was named for the Colonel, was allowed to choose his guardian and he asked for his uncle Witherel. The court assigned the younger to Witherel as well.

The Colonel had now outlived five of his children. As a practical man, not usually given to swings of emotion, he had watched the decline of his son-in-law Daniel Rogers with no illusions. Daniel may have gone a little early, though his lifespan was not unusually short for the time and place. But his passing reminded the Colonel that he was himself living on borrowed time. Even the Good Book suggested that anything beyond threescore and ten was a special gift and only came "by reason of strength." Never-the-less, an eighth decade had become a real possibility. Bowing to the inevitable, Jonathan and Lucretia asked Griswold, who had sadly lost his beloved Polly and was once again alone, to come live with them and care for the farm as the Colonel's strength ebbed away. Lucretia insisted on a great celebration for his birthday that year, with not only the family, but also all the neighbors, feasting in the open in the green fields along Station Camp Creek and enjoying not only fine food, but fiddle music as well. The Hamiltons, the Looneys, the Douglass'—they were all there. The Colonel enjoyed the festivities, but he was more preoccupied than ever with "tying up the loose ends"—his term for seeing to the future of all his children and grandchildren, the very mission which had thrust him into the wilderness more than ten years ago.

He had decided what he would do with his extensive lands to the West, now in the county named for Eusebius' old nemesis, James Robertson. His sons Daniel and Jonathan Junior would receive large tracts there for a modest sum—funds to hold in expectation of Lucretia's widowhood. Poor Nathaniel's two boys, William and Nathaniel Junior, whose loss of a father particularly touched the old Colonel's heart, were given another one hundred acres outright. He also gave one hundred acres from the land at Station Camp Creek to his grandson Lynde Latimer, who bore the name of Lucretia's illustrious grandfather, Judge Nathaniel Lynde of Saybrook in old Connecticut. It was a name to be perpetuated. After all, it was old Judge Lynde who, almost a century before, had donated the building and land which was the foundation of Yale University. Sadly, it would be generations before many of the Judge's Cumberland descendants would have the benefit of such educational institutions—or of much formal education at all. Jonathan Junior's other sons, Jacob and Jonathan III, were able to buy several hundred acres north of the Colonel's land to add to the family's growing domain.

In an age when land was everything, Colonel Jonathan had managed to make every member of his large family a landowner, with a hundred and fifty-seven acres remaining for him and Lucretia. Griswold, who remained unmarried and his parents' chief caregiver, continued to live with them and farm the place. It would be his own one day soon, the Colonel assured him. He admitted to Lucretia that all these arrangements made him proud—though he hoped not sinfully so. She assured him this was a pride born of virtue and therefore not in the least sinful.

Under his bed the Colonel had kept one of the chests the family had brought with them from New England, originally packed with necessities for their long journey. It was his personal, private box now—a place to keep those mementos that one accumulates during a long life—those physical bits and pieces that have the power to resurrect special moments and special people. And so it was a box of memories, really, and not simply of inanimate objects. One day, a few weeks before Hannah's passing, he laboriously knelt by his bed, reached under for the chest, and pulled it into view. He had not opened the box for a long time, but now he felt the need carefully to inventory its contents once more. There were decisions to be made. He sat down in his great chair, where he now spent so much of every day, bending over and lifting out one object after another.

Of course, the sword was there. There was a bit of rust on the blade, but it still looked very fine to him. It would go to Griswold, with instructions that it never leave the possession of the family. Nothing would be more representative of his life and memory than this sword which had accompanied him through every adventure now for over half a century. There were the silver spoons and the silver tankard which had belonged to his mother and father—symbols of success in old Connecticut, but too fine for common use in the Wilderness. His old carving knife. A small brass kettle, companion to the larger one which had accompanied the Latimers on their long journey more than a decade ago, which still found use in the great fireplace in the next room of the house. There were also books. Of course, he still carried one or the other of his two Bibles to church when he was able to attend; they had their place on a stand next to his great chair, where he could pick up one to read in the evenings. But the books of sermons which had belonged to Lucretia's father had long ago been relegated to the memento chest. And there was *Guthrie's Geographical Grammar*, the book that had been so carefully studied before the family set out across a thousand miles. Through it, the Colonel, Lucretia (and the children as well), had found a way to comprehend the great world beyond their relatively tiny one in New England. And finally there was the great coat which had been a part of his colonel's uniform. Or rather, the remnants of it. It was tattered and there were frayed edges here and there, and even a hole or two. No longer of any practical use, but far too precious in the world of memory to throw away.

He began to form a mental list: Griswold would become the custodian of the sword, the big kettle, and the great chair, with its ladder back, and finely turned pommels and finials, where the Colonel now spent so much of his time. It had been one of the few pieces of furniture that had accompanied the family from New England, completely dismantled so it would take only limited space and reassembled by his Cumberland grandson-in-law Thomas Murray, who was a skilled furniture craftsman. Joseph would get the silver tankard and the carving knife, Robert the small brass kettle, and Charles, Robert and Griswold would share the set of silver spoons. Lucretia would decide what to do with everything else —when the time came for deciding such things. The thought of how trivial this whole process really was crossed his mind. And yet, somehow, it seemed very important to him.

He made a mental accounting of his other possessions, besides the land, which, of course, was most important, and which was being distributed among his heirs already. There was surprisingly little else, for a man who had come from such impressive roots, a colleague of such impressive friends, and a born leader who had once wielded such power and influence: the beds and bedding, the kitchen and fireplace utensils, pewter plates, and knives and forks. There was his shotgun and a few tools, his hymnbook and his pocket dictionary. There were a few horses, not many, and a few cows for milk and meat, sheep for wool, and twenty-three head of pigs, worth 25 dollars or so. He owed the Looneys a few dollars for livestock, but not much really. No other debts.

"I have left what Lucretia and I need; nothing more," he thought. "That is as it should be."

TWELVE: LEGACY

Memory

Station Camp Creek
Sumner County, Tennessee
October 13, 1806

As October cast its cooling breeze upon the Cumberland, the Colonel found it more and more difficult to convince himself to get up and around in the morning. For years he had risen with the sun, and kept it company until it finished its course and disappeared behind the trees of the great forest, even during the long days of summer. The morning air was beginning to bite a bit, and the heavy quilts which Lucretia and her friends had made seemed warm and secure to him. And when he finally convinced himself to rise to meet the day, and breakfast finished, the most attractive place for him was near the arching fireplace, in his great chair, but close enough to the window to see and hear the world outside.

There were visitors, of course—almost every day. Peter Looney. William Douglass. His old neighbors and friends. The Reverend William McGee. Two or three of the grandchildren, eager to hear his stories. A son or daughter-in-law, coming to see that he and Lucretia were all right. He kept a book or two on a nearby stand, selected from the small but precious family library. Always more a man of action than a reader, he had found himself depending more and more on these written words to replace the busyness that had always before filled his days. Transporting him to times and places to which only they could bear him. He read his Bible and even did a little theological speculation from time to time with Peter, who tended toward skepticism, and Reverend McGee, who, of course, never expressed a doubt. He usually found himself somewhere in between.

Lucretia often found him asleep, the book he had been reading on the floor near his feet, his head bent forward as if in prayer. What she could not see were the cool mists; nor could she hear the rustling of the age-old trees, the flocks of red-breasted pigeons and chattering turkeys, the low moans of mother bears and the squeaky whining conversations of their cubs. These were sights and sounds emitting not from the window beside the Colonel's great chair, but from deep within some inner world of memory. Sometimes the sounds were unpleasant: the shattering blasts of cannon fire, the cries of fallen soldiers, the sound of horses riding off to Boston; of ships in the Sound on their way to New York Island, orders being shouted out above the rat-tat-tat of musket fire, New London burning. Then the triumphant sound of fife and drum, piercing the air with "Yankee Doodle" as the defeated Redcoats march into the village of Saratoga and throw their guns in great piles.

And often there were shadowy figures who stepped from the mists and whose faces were perfectly clear to him. His beautiful mother Borodell— had any woman every seemed more elegant and yet so warm? The tall, strong, young Nathan Hale, so full of promise—appearing for only a moment in the mists, then suddenly disappearing as if yanked by force back into the darkness. Benedict Arnold, handsome and olive-skinned, confident but somehow showing even when he smiled some fatal flaw. Colonel Selden, looking back as the Hessians dragged him away, tilting his head and cutting his eyes as if to signal, "It is up to you now, Jonathan." General Washington—called back once more from that other world where he had been residing for half a decade now, simply to show the merest touch of a reassuring smile. And from that other place, there was also his son Nathaniel, the signs of his terrible disfigurement no longer visible. And the other lost children as well. How many of them there seemed to be when they came together in one place! And then they, too, were once again lost in the mists.

Then the face of Lucretia, no longer smooth and touched with roses, but to him even more beautiful than his mother's.

"Jonathan, you have a visitor," she was saying. He realized that he had somehow returned from the land of the mists to his hearth and home on Station Camp Creek.

It was Reverend McGee.

The sight of him revived the Colonel almost immediately. The two men smiled at each other the way people smile when they are amused by some mutual bit of frivolity.

"Well, well, Bill," the Colonel said, "I am surprised to see you about. I have heard that your fellow clergymen have tossed you out of the presbytery for being a heretic!"

"They have indeed," the old minister replied, not particularly perturbed, it seemed to Lucretia.

"And what was your offense?" asked the Colonel.

"According to them, I have denied the doctrine of election, and 'held that a certain sufficiency of grace was given to every man'" he answered.

"Well, I—for one—sincerely hope that you are right and they are wrong," the Colonel said, still smiling.

Though neither let it show, Lucretia and Reverend McGee both felt the same twinge of sadness as they listened to him. The humor was still there, but the voice was weak and hardly rose above a whisper.

There was more talk about the usual small events of life—a little more theology, even some politics. Then the Colonel stopped for a moment, looked at the fire and then out into the meadow. The room was suddenly very silent.

"I think that sunset is near," the Colonel said.

Since it was hardly midday on Station Camp Creek, the visitor knew without a doubt what the Colonel meant. He only nodded in reply. Lucretia turned her face away, toward the fire.

In Pastures Green

Six tall sons carried the coffin, lovingly and skillfully constructed by Thomas Murray and carried only the day before from Nashville in a wagon otherwise packed with grieving family members. The procession moved along the path that ran eastward, leaving the house which the Colonel and Lucretia had shared with Griswold and ending near a tiny branch where the pasture land began to slope gently toward Station Camp Creek. Not too far away were two graves already marked by field stones placed head and foot, side by side: Hannah, the Colonel's first-born, and her faithful husband, Daniel Rogers. The new grave had been dug this very morning, by strong young grandsons who had risen before the sun. Throughout the night before, the family, now numbering in dozens, sat quietly throughout the house, remembering and sometimes weeping. Lucretia had insisted that the Colonel be buried in the only remaining remnant of his uniform, the coat he had worn on the cold battlefields of a land far away. It was tattered since he had used it as his winter coat for many years here in the Cumberland. It had long since lost most of its military accoutrements, except, perhaps, for an original button or two. In recent years it had rested tightly folded in his box of memories since neither he nor Lucretia could bring themselves to throw it away. That is where Lucretia found it and lovingly put it on him.

Rev. McGee spoke the eulogy, full of pathos, remembrance, and approbation. Looking out over the green fields which this family had carved from the wilderness, down toward the sparkling crystal waters of the stream below, he tried to end by singing the words to "The Lord is My Shepherd" instead of quoting them from his worn old Bible. They were the words of the old Scottish Psalter. At first, his voice was strong:

"The Lord's my Shepherd, I'll not want…"

But then,

"He makes me down to lie
In pastures green…"

The next words would have been apt indeed, looking off toward Station Camp Creek, but the Reverend McGee could not finish them:

He leadeth me
The quiet waters by…

There was a final silent, solemn moment and then the family moved away toward the house, except for two or three grandsons, who stayed behind to fill the grave with fine Cumberland soil; and Griswold, who, when they had finished, set in place two carefully selected fieldstones—one at the head and one at the foot.

A Westward Wind

Children in the Cumberland Forest, like children everywhere, used to amuse themselves by finding clusters of yellow-flowered dandelions growing in the green fields. Here they searched among the blooms for one which nature had transformed into a delicate ball of tiny parachutes, ready to be scattered by the winds. One hearty puff by childish lips at close range hurried the process and sent the little missiles off in all directions. As they were caught by the breezes, the children watched them fly high and wide, over fences, then over trees—so far into the blue sky that they disappeared into the billowy clouds above. And then, who knows where they might finally land and take root on the earth once more?

The next decades were for the Colonel's family, as for so many Americans, a similar sort of Diaspora (the word means "the scattering of seeds"). And the wind which propelled them off beyond the forest and beyond all existing boundaries and fences was a wind toward the West. For a while, after that sad gathering overlooking Station Camp Creek, the world seemed relatively settled and predictable. Charles Latimer resumed his weekly six-mile journeys over to the new little nearby town, Gallatin, to buy supplies at John Allen's County Store. (He had missed one usually predictable visit during the Colonel's decline, and his absence had caused concern among the regular customers.) On these visits, he mostly bought things ordered by the woman folk of the family—cloth, buttons, sewing supplies...things which only a short time before were only wishful dreams in the great forest.

The talk at the store was all about Andy Jackson's duel with Charles Dickinson, a professional gunslinger who had goaded Jackson into a fight by insulting his wife. Picking a fight with Jackson turned out to be a fatal mistake for young Mr. Dickinson. But overall, the most popular subject of discussion centered on Thomas Jefferson's big land deal with Napoleon. Although the papers had been signed three years before, the implications of this deal were just now beginning to dawn on the average American. The size of the county had doubled. Its boundaries had jumped across the Mississippi and now stretched all the way to the Rocky Mountains. That vast expanse, for forty years controlled by the King of Spain, and then briefly by the Emperor of France, was American now. The wind was blowing the seeds off to the West, and on their journey, they were being transformed into a wave of roaring thunderheads.

None of this was good news for Eusebius Bushnell, of course. Spain, his sponsor and protector now for more than a decade, seemed to be losing its grip. With a stroke of the pen, Eusebius found his world restricted to East Florida. His son Ezra could live and prosper in Opelousas or even in Natchez, as a Spaniard or as an American, one or the other, but he could not. Ezra had married into some wealth, started a family, and flourished as the owner of a large sugar plantation. He still kept in touch with his sisters and the other Latimers, if only in a somewhat desultory way. Eusebius' life was mostly a mystery, even to Ezra, so little was known on that score. Word of events came in bits and pieces, and there were many unanswered questions. There was the shocking news that Matthew, only eighteen years old, had been killed. By whom? For what reason? No one really knew.

At the same time as this tragedy, Eusebius built a fine water-powered sawmill on Moultrie Creek, just south of the city of St. Augustine, where he harvested and cut timber for the growing city. The Spanish Governor White, in the meantime, had forbidden Americans to participate in the timber trade and had even arrested some for trying. There was no question where Eusebius' interests and assurance of well-being lay. Then he sold his tannery to a Gringo named Samuel Robinson and concentrated on the mill, becoming in the process more and more dependent on slave labor to build his fortune. At every step, there were lawsuits and wrangling and accusations of non-payment of debts, but somehow he seemed to survive every challenge. In the midst of all this, his Irish wife Margarita suddenly died. She was only thirty-six years old.

Eusebius once again rebounded quickly. Next to his large holdings in Twelve Mile Swamp, north of the town of St. Augustine, lived a neighbor named Brian Connor. Connor ran various businesses in town as well as his plantation along the coast which was called Casacola. One day, not long after Eusebius' series of misfortunes, Connor fell out of his boat on the way to his home from town and was drowned. Eusebius stepped in immediately to help his widow, a Spanish lady from an old family, named Susanna Madin, to settle the estate. Then, after a period some regarded as a little shy of respectable, he married the wealthy widow. This union was not without its repercussions. Susanna's family insisted that Eusebius become a Roman Catholic. The thought of doing this had entered Eusebius' mind several times in recent years. He would always be an outsider in Spanish Florida if he did not share in the dominant faith of its people. And so, on December 5, 1808, at the age of fifty-nine, Eusebius was baptized in the cathedral at St. Augustine. His Christian name would be Eusebio Fernando Bushell. His new middle name he received from his godfather Fernando de Maza Arredondo, who had sponsored him in his new life. Arredondo was the wealthiest Spaniard in the colony. He owned thirty square miles of land and ran a highly profitable slave trade between Cuba and Florida. With such friends, Eusebius' future once again seemed bright and limitless.

And to top off his good fortune, he and his son Ezra were reconciled. Ezra even came with his wife Clarissa to St. Augustine to visit his father and to introduce them to his new grand-daughter. The little one was named Susanna in honor of his new step-mother. At Susanna Madin's insistence, the baby was baptized in the cathedral, and after some consideration, Ezra and Clarissa decided to convert as well. The Latimer's in Tennessee knew nothing of all this, of course, which was no doubt best for all involved. It would be difficult for the Latimers to fit these events into a worldview shaped by almost three centuries of Puritan Protestantism.

A Rumor Reaches the Cumberland

Gallatin, Tennessee
June 14, 1813

Life fell for a while into a quiet routine, except for that terrifying night in 1812 when the earth shook and the trees danced and the rivers changed their ancient paths. The center of the shaking, at New Madrid on the Mississippi, was many miles away. But the earth had trembled all the way back to New England, and the church bells of Boston were heard to chime from its shaking. Much closer, the Cumberland rocked like a gigantic cradle, and more than a few of its inhabitants thought the End of all things and the Day of Judgment was at hand. For weeks afterward the customers at John Allen's Store shared their experiences. Those who were known for fabricating tall tales did not have to resort to exaggeration this time. The truth was incredible enough.

The Colonel's son Robert, protégé of Nathan Hale, and perhaps the best educated of the sons, never in good health since his wounds during the Revolution, was too weak to sign his own will. His son Hugh held and guided his father's hand to mark the document with a wobbly "X." Hugh would soon be going off to war himself, as the new nation his family had helped to found was once again caught up in a struggle with Mother England. Along with him would be Nathaniel, whose father had died in battle on Caney Fork, Jonathan C., son of the last of the Colonel's sons to come to the Cumberland, Charles' son Nicholas, Witherel's son James, and Griswold's son-in-law William Aspley. These young men all went off to meet up with the dashing Andy Jackson, now a general, intent on liberating the mouth of the mighty Mississippi from its French overlords—and, surreptitiously, to take Florida away from the Spaniards, as well. The Latimer boys could hardly have done otherwise, given the stories they had so often heard at the feet of their towering grandfather. They mostly volunteered for Colonel Coffee's outfit, as mounted gunmen. Now they would have stories of their own, born in the bloody swamps of Louisiana and Florida.

The fruits of glory do not always ripen as expected, and this particular expedition came to nothing when the United States pulled the rug out from under ol' Hickory and his grand plan—forcing him to wait for glory at a later date. The Latimer boys were back home before the Spring flowers were in full bloom without firing a shot—but full of stories they had heard circulating in the camps nevertheless.

Charles Latimer took the information that his son Nicholas and his cousins had picked up during their long journey back home on his next trip to John Allen's country store in Gallatin. Peter Looney was there, and several other men whose sons had been with Jackson. The rumors were flying, by now having passed from mouth to mouth several times and probably suffering some distortion along the way. Nevertheless, they were finding an attentive audience.

"Well, Charley, what did your boy have to say about the war?" Peter asked his old friend.

"He said that things were moving fast, not only down in New Orleans, but over in Florida as well," Charles replied.

"And when you think of Florida, who else do you think of?" Peter said, a mischievous grin on his face, knowing his question would make any of the Latimers squirm a bit. Charles didn't like the question much, but he wasn't going to avoid it. And besides, he had heard some things worth telling.

"I suppose you are talking about Eusebius," he answered. "And as it happens, his name did come up in the rumor mill. The boys met several people who had been in Florida or knew people there. They say that for a while he was doing well in St. Augustine—lots of land, lots of deals, lots of lawsuits—you know Eusebius."

"Indeed I do," said Peter, still smiling.

"They say he had a tannery next to the Governor's House, sold it, set up a fine mill, and got into the timber business in a place called Twelve Mile Swamp, north of the town. He married a rich widow and got her land as well—his third wife from what they say. And became a Catholic!"

"Now that's something!" Peter replied, his smile fading.

"But then the governor, who was a good friend of Eusebius, got sick and died. And after that things started going sideways. Unbeknownst to him, a bunch of plantation owners in South Georgia got the idea to invade Florida and take it over. A lot of it had to do with slavery—and with the Indians. The Seminoles were a menace and kept taking in slaves who escaped from Georgia. And in fact, the Spanish were encouraging escaped Georgia slaves to live in Florida as well. They were even letting them build towns and organize armed militias, especially around St. Augustine."

Peter interrupted, "But what if all those free blacks with guns decided to come north to Georgia? What if the Spanish stirred them up and gave them help? There could have been a slave insurrection that might come up through Georgia and spread all over the place!"

"Exactly," Charles Latimer answered. "That's why the Georgia men organized their own army and headed south. They called themselves the Patriots, and claimed they were taking over Florida for the United States. And if you look close at the map, you will see that on their way to St. Augustine they had to pass right through Twelve Mile Swamp."

"Mercy! That must have put ol' Eusebius in a pickle. He would have a hard time convincing them he hadn't sold out to the Spaniards years ago."

By now Peter had been joined by everyone in the store, and a dozen others from outside, circling Charles Latimer and listening with bated breath.

"Down in St. Augustine there was a strong fort, hundreds of armed black men, and even a bunch of reinforcements sent by the Spanish from Cuba to help out. And of course, the Seminoles. The so-called Patriots soon reached the plantations north of St. Augustine, including the one that belonged to Eusebius. They started wreaking havoc upon the lumbermen and planters around the Twelve Mile Swamp. The ones they could catch, they forced to join them or face the consequences. Most of the locals fled south, hoping the blacks and the Indians and the Spanish would save them. Can you believe that? Their fine plantations went up in smoke."

"And what about Eusebius?" someone asked from among the onlookers.

"Well," Charles replied, "that's where things get murky. We don't really know exactly what happened. We do know that Eusebius could never have joined the Patriots because he was *persona non grata* in the United States and couldn't risk changing sides now. And he could hardly expect good treatment from armed runaway slaves, given his own record on slavery. Anyway, whatever exactly happened, the end fact is the same— Eusebius is dead. Whether the Patriots killed him, or the Indians, or the Blacks, we just don't know. It's likely somebody did. Not likely he died in his bed. And so here we have a patriot who fought in the American Revolution who may have been murdered for being a Spanish sympathizer by a bunch of bandits who called themselves 'Patriots.' "

"We live in a strange world," Peter said.

"Of course, you understand," Charles added, "these are all just rumors."

Eventually, the Latimers lost touch with the descendants of Eusebius. His daughters faded from the record as women did in those days, their stories swallowed up in the stories of their husbands. Ezra carried on the family name, prospered in the timber business like his father, and stayed in contact with the Latimers until his tragic death only six years after his father's. In 1818 he caught pneumonia bringing a load of timber down the River from Arkansas Territory, and died in New Orleans. As for Eusebius' Spanish wife Susannah Madin: impoverished by the deprecations of the "Patriots", she lived out her days as a shop-keeper in St. Augustine and was buried in the cathedral a few months after the death of Ezra. Bushnells may be found in the Deep South until this day.

Diaspora

With the second war with Great Britain came the raging westward winds which were to fling the Latimers toward new frontiers and new adventures. Witherel was the first to leave the green fields of Sumner alongside the still-wild Ridge, fields which were now in profitable cultivation. Just as the war was stirring the young men to action, Witherel joined his old clerical friends—the men who had planted and watered the great revival a decade before—in a move not yet west but rather a few miles to the East, to a place called the Three Forks of the Duck River. There the Reverend Samuel King and Reverend William McGee were establishing what people came to call the "Kingdom of the Revs," a complex of mill races, holding ponds, saw mills, grist mills and carding factories gathered along the river. There he would live for twenty years until, infirm and widowed, his family took him along with them as they went West in 1833, eventually to the wilderness of the Arkansas Territory. There the white men were replacing the Cherokee, who in that place had built for themselves fine farms, worked by their black slaves. But the President of the United States was sending the Indians away now, and their lands were once again being taken from them.

Along with Witherel's party, the families of his daughter Jane Latimer Wilson and his niece Fanny Latimer Hamilton was an even larger tribe, led by his son James. As a boy, James had suffered the painful years of separation from his father after the death of his mother Abigail, who lay in the old graveyard in faraway Connecticut. He was now married to Fanny's cousin Jane Hamilton. Frontier informality had nicknamed the couple "Jimmy" and "Jenny." The long processions of ox-drawn wagons were ferried across the great Mississippi River at Chickasaw Bluffs, passing through the new little town called Memphis—yet another of the entrepreneurial ventures of their old Sumner county associates James Winchester and Andrew Jackson. Ol' Andy, of course, was now President of the United States.

Though to this point they had traveled together, their destinations were different, and the two tribes of combined families, Latimer and Hamilton, who had lived through so much, were soon to take different paths to the future. To reach their new homes, they traveled part of that road which came to be called the "Trail of Tears." Following the course of the Arkansas River, they traced a path where only a few years later would follow the pitiful remnants of a once-proud race, stumbling toward their next place of exile. Even now, as they traveled, they saw clusters of the wretched precursors of this mournful exodus sharing the road with them.

Once settled in his new home, Witherel lived on his pension as a veteran of the Revolution in the homes of his younger family members. In Arkansas Territory, he renewed an acquaintance with old Chief Glass, who had led many a Cherokee war party in the old days, and had danced around many a campfire waving the scalp of some white settler, but now lived quietly in Arkansas. In the days of their youth, the two old men had tried to kill each other more than once. The aged Indian had refused to leave his little cabin in Arkansas, President Jackson or no, and with sublime irony he and Witherel, one a marauding terrorist and the other a Yankee rifleman of Buchanan's Station, lived their last days sitting on the same rough-hewn pews in the Cumberland Presbyterian Church in a settlement that took its name from the old Indian chief—Glass Village. Witherel did not survive long in this new place and is buried in an unknown and unmarked grave somewhere in what is to this day still a great forest.

Fig. 14 - Remains of Wilson Cabin in Glass Village

Lucretia

Griswold was the next to leave the Cumberland. He had faithfully cared for his mother Lucretia after the Colonel's death, just as the Colonel had planned. But now he must provide for his own children, and besides, he could count on his niece Fanny, daughter of his brother Robert and married into the substantial Hamilton family, to care for the aging matriarch. He sold the Colonel's house and farm, which he had inherited, to Fanny and her husband, Henry. One plot he carefully set aside, however, making sure that it was deeded to his brother Jonathan—now the patriarch of the Station Camp Creek Latimers. It was the quiet spot on the green slope where the Colonel slumbered, his grave still only marked by a field stone.

Then it was off to the West, to the other side of the Mississippi, just where the St. Francis River joined the mighty Father of Waters, and a new town called Helena. There Griswold became a respected leader, a Justice of the Peace and community pillar. There his daughters married and there many of his descendants live to this day.

Not long thereafter, in the summer of 1820, on a hot July morning, Lucretia Griswold Latimer bid this world farewell. She was in her ninetieth year. To merely call her life "eventful" hardly seems adequate. A childhood in the colonial home of a Yale-educated clergyman, within a family rich and powerful and sophisticated, she had been raised among books and learned piety. She could not overreach the boundaries which even her privileged world had built around her gender, however. Fifteen times she experienced the rigors of pregnancy and the struggle of childbirth. These experiences, for a woman of her day, whether privileged or not, were nothing less than journeys through the Valley of the Shadow of Death. Her handsome and caring husband, despite his powerful frame and personality, had nevertheless leaned on her fragile being all his life. She had been his friend and his compass. He was often absent during their younger years of marriage, always with the real possibility of never returning. Such was the fate of a soldier's wife. And then, as a woman of maturity, she found it necessary to leave everything comfortable and familiar and go with her family into the dark wilderness. There the work was hard, the amenities only dreams, and the danger of horrible atrocity always lurking, always imminent.

Word spread quickly, and the fine house which she and the Colonel had built was soon full of mourners. All those family and friends who were not already gone too far away toward the setting Sun came, but not so much to mourn for her. They all knew that her life had been long and full and that He who created life will ultimately and always demand it be returned to Him. Rather, they mourned for themselves—and for how she summed up all their lives had been for generations, and how the sands of Time had counted out in her almost a century, marking the march of morning and evening, winter and summer, happiness and sorrow. When the Colonel had gone away, she was still there to hold those days and years together. But now...there was a cloud of finality. Life had turned itself away from all that was past, and there remained only the uncertain future.

There were many tears as the homemade box was carried to the gentle green slope and placed beside the Colonel. There were prayers and hymns. The grandsons once again filled in the opening and Charles put a stone at the head and foot.

"We will get them proper gravestones someday," he said to those who stood by, weeping.

A Famous Friend

The Colonel's youngest surviving son Joseph was the next to be caught up by the westward winds. Already sixty years old himself, he gathered up his large extended family, along with a son of his brother Nathaniel, who had been killed by Indians many years before, and crossed the Mississippi into Illinois. First, they settled in Sangamon County, where almost immediately they became acquainted with a lanky young rail-splitter named Abraham Lincoln. Joseph's son Alexander became particularly close to Abe, and the two wrote letters to one another even after Mr. Lincoln had made a considerable name for himself and moved to Washington, D.C. One time, as Lincoln himself related, Alexander came to visit at the White House and at Abe's insistence, allowed his toddler daughter Mary to spend the afternoon playing in the oval office while the President alternated his official duties with playing childish games with her. Some people say it was Alexander who introduced Abe to a young woman in the neighborhood named Ann Rutledge—but who can say for sure?

The family acquired thousands of acres at a place they called Cherry Grove where they built homes on adjoining farms, a church, and a fine academy. Many of Joseph's descendants distinguished themselves in politics, and as authors and academicians. One of them, Clara Latimer Bacon, a distinguished mathematician, was the first woman in America to earn a Ph.D. in that discipline (at Johns Hopkins University). Another, Wendell Mitchel Latimer, was one of the key scientists who developed the atomic bomb. Latimer Hall at the University of California Berkeley bears his name. A third, who bore the Colonel's name, Jonathan Wyatt Latimer, became a famous crime fiction writer and eventually the author of movie and TV scripts (such as *Perry Mason*). One of Alexander's sons, William Guthrie Latimer, traveled furthest west—arriving in 1852 as one of the first white men to pitch a tent on the spot which became Seattle, Washington. His son Norval, a prosperous and powerful citizen of that city, built an imposing structure (still standing) on Pioneer Square which was called the Squire-Latimer Building.

The Republic of Texas

Jimmy and Jenny Latimer and their considerable ensemble left their kinsmen on the Arkansas River at a two-year-old hamlet called Little Rock and headed off down the "Southwest Trail"—bound for Texas. There were many Choctaw Indians along the way, banished from their lands and headed west. In the thriving little town of Washington, Arkansas Territory, the local tavern was full of talk about names like Sam Houston, and David Crockett, and Jim Bowie. And most of all, about Texas.

Moving on a few miles to the west the Latimers and Hamiltons came to the banks of the Red River, just at the mouth of Mill Creek. The river was muddy and wide. On its other side, they would no longer be in the United States of America. The spirit which had carried the Colonel and his tribe to new lives in new worlds lived on in his descendants. On the road to Texas, they had often spoken of him and of Lucretia, hoping their own children and grandchildren would not forget their stories. Ol' Jimmie, as he came to be called, the patriarch of this particular Exodus, still remembered vividly his long childhood journey from Connecticut to the Cumberland. Before they left the green hills and meadows of the Cumberland for the last time, he and his brothers had purchased two fine grave markers and set them up to replace the fieldstones that marked the venerable couple's resting place near Station Camp Creek. There was no one available to properly inscribe the new stones, but everyone in the family was sure that this detail would be handled in due time.

The border between the United States and Mexico was disputed, and James chose to consider his new lands to be a part of Arkansas Territory. In fact, he even served as the area's representative to the Arkansas Legislature the year after they arrived. His son-in-law Robert Hamilton was soon named to the office of sheriff. One day, a few months after the Latimers' arrival, two of Ol' Jimmie's teenaged daughters, Jane and Betsy, heard that the famous Tennessee frontiersman Davey Crockett was on his way to Texas, and had crossed the Red River. Their neighbor, the legendary frontier woman Ibby Gordon, conscripted them and they rode off to intercept him, so they could help him avoid confrontations with hostile local Indians. They reported to their families that he was not dressed in deerskin and wearing a coonskin cap, as sometimes reported, but like a gentleman, and furthermore, he was not ignorant or uncouth, as also reported, but rather dignified and well-spoken.

The family became a significant force in the Texas Revolution and in the establishment of the Republic of Texas. Ol' Jimmie's son Albert Hamilton Latimer signed the Texas Declaration of Independence. His name is separated from that of Sam Houston on the document by only two others. He was already a lawyer when the family arrived in Texas, and was a prominent legislator and judge throughout the eventful years of the Republic and the coming of statehood, eventually becoming a justice of the Texas Supreme Court. Another of Ol' Jimmie's sons, James Wellington, whom everyone called "Wake" decided to start a newspaper in the little village of Dallas (population thirty-nine). The paper became a powerful political voice, sometimes finding itself at odds with Sam Houston himself. Though he died young, Wake's paper became part of the ancestry of the *Dallas Morning News*, which is still published today. He is remembered with a monument in the Old Pioneer's Cemetery in downtown Dallas, and the Good-Latimer Expressway nearby.

The Golden State

Another family descended from the Colonel who had a significant impact in the far West was that of Robert Atwell Latimer, the grandson of Jonathan's son and Nathan Hale's student Robert. Robert Atwell "caught the fever" when gold was discovered in California and joined the hundreds of 49ers who crossed the western deserts from their homesteads in Arkansas. Like most, he soon found himself penniless and hungry. But he was not only adventuresome, he was also resourceful. If he was hungry, he figured, so were lots of other folks—some of whom had hit the payload and could afford to divest themselves of a little gold dust. So he set himself up a "vegetable ranch" near the little mining town of San Juan and at least made enough on his harvest to get back to Arkansas, where he had settled in the early 40s. The experience cured him of the "gold bug," but California still seemed to him to be the promised land. And so he headed west again, this time with sober expectations, and his family, to become a saddler and a minister in the Methodist Church.

R. A.'s daughter Sarah was a woman from the mold of her ancestor Lucretia. After helping her husband William Finley found what became Oregon State University, she was a leader in the cause of women's suffrage in California. Though a woman of social refinement, she teamed up with the rough and tumble female lawyer Fannie Martin and together they led the fight for woman's rights. Sarah wrote with skill and power on this and other issues in her son Ernest Latimer Finley's newspaper *The Press Democrat*. Ernest was a media mogul of legendary proportions and is credited with being the power behind the building of the Golden Gate Bridge.

Because the winds of the Diaspora had blown them in so many different directions, the Latimers had many different views about the issues which broke the United States apart in the 1860s. Some were slave owners; some were violently opposed to slavery. Some were ardent Unionists and some equally ardent Rebels. Some fought in blue and some in grey, and some of each died on the battlefields of the Civil War. One can only hope they did not fall at the hands of their kinsmen. But all of them, taken together, have been woven into the tapestry of a great social experiment, the United States of America, from the East, to the South, to the Midwest, and finally across the great plains to the Pacific, in one remarkable story rising from the life of a man who for one reason or another did not get painted into the iconic pictures.

Field Trip

Sumner County, Tennessee
Saturday, August 30, 2006

The enthusiastic young new history teacher at Station Camp Creek High School, fresh from her own co-ed days in Nashville, eagerly asked her principal for permission to take her class on a field trip to start the new school year.

"I'd like to take them on a little outing to places near our school," she said, "to help them see how history is all around them. And maybe even get them excited about something besides this year's football team!"

She outlined the excursion she had in mind, and the principal was very pleased. He liked to see this kind of excitement about teaching and this kind of thinking outside the box. "I'm happy to hear that you want the kids to like history," he said. "I used to be a history teacher myself, and I never could understand why history teachers somehow manage to make the subject dry and uninteresting. After all, history is just the story of people—and nothing is more interesting than people!"

So letters were sent out, parents gave their consent, one of the school's little yellow buses was commandeered (along with a licensed volunteer driver), sack lunches were prepared, and off went a dozen and a half teenagers and their pumped up instructor. They drove up Big Station Camp Creek Boulevard to where it intersects Long Hollow Pike. There on the left, alongside the beautiful creek, the teacher pointed out a large house with white wooden siding, a shiny red roof, fine black shutters on its windows, and a tall stone fireplace chimney. Most of the students had passed by this place on their way to school countless times, but had not really ever taken much notice of it.

As the yellow bus approached one student said, "This looks almost new."

"It does," the teacher replied, "but it is actually older than the state of Tennessee. And it was not only a house; it was also a sort of fortress during the time of troubles between the settlers and the Native Americans. And it was also the place where trials were held and government business was done. Andrew Jackson, who, as I hope you know, became the president of the United States, often appeared in court here as a lawyer. And maybe even more amazing, Louis Philippe, who became the King of France, once spent the night here."

The students, who were generally hard to impress, were impressed by this.

"Who built it?" one of them asked.

"The Douglass family," the teacher said. "And you would be interested to know that some of their descendants still live around here. Some may even be friends of yours. And think how much history there is, right here, only a few hundred yards from our school!"

"But now it is time to go to church—and to the graveyard!" she added with a smile.

The bus followed Long Hollow Pike until Beech Senior High School appeared on the right—known best by the class as the home of their football rivals the Buccaneers. A smattering of boos came from the back of the bus. Just past the school, they saw, again, something they had seen many times before and hardly noticed. It was a lovely stone church, and beside it, a quiet, shady cemetery.

"Some people say this is the oldest church in Middle Tennessee," the teacher said. "But I brought you here to tell you about the 'Great Revival' that you will read about in all the books on American History. Right here, where we are standing, and in several other places very near here, the huge crowds came and all the strange events you've read about—the people shouting, and falling down, and running through the woods, and crying out for mercy—it all happened here."

"And buried in this graveyard, along with many of the early settlers, is one of the preachers who made it happen. His name was William McGee."

She led the group to a weather-worn gravestone under the trees near the church. It was a strange stone. The top had been carved into the shape of a circle that made it look like the outline of a man's head, neck, and square shoulders. The teacher had one of the students read the inscription:

William McGee
Minister of the Gospel
departed this life the Sept 20, 1817
in the Triumphs of faith
aged: about 50 years

This sparked some interest among the students, and they spent the next few minutes looking at the old headstones in the graveyard, reading the inscriptions, and speculating about the lives of the people buried there.

Back on the bus, the teacher ordered the driver to turn off Long Hollow Pike onto New Hope Road and then onto a lovely country road called, according to the sign at the corner, Latimer Lane. There were beautiful multi-million dollar homes, surrounded by fine fields with immaculate wooden fences and filled with beautiful horses. Here and there the road was almost swallowed by great oak trees.

"Try to imagine what the first settlers found here," the teacher said as they drove along. "Trees much larger than these, some of them hundreds of years old, stretched in all directions. It was like a great jungle. The settlers had to hack back the forest to make these fields where the horses are grazing today."

"And why is it called Latimer Lane?" asked another student.

"I'm not sure," the teacher replied. "Probably named after some of the early settlers."

The road eventually circled back to Long Hollow Pike and lunchtime was approaching. When they reached Station Camp Creek Road, the teacher directed the bus to turn left, toward the north, where the road followed the path of the beautiful, clear stream.

"I know a farmer a couple of miles up this road," the teacher said. "And he gave us permission to hike on his land, explore a little bit, and then find a nice place to have a picnic."

The bus crossed a little steam called Brinkley Branch that ran into the larger Station Camp Creek, and the teacher asked the driver to follow the road alongside the branch a few hundred yards and then stop at the roadside. The students got off the bus and followed the teacher over the fence and along the tiny stream.

"We need to send out some scouts to find a place for our picnic," the teacher said. "May I have two volunteers?"

Two young men quickly raised their hands and were sent on their way. No more than ten minutes later they returned, running, and obviously quite excited.

"We made a discovery!" they shouted as they approached. "We found another old graveyard in the woods!"

"Why would someone have a cemetery way back here?" asked one of the girls.

"Well," the teacher explained, "in the very early days, people usually had their own little family plot somewhere on their land, not too far from their homes. Sometimes they called it 'God's Little Acre.'"

Fig. 15: Two unmarked graves in the forest

"Come and look!" the excited young men said, motioning for the others to follow and turn back up the stream. Soon the group came into a little grove of trees and sure enough, there beneath them, were two gravestones standing side by side. They seemed very old and had been almost overwhelmed by the underbrush beneath the trees.

"Even from this distance," the teacher said, "I can tell you something about them. They are quite old—they look like the style used in the early 1800's. And they are probably a husband and wife, buried side by side."

"And who do you think they are?" asked another student.

"We will know that when we

clear away the weeds and read the inscription," she replied.

But, sadly, when the students cleared away the weeds, they found that neither headstone had any inscription on it at all. They were fine head-stones, so obviously the people buried there had been loved and hon-ored. But for some reason, nothing had ever been engraved on the stones.

"What a pity that we don't know who they were," the teacher said, as the students began opening their sack lunches for the picnic. "I imagine, whoever they were, that they lived very interesting lives."

About the Author

John Francis Wilson is a field archaeologist, and writer and lecturer on archaeology in the Middle East, particularly focused on the relationship between archaeology and Christianity. He is a former dean of Seaver College at Pepperdine University, Dean Emeritus, and Professor Emeritus of Religion, and is the author of a number of publications, most notably his work on a famous archaeological site in the Middle East: *Caesarea Philippi: Banias, the Lost City of Pan*. He has also written for radio and television, produced religious television programs, and appeared on television in an A&E series about archaeology and the Bible. His love of history also extends to extensive knowledge of American history during the Revolutionary War.

If you enjoyed this book, please consider leaving an online review. The author would appreciate hearing your thoughts.

Made in the USA
Middletown, DE
10 December 2019